The alchemist's laboratory

THE STORY
OF MEDICINE

KENNETH WALKER
M.A., M.B., F.R.C.S.

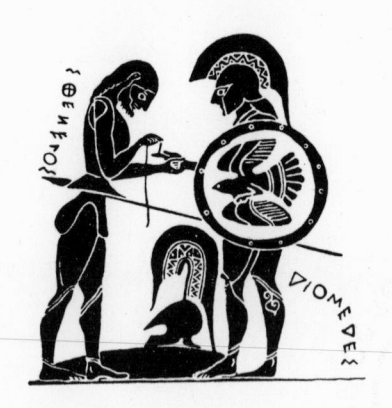

NEW YORK
OXFORD UNIVERSITY PRESS
1955

"But on that account, I say, we ought not to reject the ancient Art, as if it were not, and had not been properly founded, because it did not attain accuracy in all things, but rather, since it is capable of reaching to the greatest exactitude by reasoning, to receive it and admire its discoveries, made from a state of great ignorance, and as having been well and properly made, and not from chance." (HIPPOCRATES, *On Ancient Medicine*, Adams edition, Vol. I, 1849, p. 168.)

Contents

Disease regarded as possession by a devil to be cured by
penitence and prayer. The ceremony of the Royal Touch. The
medical school at Salerno. *De Adventu Medici*. *Regimen Sanitatis Salernitanum*. Women students at Salerno. Decline of
Salerno and rise of the medical schools of Montpellier, Padua
and Paris. Arnold of Villanova. Guy de Chauliac. Gilbertus
Anglicus and John of Gaddesden. Roger Bacon and Albertus
Magnus. The Moslem Empire. The University of Cordoba.
Moslem Hospitals. Rhazes of Basra. Avicenna. Summary of
medicine during the Middle Ages.

LIST OF PLATES

Preface

AN author does not set out to write a book for his own pleasure and instruction. He writes it to earn his living, because he hopes to amuse or to instruct other people, because he feels that it ought to be written or for a mixture of these and of other motives. Yet quite unexpectedly I have snatched both enjoyment and profit out of the task of writing this book. There was much interest as well as labour in the preliminary garnering of suitable material, in the subsequent fitting of the material together, and in the shaping of the whole into a book. And of having obtained personal profit from all this labour I am even more certain. It is as though a new dimension had suddenly been added to the subject of medicine so that instead of viewing the art which I have been practising for so long in the flat, as I have hitherto done, I begin to see it in the round. Depth has now been added to my picture of medicine, a depth which imparts to it a new meaning and richness.

Looking back on the work of the last six months, as I now do from the pinnacle of preface writing, I am no longer surprised at what has happened. It could not have been otherwise than intensely interesting this job of peering into the past of medicine in order to detect the very earliest beginnings of some important idea, and of then following the course taken by that idea throughout the whole of medical history. One notes the slowness of the idea's progress, one becomes alarmed at its disappearance, is relieved when it reappears, excited when it receives confirmation from ideas coming from another direction, and finally, one shares in the moment of triumph when the idea, no longer merely tentative, is accepted as fact by the world at large. All this is as exciting as identifying oneself with the hero of some romance, sharing in his

preliminary hardships and perils and enjoying with him the final
hour of triumph, and somehow in this case it all seems much more
real.

A great deal can be learnt from watching the slow growth of
medical theories and, amongst other things, the lesson that no
medical discovery can ever be made until the world is ready to
receive it. The history of the germ-theory of disease is a striking
example of this. Formulated during the Middle Ages by the Italian
nobleman Fracastoro, the theory was looked upon at that time
as being a fantastic dream in the mind of a poet, and even the poet
himself seems to have lost faith in his own vision. Several centuries
had to elapse and two men, Leeuwenhoek and Pasteur, had to go
through the trouble of being born before Fracastoro's idea could
even be considered as a possible approximation to the truth. A
theory, like a man of destiny, must make its entry at the right
psychological moment if it is to be accepted.

There is another and less satisfactory discovery I have made
whilst trying to narrate this story of medicine: that it is quite
impossible to tell it as it should be told. It is as though one were
watching, and at the same time trying to describe, the weaving of
a great carpet on which many people are at work. "Who is responsible," one calls out, "for the appearance of that curious device
forming itself there on the growing edge of the carpet? Which of
the weavers is in charge of its pattern?" Who, indeed, since all are
engaged on the work of weaving and each has contributed his quotum
to the pattern. No, the story of the growth of the art of medicine
cannot be properly told, for it is impossible to break it up into a
number of separate events, to be arranged tidily in chronological
order. Medical history does not admit of this treatment.

Because this is so, I make no apology for the many gaps which
will be found in my story, or for the absence from it of many
honoured medical names. I have not attempted to emulate the
thoroughness of the dictionaries of biography and of other scholarly
works of reference. All that I have tried to do has been to give
some indication of the haphazard way in which medicine advances
and to introduce to the reader some of the men who have contributed largely to its progress. And in the hope of revealing these
medical pioneers as their fellow men saw them, I have depicted them

against the background of their own times, and I have quoted as largely as possible from contemporary accounts of them.

The book fell naturally, and without any planning on my part, into two parts. In the first part, medical discoveries and the men chiefly responsible for them have been given in chronological order, so that incomplete though it be, it still maintains the form of a history of medicine. But with the rise of specialization and the breaking up of medicine into a large number of different fields of research, the effort to present a history was no longer possible. It was therefore abandoned and the manner of arranging the material changed. Events were no longer placed in chronological order, but a number of medical problems were set forth and the way in which these problems were eventually solved, described. In this second half of the book, advances in medicine are seen to be less and less the work of individual people and more and more the resultant of a number of collateral advances both in medicine and science. In other words, as the story of medicine nears its end, it becomes more and more impersonal.

Acknowledgment has been made throughout the text to a number of works from which I have quoted, but I would like to make known my special indebtedness to the following histories of medicine:

A History of Medicine, by Douglas Guthrie,

A Short History of Medicine, by C. Singer,

Medical History from the Earliest Times, by E. T. Withington,

An Introduction to the History of Medicine, by F. H. Garrison, and

The Evolution of Modern Medicine, by Sir William Osler.

Many years ago, when I had the privilege of looking after the late Sir Henry Wellcome, he spoke to me with affection of the Institute he had founded in the Euston Road, London, and urged me to visit it. Whilst writing this book I have paid the library of that Institute many visits and am specially indebted to its librarian, Mr. F. N. L. Poynter. He has put at my disposal his great knowledge of old medical works and given me much valuable help in selecting suitable illustrations for this work. It would indeed be true to say

that this book has been almost entirely illustrated by the Wellcome Library. I am grateful also to Dr. C. J. Hackett of the Wellcome Institute and to Dr. C. C. Chesterman for helping me whilst I was writing on the subject of Tropical Diseases.

Finally, I would like to thank Mr. Raymond Anderson, of Messrs. Hutchinson and Co., the publishers, for his advice in the final stages of my work, my friend, Peter Fletcher, for undertaking that tedious task the reading of proofs, and Mrs. Cannings, of Midhurst, for her patience and her skill in detecting errors in the earlier stage of typing.

THE STORY OF MEDICINE

CHAPTER I

Prehistoric Medicine

L IFE is a dangerous venture, requiring as it does a ceaseless adjustment to an ever-changing environment. When we consider the difficulties with which the living organism has to contend, the abrupt changes in surrounding conditions, from heat to cold, from moisture to dryness, from calm to storm, the unending search for food, the attacks made on it by competing forms of life, the hundred and one accidents to which it has been subjected for millions of years; when we take into account all these things it is astonishing that life has managed not only to survive on the surface of this planet but to evolve into myriads of forms. That it has been exposed to injury and illness ever since it first appeared in the brackish waters of some marsh cannot be doubted. One of the most valuable assets with which it has been endowed is its capacity to repair its own injuries and to overcome its illnesses, the healing power to which the name *vis medicatrix naturae* has been given.

Animals possess an instinct which drives them when sick to seek remedies which will aid the action of this curative force; the sick dog nibbles grass, the owl rids herself of feather-lice by taking dust-baths, and the wounded animal licks its wounds. It is from this primitive instinct in the animals to aid nature that man's healing arts have been derived. The story of medicine can be said therefore to begin with the history of disease, and disease is as old as life itself.

Probably the oldest specimen of disease to be found in any pathological museum is a relic of an illness which occurred many millions of years ago. It is a small part of the tail of a Dinosaur which was discovered by Professor Roy Moodie in Wyoming, and the disease by which it is affected is a bony tumour. We can reconstruct from this fragment of bone the sad story of a Dinosaur that developed a

pain and an increasing stiffness in its tail, a poor creature that experienced greater and greater difficulty in getting about and in finding its food, so that it grew thinner and thinner and eventually died. But in this book we are concerned only with the infirmities of humanity and with man's better-informed and more conscious efforts to heal his ills by means of medicines and other remedies of his own contriving. The oldest specimen of a disease in a man-like creature was dug up in Java in 1891 by Dr. D. Dubois. It is the thigh bone of man's ape-like ancestor Pithecanthropus Erectus and it displays near its upper end a large outcropping of bone or osseous tumour. Pithecanthropus Erectus became extinct a million years ago and when he first appeared is quite uncertain so that the age of this specimen of disease cannot be determined with any accuracy. Plate 1 shows a similar bony tumour in primitive and prehistoric man.

The oldest evidence of illness in man is to be found in bones because they alone manage to survive, and there are many excellent examples of osteoarthritis or chronic rheumatism affecting joints amongst Egyptian mummies. We can also find evidence in mummies of other diseases, such as gouty deposits in the joints, urinary calculi, gall-stones, tuberculosis of the spine, and even adhesions surrounding an old infection of the appendix. Two troubles seem to have been particularly widespread amongst the Ancient Egyptians, namely, severe infection of the gums and chronic rheumatism, and as the two conditions are often associated, it is probable that they stand in the relationship of cause and effect, the dental caries being responsible for the rheumatism. We know that dental caries and gum infections are frequently the result of insufficiencies in the diet so it is quite likely that the nutrition of the Ancient Egyptians tended to be deficient in vitamins.

Where can we best start a story which goes so far back into the past that its beginning is lost in the mists of time? We shall select as a starting point a period of time some seventeen thousand years ago when the earliest known portrait of a medical man was painted. On the walls of Les Trois Frères cave in the Pyrénées there is a rock painting of a man, wrapped in the skin of some animal, with his legs and arms painted in stripes and with the antlers of a stag fixed on his head. The artist, who lived in the Aurignacian age, has

provided us with an authentic portrait of a contemporary witch-doctor in his professional dress, and it is from the witch-doctor that the medical man of today is descended. The drawing on the walls of Les Trois Frères cave provides us therefore with a starting point for this story of medicine. (*See* Plate 1.)

It is reasonable to suppose that men who were able to fashion the remarkable flint tools and weapons dug up on these sites were sufficiently intelligent also to find some means of dealing with their injuries and sicknesses. Whatever treatment they had for these ills magic played a considerable part in it, but it is a mistake to imagine that the ancient medicine man was nothing but a sorcerer. In his book *Medicine, Magic and Religion*, Dr. Rivers points out that all primitive peoples use simple remedies of the "domestic" order for the treatment of illnesses that they do not consider sufficiently grave to require the attention of the tribal medicine man. He gives us, as a modern example of this, the Kai of New Guinea who, in addition to employing the services of the local sorcerer, make use of such simple remedies as palm-fruit poultices for wounds, bleeding for headaches, leeches for local pains and aches, and vapour baths for rheumatism. So also is it almost certain that the ancient medicine man portrayed on the walls of Les Trois Frères cave supplemented his rituals and his magical ceremonies with the use of medicinal draughts, local applications and ointments.

What we do know for certain is that prehistoric man was bold enough to undertake a surgical procedure as formidable as trephining. Innumerable prehistoric skulls with trephine holes have been dug up, chiefly in France, but also in smaller numbers in Austria, Poland, Russia, Germany and Spain. Strange to say, only a few of these trephined skulls have, as yet, come to light in Great Britain. It is believed by the majority of anthropologists that the operation was performed for the purpose of permitting the demon responsible for producing such illnesses as migraine and epilepsy to escape from the victim's head. That the trephining was not performed for the raising of a depressed fracture of the skull is proved by the absence of any signs of injury in the neighbourhood of the trephine hole. (*See* Fig. 1.) Some people have suggested that the operation was undertaken as a religious ritual, but as Professor Guthrie has pointed out, the classification of prehistoric trephining into ritual trephining

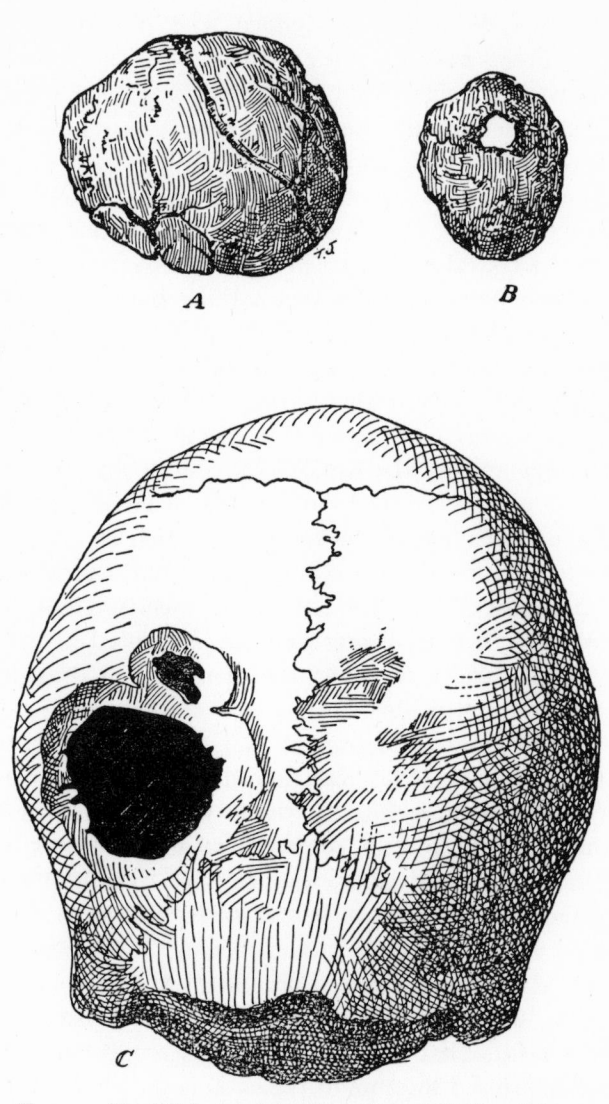

FIG. 1—Neolithic trephination. A and B, Rondelles or amulets; C, Neolithic trephined skull (*From Moodie*)

and therapeutic trephining "ignores the fact that no clear-cut distinction can be drawn between these two motives. All who have studied the early history of medicine have noted that the physician was at first a priest, and that his religious and medical duties were intimately intermingled." (Douglas Guthrie, *A History of Medicine*.)

THE NATURAL AND THE SUPERNATURAL ELEMENTS IN MEDICINE

We shall find later that the relative importance attributed to these two elements in medicine varies throughout the ages, at one time the one taking precedence and at another the other. In Ancient Egyptian medicine, for example, the supernatural element was obviously of supreme importance, the priest-physician being primarily a priest and only secondarily a medical man. The Ebers papyrus contains as many spells, incantations and magical ceremonies to be used on various occasions as it does drugs and prescriptions. Even when the patient is taking medicine he still has to utter a suitable prayer, such as the following one: "Welcome remedy! Welcome! that dost drive away that which is in my heart and limbs." Later, in the Hippocratic Age of Greece, it is the physical remedy which is regarded as important, the uttering of an invocation being a private matter that can be left to the discretion of the patient to decide upon. In the Middle Ages magic reasserts itself in medicine in the form of Church ceremonies for the casting out of devils and the exhibition of holy relics of the saints reputed to be possessed with curative powers. With the dawn of scientific medicine in the seventeenth century the priestly intruder is banished, seemingly for good, and as the centuries file past medical men become more and more materialistic in their outlook. Finally we see the reappearance of the priest but in an entirely new and secular guise. The attempts to explain life purely in terms of machinery, and to interpret disease in terms of a breakage of that machinery, have now failed and "mind" has forced itself on the physician's notice. Doctors have at last realized that it is impossible to neglect any longer the psychogenic factors in illness and a new kind of secular priest has appeared to deal with these in the shape of the psycho-therapist. Magical practices again have a place in medicine but chiefly in the form of psycho-analysis and suggestion. And thanks to the extraordinarily recuperative powers of the human body and the resilience of the human mind,

the patient generally manages throughout the ages to recover his health in spite of all the vicissitudes of treatment to which he is being subjected.

Having taken this preliminary glimpse of medicine in prehistoric times, we can now pass on to the historical period and can look at medicine as it existed in the earlier cultures. There is no unanimity of opinion as to where and at what date the thing we call civilization began, but we shall start with the ancient myth that some of the inhabitants of the legendary Atlantis were forewarned of the impending disaster and managed to escape elsewhere before their country was entirely overwhelmed. Whether this be true or not is immaterial. It provides us with the starting point that refugees from Atlantis reached the shores of Africa and Western Europe and from there spread eastwards to found three great civilizations: those of Egypt, Sumeria and pre-Aryan India. Whether they were the offspring of Atlantis or not, these three civilizations were at any rate all-important diffusion centres for culture and they provide us with excellent starting points for a history of medicine.

SUMERIAN AND BABYLONIAN MEDICINE

The more the Sumerian civilization is studied, the greater and the more interesting it is found to be. Its capital was the city of Ur situated on the Euphrates, about a hundred miles west of the Persian Gulf. The site of Ur has been excavated by Sir Cyril Woolley and we now know that the Sumerians attained a very high standard of craftsmanship and art, and that they were a well-organized community. They wrote upon clay tablets and these cuneiform writings reveal to us that there existed in Ur a medical profession possessed of a reasonably high standard of ethics. Many small copper knives have also been dug up and in all probability these were used by surgeons as scalpels. The Sumerian civilization came to an end in about the year 2000 B.C. and was replaced by two new civilizations: that of Assyria in the North and of Babylon in the South.

We possess more knowledge of Babylonian than of Sumerian medicine, and this is to a great extent due to the discovery of a code of laws engraved on a pillar of hard black stone, to be seen now in the Louvre. These laws were drawn up and recorded on this stone by command of Hammurabi (1948–1905 B.C.), an extremely able

Babylonian ruler. Fortunately he considered it important to put on record also the special laws appertaining to medical practice. Amongst these were regulations on the subject of professional fees and the following shows how carefully this matter had been considered. "If the doctor shall treat a gentleman and shall open an abscess with a bronze knife and shall preserve the eye of the patient, he shall receive ten sheckels of silver. If the patient is a slave, his master shall pay two sheckels of silver." So far all is to the advantage of the doctor, but later regulations show that medical practice in Babylon was not without its risks to the medical man. The inscription continues as follows: "If the doctor shall open an abscess with a bronze knife and shall kill the patient or shall destroy the sight of the eye, his hands shall be cut off." But this penalty was enforced only in the case of surgical failure in what, before the passing of the National Health Act, was known in Great Britain as "better-class practice". If the patient who died under the operation happened to be a slave, then all that was required of the unsuccessful surgeon was that he should "replace the slave with a new slave". Should it only be the sight of the slave's eye that was destroyed and not his life, then the penalty demanded of the doctor was that he should defray half of the purchase cost of a new slave.

The chief reason for quoting these old Babylonian medical inscriptions is that they clearly indicate that a medical profession existed at that time, that its members carried out minor operations and that they were subject to a number of medical regulations. In other words, there existed in ancient Babylon a properly organized medical profession. Nor need we be surprised at this, for archaeological research shows that older cultures were far less primitive than we formerly supposed them to be. Even the prehistoric Stone Age had its own art, and what perhaps is surprising is that the pottery left behind by Palaeolithic man is of greater artistic merit than is the pottery of his successor Neolithic man. In short, the more we learn about prehistoric man, the less does he conform to the conventional picture of him as a brutish being, half man and half ape, armed with a stone axe with which he bludgeoned all his rivals.

There are reasons for believing that medicine was regarded as a subject of considerable importance in ancient Babylon. Herodotus

writes to the effect that every educated Babylonian was interested
in it, to such an extent indeed that it was customary in Babylon to
exhibit sick people in the street so that if passers-by happened
themselves to have suffered from the same diseases or had known
other people who had suffered from them, they might recognize the
exhibited illnesses and give useful advice. The relevant passage in
Herodotus runs as follows: "They bring out their sick in the market
place for they have no physicians; then those who pass by the sick
person confer with him about the disease to discover whether they
have themselves been afflicted with the same disease as the sick
person, or have seen others so afflicted; then the passers-by talk to
him and advise him to have recourse to the same treatment as that
by which they escaped a similar disease, or as they have known to
cure others. And they are not allowed to pass by a sick person in
silence without inquiring the nature of the distemper."

Herodotus is referring here to the earlier part of the Babylonian
era. It is obvious that a people so interested in the causes of sickness
as the Babylonians would not be content to leave the matter of
treatment for good in the hands of the amateur doctors of the
market place. So the professional physician eventually appeared
and, still later a great deal of specialization took place, so that in
Babylon as in Egypt there was a different expert for every type of
disease.

INDIAN MEDICINE

Our knowledge of ancient Indian medicine is very scanty. The
earliest Sanskrit documents relevant to medicine are the Rig Veda
(1500 B.C.) and the Ayur Veda (700 B.C.). From these it is apparent
that ancient Indian medicine was strongest in surgery and, strange
to say, weakest in that subject on which surgery is based—anatomy.
The plastic surgeon of today still refers to the Indian method of
rhinoplasty, in other words, to the method of turning down a flap of
skin from the forehead, a procedure adopted by the ancient Indian
surgeons when they wanted to cover a gross defect in a patient's
nose. Infidelity in a wife was punished in ancient India by cutting
off her nose and Indian surgeons devised this particular flap operation
for the repair of this mutilation. It was in surgery that the ancient
Hindus excelled. Susruta, a surgeon who lived about A.D. 400,

describes nearly a hundred different surgical instruments used by himself and his colleagues. Caesarian section was performed in ancient India as well as operations for the removal of calculi.

The earlier Sanskrit document, the Rig Veda, contains philosophical and scientific knowledge of great interest but it contributes little to our knowledge of ancient Hindu medicine. It is to the Ayur Veda that we must refer for medical information and in this work we find a description of the vascular system which strongly suggests that the Hindus of this period anticipated Harvey's discovery of the circulation of blood. The Ayur Veda also contains the highly intelligent observations that plague is likely to appear when many dead rats are found lying about, and that malaria is caused by mosquitoes. It gives a description of phthisis, a disease characterized by a persistent cough, fever and the expectoration of blood. Over seven hundred medicinal plants are mentioned in this great Hindu work, and information is given about the dispensing of a number of useful ointments, inhalations and sneezing powders.

The physicians of the Vedic Age belonged not to the Brahman but to the Vaisya caste. Because, according to the ancient laws of Manu they were regarded as being unclean, they were excluded from the funeral feasts. Although the Ayur Veda is not one of the four great religious Vedas of India, it is regarded as being knowledge revealed to the great physicians Charaka and Susruta, either by the divine healer Dhanwantari himself or else through the inspired utterances of some other great "rishi" or teacher.

EGYPTIAN MEDICINE

The third ancient civilization to be considered is that of Egypt. Medical practice in Egypt was so much in the hands of the priests and so closely tied to theology, that we know far more about the Egyptian gods and demi-gods who presided over medicine than we do about medicine itself. Imhotep became the Egyptian god of healing and he has therefore the unique distinction of being the only medical man ever to achieve deification. Imhotep is also one of the earliest doctors known to us by name and no name could have better befitted a great physician, meaning as it does, "he who cometh in peace". After the great physician Imhotep had died he was regarded first as a demi-god and then later he was promoted to full deityship.

Many centuries afterwards the Greeks claimed that Imhotep was identical with their own god of healing, Æsculapius.

Unfortunately we know less about Imhotep's achievements as a physician than we do about his work as a great architect. He designed the Step Pyramid at Sakkarah, and in the many bronze statuettes of him that are to be found he is generally represented as seated and gazing at a papyrus, presumably an architectural plan, resting on his knees. Yet Imhotep must have been at least as great a physician as he was a designer, for as has already been said, he was worshipped as the divine physician for many hundreds of years after his death.

In the earlier years of the Egyptian civilization the priest and the physician were one and inseparable and it was only in the later dynasties that medicine freed itself from religion sufficiently for the Egyptian physician to appear. The Egyptians did not regard disease and death as natural and inevitable human events but believed that they were contrived and imposed on men by a hostile force. Maspero describes the Egyptian's view of illness as follows: "Often, though, it (the hostile force) belongs to the invisible world, and only reveals itself by the malignity of its attacks: it is a god, a spirit, the soul of a dead man, that has cunningly entered a living person, or that throws itself upon him with irresistible violence. Once in possession of the body, the evil influence breaks the bones, sucks the marrow, drinks the blood, gnaws the intestines and the heart, and devours the flesh. The invalid perishes according to the progress of this destructive work; and death speedily ensues, unless the evil genius can be driven out of it before it has committed irreparable damage. Whoever treats a sick person has therefore two equally important duties to perform. He must first discover the nature of the spirit in possession, and if necessary its name, and then attack it, drive it out, or even destroy it. He can only succeed by powerful magic, so he must be an expert in reciting incantations, and skilful in making amulets. He must then use medicine (drugs and diet) to contend with the disorders which the presence of the strange being has produced in the body." (Maspero, *Life in Ancient Egypt and Assyria*. London, 1891.)

An examination of the translations of Egyptian papyri that are concerned with the art of healing shows them to be filled with

incantations, symbols and magical formulae to be used in the curing of the various ailments. There are also descriptions of a great number of physical remedies in the way of draughts, gargles, salves, snuffs, inhalations, suppositories, plasters and poultices. The papyri show that the priest-physicians of ancient Egypt knew and made use of the following drugs: opium, hemlock, salts of copper, squills and castor oil. Their surgery was very primitive but their hygiene and public health measures were often of a very high order, much superior to those to be found in Europe during the Middle Ages. By far the most valuable of the papyri from the point of view of medical history are the Ebers and the Edwin Smith papyri. Both of these papyri show that advances are being made in clinical medicine during the later Egyptian epochs. Although charms and rituals are still being used, the priest physicians have learnt to examine their patients in order to discover what is physically amiss with them. The following instructions given in the *Ebers Papyrus* for palpating swellings or tumours are quite practical.

"When thou meetest a tumour of the flesh in any part of the body of a person, and thou findest it like hide in his flesh, he is clammy, it goes and comes under thy finger, except when the finger is kept still, because the matter escapes through it, then thou sayest, 'It is a tumour of the flesh. I will treat the disease. I will try to heal it with fire, like cautery heals'.

"When thou meetest a tumour that has attacked a vessel, it has formed a tumour in his body when thy finger examines it and it is hard stone under thy fingers, then say thou, 'It is a tumour of the vessels. I shall treat the disease with the knife'.

"When thou meetest a pustular tumour in the limb of a person, and if, in palpating it, thou findest that it goes and comes and that the flesh thereunder is drawn over, then say thou, 'A gathering of pustules. Use the knife against it'." (The *Ebers Papyrus* translated from the German version by C. P. Bryan.)

The *Edwin Smith Papyrus* has been translated and commented on by J. H. Breasted, and it is best described as a medical guide to the treatment of wounds and sprains. (J. H. Breasted, *The Edwin Smith Surgical Papyrus*. Chicago, 1930.) It is interesting to note that the

Edwin Smith Papyrus contains a description of a method of reducing a dislocation of the jaw which very closely resembles that used at the present day.

A medical author of the time of Rameses I presents his qualifications for authorship in the preface to his book as follows: "I have come out from the school of medicine at Heliopolis, where the venerable masters of the Great Temple have inculcated their remedies within me. I have come out from the Gynaecological School of Sais, where the Divine Mothers have given me their prescriptions. I am in possession of the incantations composed by Osiris personally. My guide has always been the god Thoth, the inventor of speech and writer of infallible prescriptions, he who alone knows how to give reputations to magicians and physicians who follow his precepts. Incantations are excellent for remedies and remedies are good for incantations."

We find here the attainment of an excellent compromise between the two ingredients of Egyptian medicine, magical incantations and physical remedies. It is the earliest reference in medical literature to the psycho-somatic school of medicine, the incantations providing the psycho-therapy and the physical remedies the treatment of the body.

In the year 525 B.C., after the Persian conquest, a medical school was founded at Sais in Lower Egypt and Herodotus praises the high standard attained by this school and also draws attention to the large number of specialists working in it.

CHINESE MEDICINE

China must also be mentioned as one of the great centres of ancient medical learning. The first physician mentioned in Chinese literature is the Emperor Shen Nung who lived about 3000 B.C. Shen Nung was only an amateur doctor, but he was very far from being an imperial dilettante toying with novel medical theories. He made many experiments on himself over a great many years, and is credited with having discovered a large number of new drugs and poisons. The work in which he gives an account of these researches of his, the *Pen Tsao or Great Herbal*, has run through countless editions since it first appeared and was apparently reprinted in Egypt as late as the year 1911. Very few writers have produced

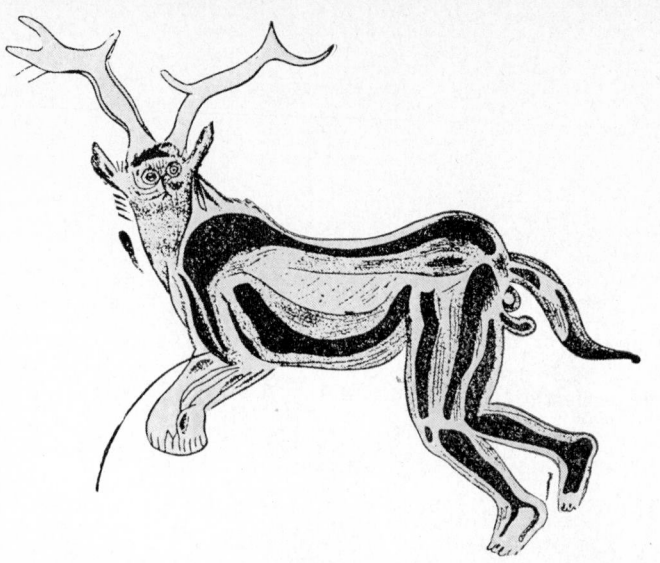

"Medicine Man" as depicted in Cave Trois Frères,
France

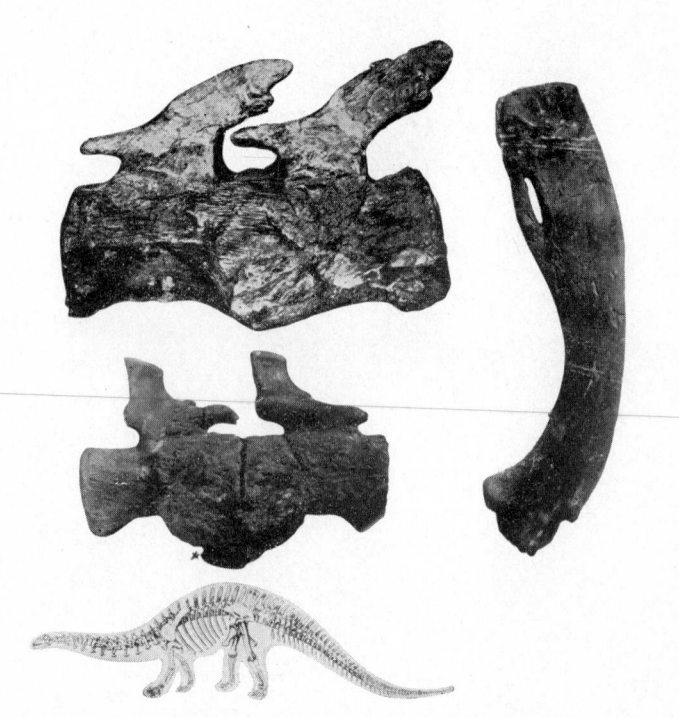

Severe arthritis in a dinosaur likely to have caused
difficulty in getting about

(From *Palaeopathology*, Roy Moodie)

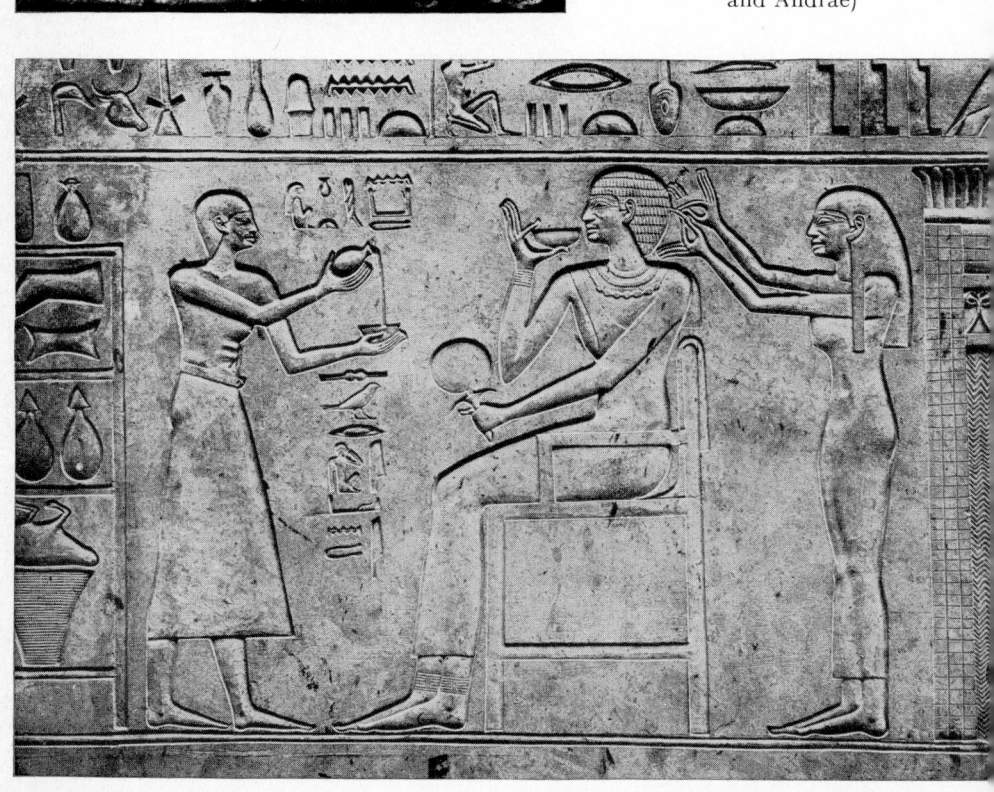

Poliomyelitis as depicted in an ancient Egyptian stele of the XVIII Dynasty

(From *Magician and Leech*, Warren Dawson)

Toilet of Princess Kivait

(From *Kunst der alten Orients*, Schafer and Andrae)

books that have remained in print for four thousand years, a feat that the Emperor has succeeded in achieving.

Professor Guthrie gives the following quotation from the writings of yet another Chinese Emperor interested in medicine and physiology, this time the Emperor Hwang Ti (2650 B.C.). In *Nei Ching* (The Book of Medicine), the Emperor Hwang Ti writes: "All the blood in the body is under the control of the heart . . . the blood current flows continuously in a circle, and never stops." It is difficult to say how the Emperor managed to arrive at this correct conclusion that the blood circulated on the basis of knowledge extant at that time. Harvey's discovery of the circulation of the blood was to a large extent founded on a very careful consideration of the anatomy of the vascular system, but in ancient China little was known about the anatomy of the human body, as the dissection of bodies was strictly forbidden and therefore very rarely carried out. It is of course possible that an absolute ruler with powers of life and death over his subjects enjoyed greater facilities for anatomical research than did ordinary mortals.

The third Imperial patron and student of Chinese medicine was the Emperor Kien Lung who appointed a committee of experts to bring out *The Golden Mirrors of Medicine*, an elegant Chinese name for an immense encyclopaedia of medicine which was eventually published in forty volumes. In this imposing work the principles of Chinese medicine were laid down and an account was given of a great many different kinds of treatment, including treatment by massage and acupuncture. A study of these works shows that there were two great theories in ancient Chinese medicine, the first being the doctrine of the five elements: earth, fire, water, wood and metal. The body was said to be composed of these five components and it was from this much older doctrine of five principles that the European theory of the four body humours was probably derived. The second great doctrine of ancient Chinese medicine is the idea of the two fundamental principles, the Yang and the Yin.

The Yang and the Yin were looked upon as being two opposing forces which entered into the genesis of phenomena of every kind. Examples of these two opposing, and at the same complementary, principles are to be found in the dualities of action and reaction, male and female, heat and cold, life and death, and so on. Every-

thing in the universe, including human health, was said to depend on a proper balance being maintained between these two opposing forces, and also between the five different elements of which the body was composed. And, philosophically speaking, there is much to be said in favour of this idea that health is a state of harmony between a number of different elements, and that disease is a disturbance or disharmony in that balance.

ANCIENT JEWISH MEDICINE

Ancient Jewish medicine was very primitive, and except for the excellent preventive measures laid down by the Mosaic Law it is of little interest to us. The physician scarcely exists so far as the Old Testament is concerned for disease was regarded as being an expression of the wrath of God, for the treatment of which the patient must seek the aid of the priests. The latter taught that provided a man lived in accordance with the law of Moses he would remain healthy. "I will put none of these diseases upon thee, which I have brought upon the Egyptians, for I am the Lord that healeth thee" (Exodus xv, 26). It should be noted however that the reference here is to diseases on a very large scale, in other words, to epidemics, and it was in dealing with epidemics that ancient Jewish medicine excelled. The Jewish priests, who wielded far more power than the few insignificant private physicians who existed at that time, acted as medical officers of health, and remarkably efficient officers they appear to have been. Whereas the Greeks of a much later age seem to have taken very little notice of the direct transmission of disease from one individual to another, the Jewish priests were keenly aware of it and took whatever steps were possible to guard against it. The Book of Leviticus lays down clear and efficient instructions on such subjects as proper and improper food, clean and unclean objects, the hygiene of childbirth and of menstruation, and the prevention of contagion. Pigs transmit such parasites as cysto-cercus and tape-worm to human beings and it was a wise precaution to forbid the eating of pork. References are made in Leviticus to the diagnosis of gonorrhoea, leucorrhoea and leprosy, and in each case special emphasis is placed on the need for preventive measures. Directions are also given on such subjects as the isolation of infected people and the disinfection of their property, the latter being

carried out so thoroughly as to include scraping the walls of the house or, in certain cases, razing the house to the ground. So efficient were the Bible's instructions for the handling of the leprosy problem that when that disease started spreading through Europe during the Middle Ages, the preventive methods adopted were those recommended in the Old Testament. It may be said therefore that the sole contribution made by the Jews to medicine were in the fields of hygiene and of preventive medicine.

As the Pentateuch is the written version of the Mosaic Law, so is the Talmud the law according to oral tradition, and the Talmud contains far more precise knowledge of medicine than does the semi-legendary narrative of the Old Testament. Yet even in the Talmud the physician appears to be a person of very little importance. The text in the Old Testament that is so frequently quoted about honouring the physician was added at a much later date when physicians became of more account. "Honour a physician according to thy need of him with honour due to him; for verily the Lord created him." According to the scholars these words were contributed about 180 B.C. by Jesus the son of Sirach and they therefore express a later and amended view of the medical profession.

There is no evidence that any Jewish physician attained a position of any eminence until the Middle Ages and even then the eminence was a very limited one for the Church forbade the employment of Jewish doctors on the grounds that they were pagans. Yet, as everybody realized at that time, the Jewish doctor was the only one worth consulting. He and his pagan colleague the Greek physician were the only medical men who retained any knowledge of Hippocratic medicine during those dark years of ignorance and mental lethargy. The difficulty was overcome by means of an excellent compromise; in public the Jewish doctor was banned and abused, as enjoined by the Church, but in secret he was employed. Every monastery is said to have possessed its own Jewish physician carefully hidden from the eyes of the world but consulted in secret by the monks and the Abbot whenever they felt in the least indisposed. It was the lot of the Jewish physician during the Middle Ages, as it has been the lot of the Jewish nation throughout the whole of history, to be simultaneously abused and used, hated and liked, praised and blamed. The Jewish doctor was a contraband commodity,

a luxury prohibited by the Church, yet used in secret by every ailing prelate in the land. The same treatment was meted out to the Jewish doctor in Spain. He was permitted to practise there until he was no longer required and then in 1492 when other doctors were available he was hounded out of the country. Jewish doctors were likewise utilized by the Medical School of Palermo in Southern Italy until it was possible for the school to get on without them. This was the fate of the Jewish doctor in Europe and to a certain extent it has been his fate recently, as the pre-war medical exodus from Germany and Austria has shown.

CHAPTER II

Greek Medicine (600–372 B.C.)

SOMEBODY has said that we owe everything we possess either to Nature or to the Ancient Greeks and this is certainly true of the healing arts. Nature is the Great Healer and it was Hippocrates who taught us how to assist and not to hinder her work. The Greek era is an extremely important one in the history of medicine and we are apt to forget how long it lasted. It spanned a stretch of eight hundred years, beginning in the sixth century before Christ and ending at the close of the second century of the Christian era. Our own period of European Medicine, which may be said to date from the Renaissance, has only endured half the time that the Greek School of Medicine lasted.

Nothing begins entirely anew and Greek medicine derived knowledge from a great many older sources, Egyptian, Babylonian and probably Indian. Greece also learnt much from the remarkable people who had their headquarters in Crete, the Minoans. It is now realized that the Minoan civilization, like many other ancient civilizations, was far more advanced than the archaeologists of an older school believed it to be. It was particularly advanced in matters of Public Health. The drainage systems, water-supply, bathing arrangements and methods of disposal of refuse uncovered in the excavation of Minoan cities are much superior to those which existed in our own British cities in the time of the Stuarts. It is likely, therefore, that the Greeks in the process of over-running the Minoan cities in Eastern Europe, in about the year 1000 B.C.— Troy was one of the last of these Minoan strongholds—learnt a great deal from the people whom they vanquished.

Originally the Greeks came from the north in two great invading

37

streams: the Dorians, who spread into Crete, the island of Cos and the neighbouring peninsula of Cnidus; and the Ionians who colonized Western Asia Minor. The medical system evolved by these Greek conquerors took shape first in Asia Minor and thence slowly spread throughout the whole Greek world. The Greek colonists in Asia Minor were very well placed strategically for the collecting and the collating of medical knowledge reaching them from outside sources, since they lay on the fringes of the great civilizations that had been cradled in the valleys of the Tigris and the Euphrates. They were also able to maintain close touch with the great culture which had grown up along the banks of the Nile. Finally, as we have already seen, the Greeks learnt a great deal from the people they conquered.

It was in the islands lying off the Greek coast that the knowledge coming from all these different countries was sorted out and collated, and more particularly in the island of Delos. According to an old tradition, this island was the birthplace of Apollo. Whilst still a child, Apollo was transported from Delos to Delphi and there, young though he was, he slew the python or monster that was rendering that region uninhabitable to man. Delphi later became the site of the world-famous oracle, and Professor Guthrie makes the interesting suggestion that many of the problems that were submitted to the oracle may well have been questions concerned with health and the treatment of illness. According to legend, Apollo taught the healing arts to the gifted and sagacious centaur Chiron and from him it passed on to Chiron's young pupils Jason, Achilles and Æsculapius. But it is with the last named that we are alone concerned here for Æsculapius became for the Greeks what Imhotep had previously been for the Egyptians, their God of Healing. So active was Æsculapius as a healer, so skilful was he in averting death, and so many astonishing miracles did he perform in the way of raising the dead, that Pluto, the jealous ruler of the Underworld, complained to the father of the gods of his interference. "The supply of new souls to the Shades," he grumbled, "is being endangered by all this healing," and Zeus, realizing that Pluto had just grounds for complaint, slew Æsculapius with a thunderbolt. (*See* Plate 4.)

Many temples, known as Asklepieia, were erected to the slain god's memory and to these the sick were brought for treatment.

The great ruins of one of the most famous of these Asklepieia are still to be seen at Epidaurus. Simple measures such as dieting, baths, exercises and massage were used at the temples but the main treatment was a form of psycho-therapy known as "incubation". On arrival at the temple the sick person started his treatment by making a sacrificial offering and taking a purifying bath. He then made a bed for himself on the "abaton" or the colonnaded terrace of the temple which lay open to the air. There he would recline at night, to be visited perhaps in his dreams by Æsculapius, or if not so favoured as this, to be given treatment at the hands of the god's human representatives, the temple priests. (*See* Plates 4 and 6.) A revealing description of a night spent by a patient on the abaton of a temple is to be found in the Plutus of Aristophanes.

"Soon the Temple servitor
Put out the lights and bade us fall asleep,
Nor stir, nor speak, whatever noise we heard.
So down we lay in orderly repose.
And I could catch no slumber, not a wink,
Struck by a nice tureen of broth which stood
A little distance from an old wife's head,
Whereto I marvellously longed to creep.
Then, glancing upwards, I beheld the priest
Whipping the cheese-cakes and figs from off
The holy table; thence he coasted round
To every altar spying what was left.
And everything he found he consecrated
Into a sort of sack."

Aristophanes does not tell us the nature of the illness from which his character is suffering but his intense interest in food suggests that his appetite is not impaired by it. Eye troubles were very common in ancient Greece and a well-known remedy for them was an application containing extract of cloves, garlic, squills, vinegar and verjuice. Aristophanes continues his account of night on the abaton and reaches the dramatic moment when a patient who is suffering from one of these eye troubles is cured.

"Then the god clucked,
And out there issued from the holy shrine
Two great, enormous serpents . . .
And underneath the scarlet cloth they crept,
And licked his eyelids, as it seemed to me;
And, mistress dear, before you could have drunk
Of wine ten goblets, *wealth* arose and saw . . ."

(B. B. Rogers' translation of *Aristophanes*.
London, Bell & Sons, Vol. VI, II, 668.)

Some sort of research was carried on in the Asklepieia, notes being taken of cases under treatment and the results of the treatment recorded. Ordinary medical remedies were applied by the temple attendants, abscesses opened and other operations of a minor kind performed. As Aristophanes has described in the above verse, harmless snakes played an important part in the temple ritual by licking the eyes and exposed sores of the patients. Small buildings containing a paved and circular pit have often been found close to the ruins of an Asklepieia and it is probable that they were used for housing the temple snakes.

When the God of Healing failed to appear and to bring about a miracle, the patient remained for a time in the temple in order to take the baths and the other forms of spa treatment prescribed by the temple authorities. Amusements were even provided for the friends and relatives waiting until the patients had finished their courses of treatment. The immense theatre at Epidaurus with seating accommodation for about twenty thousand spectators is one of the most imposing of these. That fairly satisfactory results were obtained from the temple treatment is supported by the fact that it survived for many centuries, from about 700 B.C. till far into the Christian era. Professor Guthrie tells us that traces of the old temple rituals and practices are still to be found in Southern Europe at the present time. "In the churches of Palermo, Naples, Sardinia and Styria the custom survives to this day. On the sacred island of Tenos, close to Delos, a great religious festival is held twice a year, and many sick persons sleep in the church in expectation of a cure. . . . Incubation is also still practised on a small scale

in Cyprus, in Rhodes and at many country churches on the mainland of Greece and in Asia Minor."

The old Greek temples of healing were built in places which would now be used as health resorts. They were situated on hills near to a spring of pure water, or in some sheltered valley near to the sea, and some of them owed their fame to their proximity to mineral or hot springs. The patients applying for treatment were carefully selected. "Access to the shrine was forbidden to the unclean and the impure, pregnant women and the mortally afflicted were kept away; no dead body could find a resting place within the holy precincts, the shelter and the care of the sick being undertaken by the keepers of inns and boarding-houses in the neighbourhood. The suppliants for aid had to submit to careful purification; to bathe in sea, river or spring, to fast for a prescribed time, to abjure wine and certain articles of diet, and they were only permitted to enter the temple when they were adequately prepared by cleansing inunction and fumigation. This lengthy and exhausting preparation, partly dietetic, partly suggestive, was accompanied by a solemn service of prayer and sacrifice, whose symbolism tended highly to excite the imagination." (Max Neuberger, *History of Medicine*. English Translation. Oxford, 1910.) In other words, the Asklepieia combined the curative assets of Carlsbad and Lourdes.

It was the custom for the cured to give votive offerings and accounts of miraculous cures happening at that temple were inscribed on stone (*see* Plate 5) in the same way that cures are recorded in the official files at Lourdes. The following reports were found engraved on stone tablets at Epidaurus.

"A dumb boy came as a suppliant to the temple to recover his voice. When he had performed the sacrifices and fulfilled the rites, the Temple priest who bore the sacrificial fire turned to the boy's father and said, 'Do you promise to pay within a year the fees for the cure, if you obtain that for which you have come?' The boy replied that he would. His father was greatly astonished at this and told his son to speak again. The boy repeated the words and so was cured."

"Enippos had had for six years the point of a spear in his cheek. As he was sleeping the god extracted the spear-head and gave it to him into his hands. When the day came Enippos departed cured and he held the spear-head in his hands."

"Hermodites of Lamosakos was paralysed in body. In his sleep he was healed by the god, who ordered him to bring to the temple as large a stone as he could when he left the abaton. The man brought the stone, which now lies before the abaton."

The study of dreams appears to have been an important part of the temple treatment. It is likely that the early Greeks learnt this interest in dreams from the Babylonians who were great experts in the interpretation of dreams. The priests of the Greek temples of healing paid attention to dreams for the same reason that the followers of Jung pay attention to them, because they throw light on the contents of the less conscious levels of the mind. The patients of the Asklepieia were required therefore to report their dreams in order that they might be interpreted by the priests. In other words, temple practice included a small amount of psycho-analysis as well as a great deal of suggestion. This interest in the study of dreams persisted for a long time in Greece so that we find Aristotle commenting on it. "Even scientific physicians tell us that one should pay diligent attention to dreams, and to hold this view is reasonable also for those who are not practitioners, but speculative philosophers." (Aristotle, *Parva Naturalia, De divinatione per somnum.*)

MEDICINE IN THE PRE-HIPPOCRATIC OR HOMERIC AGE

There are men in human history who have exerted so powerful an influence on their fellows that their names are used as boundary marks dividing off one epoch from another. For example, we speak of the Shakespearian and the Homeric Ages and, when discussing the development of physics, we sub-divide it into the Newtonian and post-Newtonian eras. Greek medicine is sharply sub-divided in this way by the life of Hippocrates into the pre- and the post-Hippocratic Ages. At present we are concerned only with the pre-Hippocratic Age and much of our knowledge of it is derived from Homer.

Homer sang of the Trojan War and what he has to tell us about medicine in the Iliad is almost exclusively concerned with war surgery. (*See* Fig. 2.) As a consequence of this, there is a monotony about Homer's reports of the work of the army doctors during the Trojan War, just as there is a monotony about the official medical records of the two recent world wars. We grow tired of Homer's

accounts of wounds and of the efforts made by army surgeons to deal with them, for one report very closely resembles another. We learn for example that "Agamemnon ordered his herald that he should with all speed call Machaon hither, the hero son of Aesculapius, the noble leech, to see Menelaus, whom one skilled in archery hath wounded with a bow shot, to his glory and grief. . . . The god-like

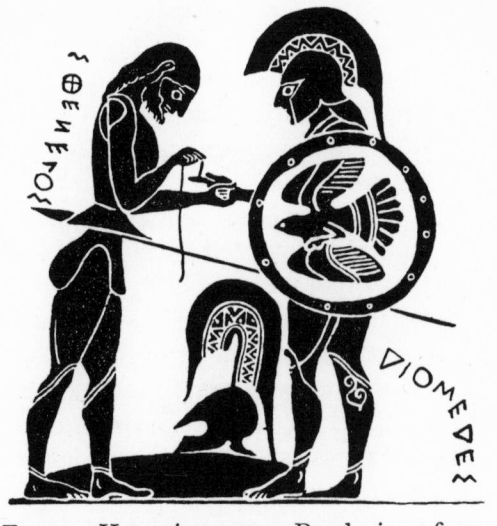

FIG. 2.—Homeric surgery. Bandaging a finger.
From a Greek vase.

hero came and drew forth the arrow, and as it was drawn forth the keen barbs were broken backwards . . . and when he saw the wound where the arrow had lighted, he sucked out the blood and cunningly spread soothing drugs such as Chiron of his good will, had imparted to his sire."

With characteristic Teutonic thoroughness D. H. Frölich has made a statistical survey of all the injuries recorded by Homer in the Iliad, and he has found that out of a total of 147 wounds, 106 were due to spear thrusts and that 80 per cent of these spear wounds ended fatally. Arrow wounds, as was to be expected, proved much less dangerous, and the total mortality from all forms of wounds worked out at as high as 77.6 per cent. It is not surprising that with this lack of variety and with the disappointing results obtained, the

medical records of the Trojan War make dull reading, in spite of Homer's surprisingly good knowledge of anatomy and of his poetic genius. Frölich is so impressed with Homer's remarkable knowledge of anatomy that he has put forward the novel theory that the author of the Iliad, about whom we know next to nothing, was an army surgeon with an unusual flair for poetry. His theory is only a little less surprising than Samuel Butler's alternative suggestion that the author of the Iliad was a woman.

Even although the Greeks attained a higher level of culture and were less superstitious than their predecessors the Babylonians, the doctors of this pre-Hippocratic period would appear to have had more faith in rituals and magical ceremonies than in physical remedies. And they were quite logical in showing this preference, for illnesses were still regarded as being the result of malignant influences or as punishments meted out by the gods. It was reasonable therefore to try to appease the gods by means of ritual sacrifices, or to do one's best to cut short an illness, when it had occurred, by various purification ceremonies. It must be borne in mind that the physician of that time was not a highly educated man but a member of the artisan class. No special qualification was required of him. He started his professional life by serving an apprenticeship and as doctoring ran in families he was often apprenticed to his own father. On completing this apprenticeship he usually went off on his travels, settling down eventually in any city which seemed to offer him good opportunities for starting a practice. A medical newcomer to a city often began by offering to treat people without any charge and then, after he had gained a good reputation, he was able to recoup his previous losses.

Although physicians belonged to the artisan level of society and were seldom well-educated men, they were often highly esteemed by their fellow citizens. It is true that Plato banned them from his Republic but it is also true that he admitted a medical man to the exclusive coterie of his Symposium. Not only was the physician honoured by his fellow men but he might be competed for if he happened to be an exceptionally good one. One city would outbid another to secure his services, just as one city outbids another today in order to obtain a successful footballer. And if the acquired doctor served his city well he was honoured as the modern footballer

or film star is honoured. Thus we find the people of Brykounti
decreeing that, on account of his services, Menocritus shall have a
golden crown and a seat of honour at all the festivals, and that the
decree to this effect shall be read publicly at the games and engraved
on a pillar of the Temple of Poseidon. Even a private patient might
on occasions pay for an inscription being made in order to put on
record the particular skill of his own practitioner, as the following
words carved in stone and dating from the first century B.C. show:

> "If ever mortal by wisdom discovered ought worthy
>   of honour,
> Surely, Argaeus, 'tis thou, O man of marvellous
>   mind:
> Thou who hast gathered from books of learning
>   and lore of physicians,
> Thou who dost heal with sweet wine wearisome
>   pains in the joints,
> Passing in brightness the stars shining for ever on
>   high."
>
> (*Corpus Inscriptionum Allicarum*, III, 779.

Hygnius, the fabulist, states that the Athenians thought so
highly of medicine that they forbade women and slaves to practise
it. Because of this edict many Athenian ladies are said to have died
of gynaecological ailments untended rather than submit to the
outrage of being examined by a man. According to another story,
an enterprising woman, named Agnodice, felt the injustice of this so
strongly that she disguised herself as a man in order to discover all
that was to be known about obstetrics. Later she was accused
by her gynaecological colleagues of corrupting women, but by
declaring her true sex she not only obtained her acquittal but also
the repeal of the law which forbade women to practise medicine.
This story is apocryphal and may well have been invented by someone in the hope that it would secure a greater freedom for women
in Athens.

THE PHILOSOPHER-PHYSICIANS OF ANCIENT GREECE

The philosophers who later became interested in and actually practised medicine form a bridge connecting the cruder

medicine of the Homeric Age with Hippocratic medicine. The three greatest of these physician-philosophers were Pythagoras, Alcmaeon and Empedocles. We know very little about Pythagoras (580–498 B.C.) beyond the facts that he was born in Samos and spent a great deal of his life at Croton in Southern Italy. We know also that in the earlier period of his life he travelled extensively and it is probable that the system of philosophy he subsequently taught came originally from India. He was interested in a theory of numbers and for this reason some people have called him the father of arithmetic. Little is known about the school he founded and the teaching he gave in it, chiefly because his instructions were imparted to his followers orally and not by means of books. There can be little doubt, however, that his thought strongly influenced the medicine of that time.

It is from Alcmaeon of Croton (500 B.C.), a devoted follower of Pythagoras, that we learn a little more about Pythagorean medicine, although it is impossible to say what Alcmaeon actually obtained from his great teacher and what he discovered for himself. Alcmaeon certainly dissected animals and distinguished between veins and arteries, but he subscribed to the current error that the latter were filled with air. He regarded the brain as the seat of the intellect and described health as a state of harmony and illness as one of discord.

Empedocles (504–443 B.C.) also belonged to the Pythagorean school of philosophy but even less is known about him than about Alcmaeon and Pythagoras. He is said to have stopped a serious epidemic of some sort in his own home town by draining a marsh and fumigating the houses, and it is also known that he propounded the theory of the four body humours. But legend has been so busy with his name that it is difficult to separate the actual from the imaginary. He is said to have performed several miracles and then to have ended his days by leaping into the mouth of Mount Etna with the intention of becoming a demi-god.

THE GOLDEN AGE OF GREECE

It is unlikely that there have ever appeared in the world's history so many men of genius within such narrow limits of time and space as appeared in the small country of Greece in the fifth century B.C. Into the Periclean or Golden Age of Greece were

squeezed not only Pericles, the great leader who gives it his name, but Sophocles, Euripides, Aristophanes, Socrates, Plato, Herodotus, Thucydides and Hippocrates. Actually we know surprisingly little about the man who was to earn for himself the honourable name of Father of Medicine. We know that he was the son of a physician and that like many another youth he received the beginnings of his instruction in medicine from his father. We read that he studied in Athens and afterward—again in accordance with Greek custom—widened his experience by travelling and by practising the art of medicine in the various cities of Thrace, Thessaly and Macedonia. It has been said also that he belonged to a guild of the Asklepeiad and was connected with the Asklepieion, whose ruins can still be seen standing on a beautiful hillside in the island of Cos, but modern authorities discount this statement on the grounds that the Aesculapian cult did not reach that island until after Hippocrates was dead. Nor is this story of Hippocrates being connected with a temple of healing at all a likely one, for his whole approach to medicine was entirely different from that of the priest. One of the fundamental principles in his teaching was the doctrine that medicine must be entirely dissociated from the studies of theology and philosophy. (*See* Plate 3.)

What cannot be doubted is that Hippocrates lived and worked for a long time on the island of Cos. Visitors to that island are still shown an oriental plane tree with a gigantic spread and obviously very old, under which Hippocrates is said to have taught his pupils. Two thousand and five hundred years is a very long time for a tree of this kind to live, but it is pleasant to picture to oneself Hippocrates holding an open-air clinic in the shade of this tree or if not actually this tree, the tree from which it is descended. Although we know so very little about the Father of Medicine and possess no statue of him, we have inherited something of much greater importance, the Hippocratic collection of books. This library consists of about a hundred volumes, written by different authors and at various dates. Occasionally the authors of these books express different opinions and sometimes they flatly contradict each other, but the writings of the Hippocratic collection are all inspired by the new spirit which Hippocrates breathed into medicine. We find in these books an entirely different outlook from that to be found in

older medical works. The tortuous practices of the magician and the muddled theology of the priest have been scrapped and replaced by an honesty and a serener wisdom than had ever been present in medical works before. Instead of reading about magical rites and incantations, we learn instead about the necessity for maintaining a high standard of professional conduct, and about the need in medicine for a much greater accuracy in the observation of the symptoms and the recording of the physical signs of the disease. Doctors are encouraged for the first time to strive to discover the *physical* causes of the illness and it is this last fact which is of such paramount importance in Hippocrates' medicine that a disease is regarded as a phenomenon with a natural and not a supernatural explanation. The days of the sorcerer, the witch-doctor and the magician have been brought to an end and the days of the clinical physician have begun. Hippocrates succeeded not only in changing the direction of medicine but in providing it also with certain fundamental principles which it had previously lacked. We are entirely justified therefore in dividing Greek medicine sharply into the pre-Hippocratic and the post-Hippocratic eras.

It is unfortunate that we know so little about the life of the man who freed medicine from superstitions and converted it into an empirical art which must be studied and mastered by the slow process of trial and error, and yet all that we know for certain about him is that, like most of the philosophers of his day, he travelled a great deal and practised medicine in the city of Athens as well as on the island of Cos. From the Hippocratic writings we gather that he placed far more reliance in his practice on the use of general measures than in the prescribing of drugs. For example, he made great use of poultices, he bled his patients occasionally but not too frequently, and he paid particular attention to their diet. He ordered purgatives and diuretics only when he felt that they were really required, and never used them as routine measures. Like the modern spa physician he made considerable use of medicated baths and he often prescribed a "change of air" when a certain phase of convalescence had been reached. Hippocrates makes particularly shrewd observations on the subject of dietetics. He relates the food he orders his patient to the amount of work that he is doing, realizing that the body is an engine which requires a variable quantity

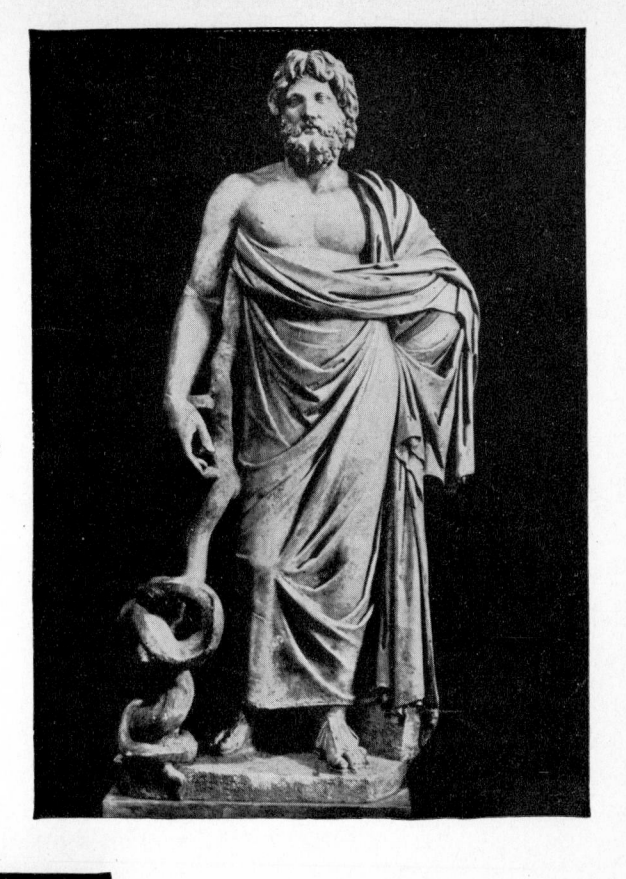

Æsculapius
(From Museo Laterano, Rome)

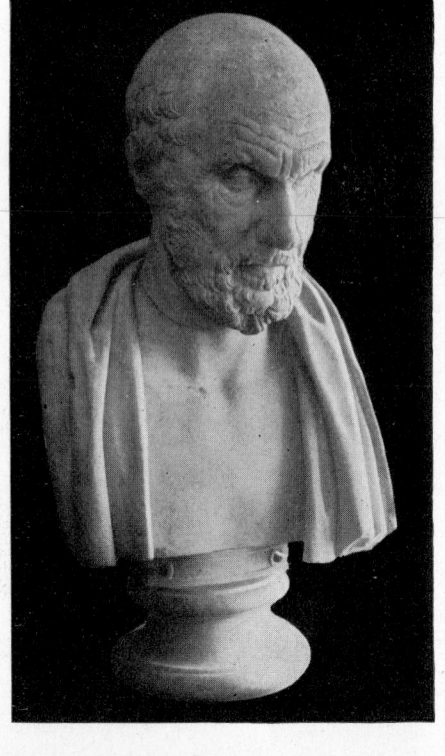

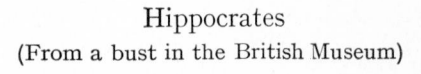

Hippocrates
(From a bust in the British Museum)

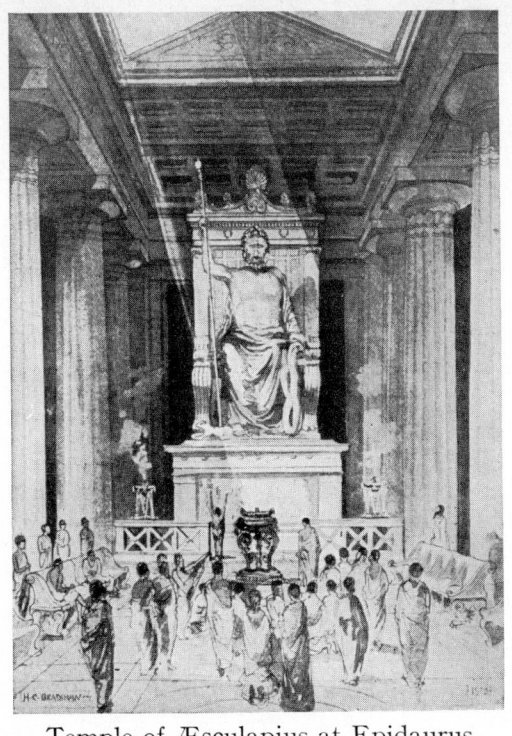

Temple of Æsculapius at Epidaurus
(Drawing by H. C. Bradshaw)

Temple of Æsculapius reconstructed

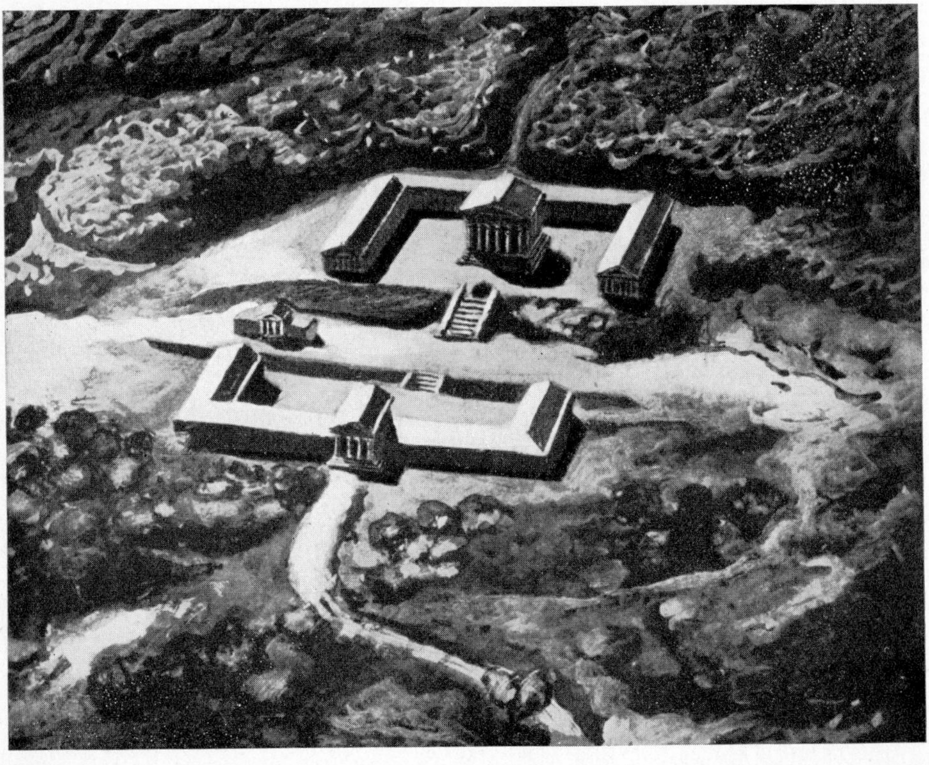

of fuel. He writes that the "performances of work are directed to the consumption of what exists, while food and drink are intended to replenish the void". As R. C. Macfie points out in *The Romance of Medicine*, the Hippocratic school of medicine was not content merely to speculate and propound theories as other schools of medicine had done, but it carried out clinical experiments as well; and one of the clinical methods it employed resembles very closely the modern "test-meal". The patient was given different kinds of food to eat and afterwards vomiting was induced in order that the amount of digestion which had taken place in the various ingredients of the meal might be investigated.

Advanced though these experimental studies in clinical medicine undoubtedly were, it has to be admitted that the knowledge of anatomy possessed by the Hippocratic school of medicine was very defective. It was realized that the blood vessels were continuous with the heart but no distinction was made between the arteries and the veins. What was perhaps still stranger was that the Hippocratic physician failed to make any division between nerves, tendons and ligaments, and seems to have lumped them all together as parts of the muscular system. That he paid so little attention to individual muscles is a little surprising when we remember that in the preceding Minoan civilization statues had been made in which the contours of the various muscles were beautifully portrayed. Some of these Minoan statuettes show the smaller muscles of the forearm and even represented the superficial veins of the hand with great anatomical accuracy.

There is nothing in the Hippocratic collection of writings which reflects better the spirit of that school and gives a clearer idea of its lofty aims than the oath which its students were required to take on entering their medical apprenticeship. Familiar though the Hippocratic Oath may be, and frequently quoted, any account of Hippocrates and his school which did not give it would seem defective:

"I swear by Apollo the healer, by Aesculapius, by Health and all the powers of healing, and call to witness all the gods and goddesses that I may keep this Oath and Promise to the best of my ability and judgement.

"I will pay the same respect to my master in the Science as to my parents and share my life with him and pay all my debts to him. I will regard his sons as my brothers and teach them the Science, if they desire to learn it, without fee or contract. I will hand on precepts, lectures and all other learning to my sons, to those of my master and to those pupils duly apprenticed and sworn, and to none other.

"I will use my power to help the sick to the best of my ability and judgement; I will abstain from harming or wronging any man by it.

"I will not give a fatal draught to anyone if I am asked, nor will I suggest any such thing. Neither will I give a woman means to procure an abortion.

"I will be chaste and religious in my life and in my practice.

"I will not cut, even for the stone, but I will leave such procedures to the practitioners of that craft.

"Whenever I go into a house, I will go to help the sick and never with the intention of doing harm or injury. I will not abuse my position to indulge in sexual contacts with the bodies of women or of men, whether they be freemen or slaves.

"Whatever I see or hear, professionally or privately, which ought not to be divulged, I will keep secret and tell no one.

"If, therefore, I observe this Oath and do not violate it, may I prosper both in my life and in my profession earning good repute among all men for all time. If I transgress and forswear this Oath, may my lot be otherwise."

As has already been pointed out, the Hippocratic books are explicit and entirely practical and the terse manner in which the requirements for a surgical operation are summarized in the following passage recalls a modern text-book on surgery:

"Operative requisites in the Surgery; the patient, the operator; assistants; instruments; the light, where and how placed; the patient's person and apparatus. The Operator, whether seated or standing, should be placed conveniently to the part being operated upon and to the light, each of the two kinds of light ordinary or artificial, may be used in two ways, direct or oblique." (*See also* Plate 6.)

The Aphorisms of Hippocrates, like the Hippocratic Oath, have been so often quoted that some of the virtue has gone out of them so that they seem a little trite. This is because we have forgotten that what is so familiar to us now as to be a cliché was entirely revolutionary at the time at which it was written. Many of the aphorisms are pure distillations of clinical wisdom, as the following examples show:

"Do not disturb a patient either during or just after a crisis, and try no experiments neither with purges nor with diuretics."

"Old men endure fasting most easily, the man of middle age next, youth very badly and worst of all children, especially those of a liveliness greater than the ordinary."

"When sleep puts an end to delirium it is a good sign."

"Old men generally have less illness than young men, but such complaints as become chronic in old men generally last until death."

"All diseases occur at all seasons, but some diseases are more apt to occur and to be aggravated at certain seasons."

"In winter occur pleurisy, pneumonia, colds, sore throats, headaches, dizziness, apoplexy."

"Consumption occurs chiefly between the ages of eighteen and thirty-five."

Enough of these Hippocratic aphorisms have been given to reveal the rapid change that has taken place in medicine as the result of Hippocrates' influence. The doctor's attention is now directed entirely on to his patient and he is no longer concerned with religious or philosophical theories about the genesis of disease. The illness is being watched as a natural process and accurate notes are being kept so that the same signs may be recognized should they be seen again in another patient. The doctor will then be able to profit by his previous experience and be able to intervene more effectively and earlier on his patient's behalf. For this reason great attention is paid to exact observation. What could be more penetrating than the following observations on a case of fever ending in a low muttering, delirium and death. They are terse notes but they record all that it is necessary for the physician to remember.

"In Thasos, the wife of Delearces, who lodged in the plain, through sorrow was seized with an acute and shivering fever. From first to last she always wrapped herself up in her bed clothes;

kept silent, fumbled, picked, bored and gathered hairs (from the clothes); tears and again laughter; no sleep; bowels irritable but passed nothing; when urged drank a little; urine thin and scanty; to the touch the fever was slight; coldness of the extremities.

Ninth day talked much incoherently and again sank into silence.

Fourteenth day. breathing rare, large and spaced and again hurried.

Seventeenth day. After stimulation of the bowels she passed even drinks nor could retain anything; totally insensible; skin parched and tense.

Twentieth day. Much talk and again became composed, then voiceless; respiration hurried.

Twenty-first day died. Her respiration throughout was rare and large; she was totally insensible; always wrapped up in her bed clothes; throughout either much talk or complete silence."

Every medical man who has watched this same sequence of events in the course of some grave infection such as typhoid fever and who has listened to his patient's breathing, at one moment "large and spaced, and again hurried", will appreciate the exactitude of this report. The breathing described in it is generally a sign of grave import and is known as "Cheyne-Stokes" respiration. Here we see scientific medicine in the earliest stages of its making by a great genius in the lovely island of Cos, in other words, medicine as it was taught by the Father of all physicians.

But doctors were not yet able to dispense with the supernatural element in medicine, and soon after his death the deification of Hippocrates himself began. Magic was not to be banished from medicine as readily as Hippocrates had believed. As R. C. Macfie points out in *The Romance of Medicine*, "he who had performed no magic living was reputed to perform magic dead. A pagan physician writes to his friend: 'I have a brazen Hippocrates of near a cubitt in length, who when the lamp before him is out, takes a tour all round my house, rattling and rummaging over all my boxes, mixing or jumbling together all my medicines, throwing open my doors etc., and this more especially if we delay the annual sacrifice that is usually made to him. I must therefore declare that Hippocrates the physician still requires sacrifice, and is highly displeased at neglecting the festivals of divine worship to him'."

ARISTOTLE (384–322 B.C.)

Close upon Hippocrates' heels came a Greek who although not a physician himself was destined to have a profound effect on subsequent medical thought. Plato is regarded by many authorities as the greatest philosopher who has ever lived, and Aristotle, his disciple, can be regarded as one of the greatest figures in the whole history of science. By birth he was a provincial Greek, the son of a Macedonian physician, and he was fortunate enough to come under Plato's influence at the early age of seventeen. In 347 B.C., after Plato's death, he left Athens and took up his residence in Asia Minor in order to continue there his study of biology, a subject in which he was particularly interested. He made many dissections on different animals and can be said to have founded the sciences of Comparative Anatomy and Embryology. Five years later his work was suddenly interrupted. At the request of Philip of Macedon he became tutor to his son, the young man who was later to earn the name of Alexander the Great. Fortunately, when Alexander marched off to conquer Asia, Aristotle was able to sever his connection with his pupil and to return to his right work in Athens where he remained for the rest of his life.

The views of Aristotle influenced science for hundreds of years after his death and indirectly affected the whole course of medicine. His field of research was so wide that few topics can be discussed without the views of Aristotle on the subject having to be mentioned, but Aristotle's interest in medicine was entirely philosophical. He was too occupied with science to have any time to study the clinical problems of medicine. He held, as Hippocrates had done, and as doctors were to believe for many centuries, that the human body was composed of four "humours"—blood, phlegm, yellow bile and black bile, and he regarded a disturbance in the balance maintained by these four humours as the root cause of disease. This theory, afterwards expounded by Galen, was destined to remain a fundamental doctrine in medicine for many hundreds of years.

The school of Aristotle was carried on for a while after its founder's death by Theophrastus (372–287 B.C.), a former pupil of Aristotle's, and then it came to an end. From that time onwards biology ceased to be considered a subject worthy of separate study and it was relegated

instead to a small and rather unimportant part of the general field of medicine. Neglected thus it made no further progress. Nor was biology the only subject ancillary to medicine which ceased to advance after the death of Aristotle, as the Golden Age of Greece drew to its close. For a few centuries medicine, still invigorated by the new spirit Hippocrates had breathed into it, managed to remain alive and then it, like science, was overcome by the mental stagnation of the Middle Ages.

CHAPTER III

The Medicine of Alexandria and Rome
(300 B.C.–A.D. 200)

LONG after Greece had lost both her independence and her intellectual leadership Greek culture still exerted its influence on the world. Alexandria, the great city founded by Alexander a year before his death at the early age of thirty-three, became the hub of the world's activity and the exchange and mart of its thought. Its situation in the Delta of the Nile and on the Mediterranean coast brought it into relationship with the neighbouring maritime nations and also made it a bridge between Eastern and Western civilizations. Alexandria was also fortunate in its rulers. Ptolemy Soter (323–285 B.C.), formerly one of Alexander's generals, and now the founder of a new Egyptian dynasty, drew around himself from different parts of Europe, and particularly from Greece, men who were eminent in literature and philosophy. He gave them every facility for the prosecution of their researches, built for their benefit a great museum and laid the foundations of a still greater library. The work begun so splendidly by him was vigorously continued by his successors so that the fame of the school of Alexandria grew and spread throughout the whole civilized world.

The intellectual movement radiating from Alexandria persisted for many centuries—to be more precise, from the fourth century before Christ until the seventh century of the Christian era—and this long period falls naturally into two parts. The first of these parts extends from about 300 B.C. to 30 B.C., that is to say, from the beginning of the Ptolemaic dynasty to its final subjection by the Romans, whilst the second ends with the destruction of Alexandria's university and the burning of its great library by the Arabs. During

this long period Greek thought remained supreme at this great centre of learning and nowhere was its supremacy more in evidence than in the departments of the university dealing with anatomy, physiology and medicine. The first teachers of anatomy and medicine at Alexandria were Herophilus of Chalcedon and Erasistratus of Chios, both born about the year 300 B.C. These two were not only the earliest but also the greatest of the anatomists of the Alexandrian medical school.

HEROPHILUS OF CHALCEDON

Herophilus was probably the first man ever to make dissections in public and he is particularly well known for his researches on the brain. It is obvious that he grasped the nature and significance of the nerves, realizing that they were connected with the life of movement and sensation. He repudiated Aristotle's views about the respective functions of the brain and the heart. Aristotle had regarded the heart as the mainspring of life and the seat of the intelligence, and had assigned to the brain an entirely subsidiary position. It was nothing more than a cooling gland which helped to chill the heart's unruly ardours. Herophilus scouted this idea entirely since he had come to the conclusion that the brain was the headquarters of the central nervous system and if this were the case then it must follow that it was also the seat of thought. Herophilus showed considerable knowledge of the major anatomy of the brain, differentiating the cerebral hemispheres from the cerebellum, describing the circle of blood vessels which has been named after him, and giving an excellent account of the fourth ventricle of the brain. At a later date he was accused by Celsus of having gained this intimate knowledge of human functions from human vivisection, an accusation which was almost certainly a false one. But that he had dissected human corpses is almost certain, for his knowledge of the human brain is far too exact to have been inferred from the dissection of the brains of animals.

ERASISTRATUS OF CHIOS

Erasistratus was also particularly interested in the anatomy and the physiology of the brain. He made observations on the convolutions of the cerebral hemisphere and realized that their greater

complexity in man, as compared with the convolutions of the brains of animals, was connected with man's greater intelligence. He postulated that the ventricles or cavities within the brain were filled with something which he called "animal spirits" and he believed that these animal spirits were conveyed by the nerves into the muscles so that the latter were compelled to shorten themselves. If we substitute the term "nervous impulse" for the words "animal spirits", then Erasistratus' theory of the activation of the muscles is substantially correct.

He believed that "plethora" or an excess of blood was the commonest cause of disease and, whenever he found this condition in his patients, he treated it by bouts of starvation. Some of his contemporaries supplemented starvation by blood-letting but because Erasistratus was, on principle, opposed to all treatments of a drastic nature, he rarely combined the two. He also wrote a treatise on hygiene and complained that his Greek medical contemporaries showed far too little interest in the subject of the prevention of illness as opposed to its treatment. Erasistratus was justified in making this criticism of Greek medicine for whereas the Minoans, whose civilization had preceded that of the Greeks, paid great attention to sanitary measures, and provided for drainage and the disposal of waste products in their cities, no hygienic structures of this kind are to be found in the ruins of the Greek cities of this period.

After a century or two, the impetus which had led to the founding of the great Alexandrian school of medicine and to its maintenance began to slow down and no teacher of any repute appeared there to revive its former fame. Branches of science other than that of medicine managed to flourish there for a little longer and then, with the absorption of Egypt into the Roman Empire in about the year 50 B.C., Alexandria ceased to be of any importance at all. Even if Egypt had retained some of its former importance it would have been difficult for a centre of learning and culture to have remained located in such an outlying part of the Roman Empire as Alexandria. Anything of such importance would have had to be situated in the very heart of that great Empire, in the city of Rome itself. The transference of power from Greece to Rome rendered the decline of Alexandria inevitable.

Rome was undisputed mistress of the world and the story of medicine now becomes synonymous with the story of medicine within the Roman Empire.

ROMAN MEDICINE

The little art that Rome possessed was inherited from Greece and what did not come from Greece came to her from Babylon and Egypt. Medical knowledge was derived from the same sources for her own native system of medicine was primitive and unscientific. In Rome medicine was not considered worthy of separate study, and to practise as a doctor was beneath the dignity of all Roman citizens of education and standing. As a consequence of this, the quality of medical practice declined very rapidly within the Roman Empire. Rome's chief contributions to the world, and they were of no mean order, were a fine code of law, a magnificent military tradition and an aptitude for the building of roads, viaducts and other great public works.

H. G. Wells criticizes the Romans for being singularly lacking in imagination and this is certainly true also of Roman medicine. Not only did the Romans contribute little or nothing new to the healing arts but they were even suspicious of the little medical knowledge which they had taken over from the Greeks. Cato the Censor (234–149 B.C.), who never found anything admirable in the Greeks, wrote quite childishly to his son on the subject of Greek Physicians. In his *Praecepta ad Filium* will be found his paternal instructions: "They (the Greeks) have sworn to kill all barbarians with their drugs and they call *us* barbarians. Remember that I forbid physicians for you." Guthrie refers also to Martial's protest against the clinical method of teaching medicine introduced by Hippocrates, that is to say the method by which the medical student learns directly about diseases at the patient's bedside instead of indirectly in the lecture hall or the library. Martial utters his complaints on this subject in the following doggerel:

"I'm ill . . . I send for Symmachus; he's here,
A hundred students following in the rear.
All paw my chest with hand as cold as snow;
I had no fever but I have it now."

Such strong personal indignation is being voiced here and it is so reminiscent of the kind of objection raised at the teaching hospitals of today by certain patients that it would seem certain that Martial had actually experienced what he was talking about. Whether this be true or not, his doggerel at any rate proves that clinical teaching in accordance with Hippocratic principles was still being carried on in Rome at that time. The Romans had little liking either for Greek doctors or for Greek medicine but they were in a weak position for they had no proper doctors of their own with which to replace them.

The Roman's distaste for Greek physicians and their methods continued right up to the Christian era, for again we find Pliny the Elder (A.D. 23–79) condemning them at a later date in his rather discursive work on Natural History and regretting "that there is no law to punish ignorant physicians, and that capital punishment is not inflicted on them. Yet they learn by our suffering," he continues, "and they experiment by putting us to death." It is quite possible that the Romans had some measure of justification for their complaints against Greek physicians for there is evidence that theories and dogmas began to creep back into medicine in this post-Hippocratic era. Instead of following Hippocrates' practical methods, physicians became involved in argument again so that a number of different schools of medicine arose, known as the Dogmatists, the Empirics, the Methodists and the Pneumatists.

The only medical advances made by the Romans themselves were in public health measures and in the organization of the medical services of the army and in both of these spheres the Romans showed great enterprise. They must be credited with having introduced extremely useful sanitary measures by the issuing of government decrees. One proclamation made in the year 450 B.C. forbade all burials within the city walls and another ordered city officials to attend both to the cleanliness of the streets and to the water supply available to Roman citizens. The efficiency with which the latter requirement was carried out is clearly demonstrated to us today by the remains of the fourteen great aqueducts which formerly supplied Rome with its three hundred million gallons of drinking water per day. A public medical service of physicians was also organized to look after the needs of poor Roman citizens. But,

as is to be expected, it was in its army medical services that Roman efficiency was most apparent. The army medical service appears to have been well run, its main defects being those of most services of this kind, namely, a lack of elasticity and a greater respect for army regulations than for professional skill in the treatment of the sick and wounded.

In spite of the Roman's lack of imagination and of his strong distaste for the clinical medicine inherited from the Greeks, we owe to him an innovation which still survives at the present day and which is of primary importance to our recent Health Act—the hospital system. The legend concerning the founding of the first hospital in Rome is well known but it can bear repetition. A great pestilence broke out in the city in the year 293 B.C. and a Roman mission was despatched to seek help and advice from the only quarter where good medical advice could be obtained, the Greek school of medicine situated at Epidaurus. The mission eventually returned with one of the sacred serpents used in the Greek Asklep-ieia on board, and as the ship sailed up the River Tiber this Greek emblem of the healing arts slipped quietly overboard, swam to the shore and landed on the island of St. Bartholomew. From that moment the plague was stayed and a hospital was afterwards built on the exact spot at which the serpent had landed. From this hospital came, many years later, a certain monk, by name Rahere, who was afterwards to found St. Bartholomew's Hospital in London.

The first Roman hospital may well have been built, as the legend proclaims, by the action of the civic authorities, but the spread of such institutions throughout the Empire was brought about chiefly through the army. As the frontiers of the Roman Empire were pushed further and further away from Rome, great military hospitals were erected at various strategic points on the lines of communication and many remains of these are still to be found. The immense ruins which have been excavated at Düsseldorf are the best known of them. At a later date "valetudinaria" or infirmaries for poor sick civilians were opened in Rome by the civic authorities and recent excavations at Pompeii suggest that a physician's house was also used at times as a kind of private "nursing home" for better-class patients.

It may be said, therefore, without any unfairness to the Roman, that he was far more interested in organizing his own health services than in advancing the frontiers of medicine, and that any progress made at this period of history was due generally to the enterprise of Greek physicians in Roman employ. A good example of such progress is the great improvement in the Roman Pharmacoepeia brought about by Dioscorides (A.D. 60). He was a Greek keenly interested in the study of botany who was continually seeking for plants which might prove of service to the doctor. In order to be able to collect and study plants growing in countries far from Rome, he enlisted as a surgeon in the army of Nero and saw a great deal of foreign service. During all that time he never forgot his main interest. He collected a large number of plants, experimented with extracts made from them, and, at a later date, wrote his great work, *De Universa Medicina*, a book which remained the standard work on pharmacology for many centuries. Some of the illustrations taken from this book are extremely beautiful. (*See* Plate 7.)

A still more striking example of a Greek in Roman employ who made great discoveries in medicine and in allied subjects is provided by Galen. Galen is a man of such great importance in the history of medicine that he must be dealt with at some length.

GALEN

The physician who was destined to dominate medicine for many centuries and who wrote with such conviction and dogmatism that few doctors dared to criticize him was born at Pergamos in Asia Minor in the year A.D. 130. He was a prodigious writer and in one of his many books he gives us an account of his own parents, describing his father as amiable, just and benevolent, and his mother as thoroughly objectionable, a woman who was always shouting at her husband and displaying her evil temper by biting her serving-maids. It is said that it was revealed in a dream to Galen's father, an architect by profession, that his son was destined one day to become a very great physician and, having great confidence in his vision, he started by sending his son to Pergamos and to Smyrna for a preliminary grounding in philosophy. After the boy had acquired a good knowledge of philosophy he was despatched to Alexandria, there to specialize in medicine.

After qualifying at the age of twenty-eight, the young Galen was appointed surgeon to a school of gladiators, a post which provided him with excellent opportunities for studying wounds. From the very start he showed great aptitude in his profession and being supremely confident of his own ability he decided to resign his job with the gladiators and to seek his fortune in the city of Rome itself. He went to that great city and continued to work there for several years; and then quite suddenly and unexpectedly he returned to Pergamos. Some said that he had fled from Rome in order to escape the plague but a more likely explanation of his abrupt change of plans was that he had incurred the enmity of his Roman colleagues. Galen was a self-opinionated and pushing man who had a ready answer for every question put to him and he would not be an easy person to work with. He may well have offended his colleagues and have come to the conclusion that it would be prudent to retire from the city into the provinces for a few years and then perhaps return later when the matter had blown over. That he had already made his mark in Rome in high quarters is shown by the fact that he was eventually summoned back again to the city by no less a person than the Emperor Marcus Aurelius himself.

Galen was a greater physiologist than a physician. He also made important contributions to anatomy, but in this field of research he was severely handicapped by the fact that during the whole of his life-time it was illegal to dissect human bodies. His anatomical researches were carried out on the bodies of Barbary apes and pigs and Galen was over-ready to infer that what was true of the anatomy of these animals was equally true of the anatomy of man. Yet in spite of this serious handicap to research, he made many important discoveries in anatomy and physiology. For example, he corrected the error current up to that time, that the arteries contained air and proved that they were filled instead with blood. He also proclaimed that there was an ebb and flow movement of the blood in the body and that this movement was brought about by the pumping action of the heart. But he completely missed the point that the blood made a complete tour of the body. In his opinion all that the pumping of the heart did was to impart to the blood a sort of tidal motion and to recharge it with the "Vital Spirit" during its passage through the lung. Like his predecessors

and like all other medical men of the day, he believed that the blood percolated through the intervening septum from one auricle of the heart into the other and this strongly entrenched doctrine was destined to cause confusion for hundreds of years.

Galen is said to have written more than five hundred books, of which only eighty survive, the rest perishing in a fire which destroyed Galen's Roman home. Galen acknowledged his indebtedness to his great predecessor Hippocrates and his general attitude to medicine was in many ways similar to that of the great physician of the island of Cos. But he was an entirely different type of man from Hippocrates, a man remarkable for his energy and industry rather than for his judgement. He collected a vast amount of information and possessed a great deal more knowledge than wisdom. Having accepted the Aristotelian view that Nature makes nothing without some purpose, Galen set out to explain and to justify the form taken by every structure of the human body. This was a task that neither he nor any other man was properly equipped to undertake. He could only carry it out by claiming a far completer knowledge of the laws of Nature than he actually possessed. Galen's character was such that he had no difficulty in doing this and because he wrote with such firm confidence in the correctness of his views, his readers were misled into believing that he knew a great deal more than he actually did.

Galen's physiology and pathology were based on the fashionable theory of the day, that of the four humours. The body was supposed to be made up of four humours and in health they were nicely balanced but in illness the balance became disturbed. Treatment therefore consisted in administering the appropriate drug for restoring the dispelled harmony. The various drugs used were believed to possess the different characteristics of the four humours; some were cooling, others heating, and yet others moistening and drying. A disease associated with fever had therefore to be treated with cooling drugs, whilst "chills" of the body were counteracted by administering heating drugs. Each drug was said to possess varying degrees of its predominant quality. For example, bitter almond was heating in the first degree and drying to the second degree, whilst pepper was heating to the fourth degree. Several thousand drugs were available for treatment along Galenic lines, and sometimes a

hundred of them would be included in a single prescription. In Roman times physicians were compelled to dispense their own prescriptions because otherwise the difficult art of the apothecary would have had to be confided to unreliable, and in all probability, unscrupulous people. Such pharmacists as existed in Rome were men and women of low intelligence and character, the dispensing of medicines often being used by prostitutes as an additional method of making a living.

Withington narrates a story of Galen which is a striking instance of the contrast between his methods and attitude to his profession, and those of his great predecessor Hippocrates. When Marcus Aurelius returned from his victorious campaign against the Teutonic tribes he was welcomed with many festivities and triumphs and it is probable that, philosopher though he was, he partook of these a little too freely. Believing that he could put things right without the help of a doctor, he dosed himself with bitter aloes, but without any benefit. Galen was therefore sent for in order that he might examine the Emperor and advise him. "On special command," writes Galen, "I felt his pulse and finding it quite normal, considering his age and the time of day, I declared it was no fever but a digestive disorder, due to the food he had eaten. . . . Then the Emperor repeated three times 'That's the very thing', and asked what was to be done. I answered that I usually gave a glass of wine, with pepper sprinkled on it, 'but for you Kings we only use the safest remedies and it will suffice to apply wool soaked in hot nard locally'. The Emperor ordered the wool and the wine and I left the room." But this report was not sufficient for Galen's purposes and he is careful to complete his account of the episode by adding the following: ". . . and after drinking the peppered wine he said to Pitholaus 'We have only one doctor and that an honest one', and went on to describe me as the first of physicians and the only philosopher, for he had tried many before who were not only lovers of money but also contentious, ambitious, envious and malignant."

The account given by Galen of his perfunctory examination of the Emperor is very different from the accounts given by Hippocrates of cases he had examined, and Withington comments on the different outlooks of the two men. "Hippocrates," he writes, "tells us briefly and simply what he has observed of the natural history

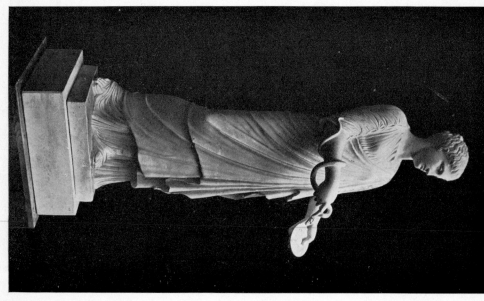

Hygiea. Greek goddess
of health and one of the
two daughters of Æscu-
lapius

(The statue is in the Louvre)

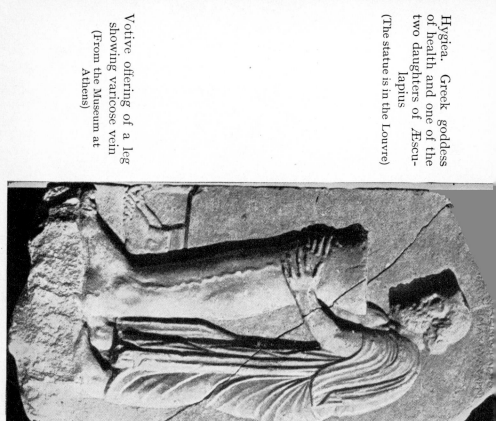

Votive offering of a leg
showing varicose vein
(From the Museum at
Athens)

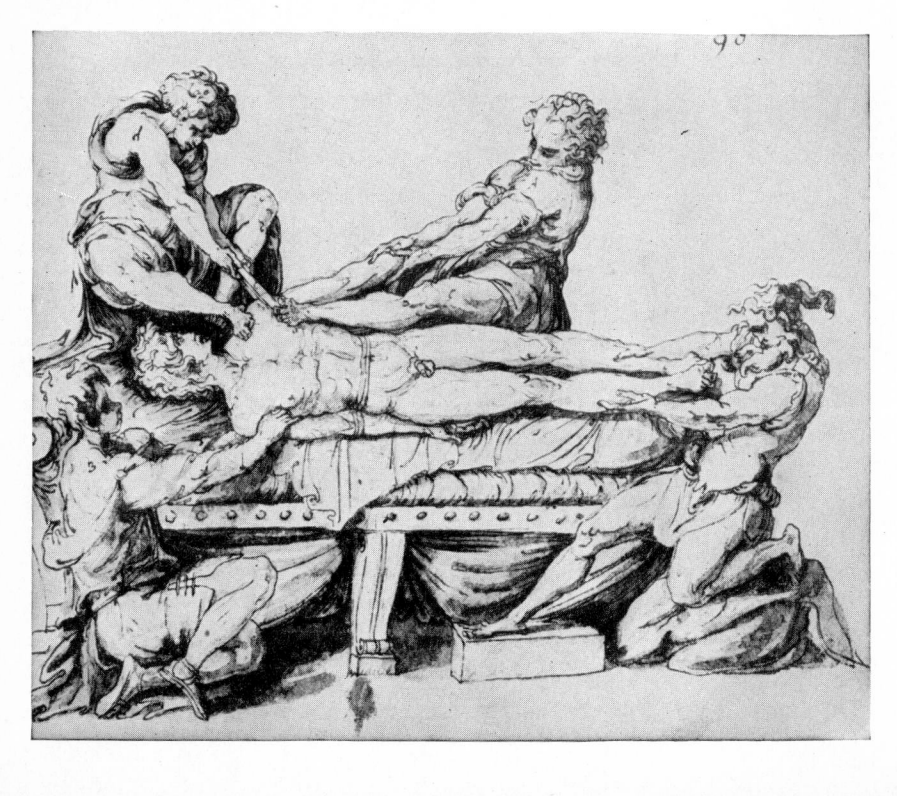

The reduction of a
dislocated shoulder.
Drawing by Primatice
illustrating a Greek
manuscript on surgery
(*Bibliothèque Nationale*)

Another method
(From the same source)

of various diseases in order that others may do likewise, and that some definite knowledge may be obtained of what disease is, how it affects the human body, and its probable course in each case. But the stories which from time to time enliven the endless discussions of Galen are introduced either to show how much cleverer he was than his colleagues, or at best to exemplify and support some particular theory."

Nevertheless Galen gained a great reputation during his life-time and a still greater fame after his death. But he established no school of medicine and collected round himself no group of devoted followers as Hippocrates had done. This is not in the least surprising for he was a quarrelsome man by nature and not one who would be likely to attract to himself young disciples. He lacked those essential qualities which endear men to their fellows and which inspire younger men to follow their methods. But his reputation as a scientist was immense and after his death in A.D. 203 all serious anatomical and physiological research came to an end on the assumption that Galen had discovered and described in his books all that it was necessary for a doctor to know about anatomy and physiology.

CELSUS

Although medicine was in Greek hands, the best account of it, as it was practised in Rome, was given by a pure-blooded Roman, Aurelius Cornelius Celsus. Celsus was not a physician and, in all probability, he would have been insulted if anybody had mistaken him for one. He was a member of a patrician family and a man of catholic tastes who liked to keep in touch with all interesting new developments in philosophy, politics and science. He is the first of that band of gifted amateurs to whose enterprise and industry medicine is so deeply indebted and there have been many such people in the long history of medicine. We shall hear much of these men later, of men such as Veronese nobleman Fracastoro, who has rightly been called the first epidemiologist, van Leeuwenhoek, the well-to-do Delft draper who was the first to explore the world of micro-organisms through his home-made microscope, the Rev. Stephen Hales, who devised new modes of investigating the circulation, and a great many other similarly gifted men whose amateur

but highly skilled work has materially contributed to the progress of medicine.

Celsus was evidently a man of encyclopaedic mind for he completed in the year A.D. 30 an immense work dealing with philosophy, military strategy, law and medicine. The only part of this work which survives is *De re Medica*, a book described by Dr. Singer as "in many ways the most readable and well arranged ancient medical work that we have". It is not really an original work but a compilation made from various Greek treatises existing at that time, including, almost certainly, works forming a part of the Hippocratic Collection. What is surprising is that operations of a very elaborate nature are described in *De re Medica*, and yet as we have seen, Greek surgery was inferior to Greek medicine. Despite this Celsus gives accounts of the following complicated surgical procedures: a number of complicated plastic operations on the face; a method of enucleating tonsils very similar to that used today; and finally a particularly bold operation for the removal of a goitre. He also describes operations for stone, hernia and cataract. Having given his accounts of techniques Celsus then lays down the attributes of a good surgeon. He "should be youthful or in early middle age, with a strong and steady hand, as expert with the left hand as with the right, with vision sharp and clear, and spirit undaunted; so far void of pity that while he wishes only to cure the patient, yet he is not moved by his cries to go too fast, or cut less than necessary". It is a fair enough description of what was undoubtedly needful in the pre-anaesthetic era of surgery when boldness and speed were all-important requisites.

That the Romans were far more interested in surgery than in medicine and that they sought to develop the surgical side of the healing arts was quite natural for they belonged to a virile and a military type of nation and were men who, even in peace-time, enjoyed gladiatorial shows. It must be borne in mind that Rome was more often at war than at peace, and war has always had a stimulating action on the study of surgery. That surgical technique in ancient Rome was far from being crude is confirmed also by the elaborate nature of many of the surgical instruments dug up in such excavations as those made at Pompeii. (*See* Plate 7.)

The works of Celsus are the oldest medical documents in existence

except for the Hippocratic writings and they are also of a very high quality. Because they were written in Latin and by a Roman they received very little attention from contemporary Greek practitioners or, indeed, from doctors of a later age. Even during the Middle Ages they remained neglected and it was only at the Renaissance that the excellence of Celsus as a medical reporter was recognized.

THE FALL OF THE ROMAN EMPIRE

The second century, in which Galen lived, was a prosperous one for the western world but even then there were certain signs that the ramparts of the far-flung Roman Empire were not quite as secure as they had formerly been. Later the Goths, Vandals and Huns became much more threatening in their behaviour and although Marcus Aurelius dealt with them astutely by means of a mixture of diplomacy and military punitive expeditions, the frontiers of the Roman Empire became the scene of more and more disturbing incidents. Constantine managed to avert the final disruption until the fifth century by transferring the capital of the Empire from Rome to Byzantium, and during this period medicine was kept alive by a number of scholarly physicians who preserved what was already known rather than made fresh advances.

The causes of the collapse of the mighty Empire were many: moral and political corruption, onerous taxation, and the decline in the level of agriculture have all been blamed for it. These were undoubtedly important factors in the decline of Rome but there are reasons for believing that the malaria which was a continuous source of ill-health to those living in the swampy country around Rome, and the severe epidemic of plague in A.D. 542 which wiped out at least half of the inhabitants of Byzantium, were also contributory causes of Rome's final and sudden collapse.

As has already been said, Rome's contributions to medicine lay in the realms of hygiene and public health, and not in that of clinical medicine. Excavations in Rome show not only that every house was supplied by the main aqueduct but also that every house possessed its own private cistern and service of taps. In order that water might be pure, settling tanks and other methods of cleansing were employed on a very large scale. The Cloaca Maxima, constructed in the earliest days of Rome, shows how far the Roman's ideas on the subject of

drainage were in advance of those of the Greeks. Nor was it only the great city of Rome that was provided with a good drainage system. Even obscure frontier posts had well-planned drains, such as those that have been found at Housestead on Hadrian's Wall in Northumbria. Excavations have also revealed the existence of latrines that were periodically flushed by surface water and by water coming from storage tanks. The remains of hospitals at the more important of these frontier posts are also very impressive. At Novaesium on the Roman road to Cologne are to be seen the ruins of a Roman military hospital containing about forty wards arranged round long corridors. The refectory was situated in the centre of the building, and attached to the main block were various administration buildings, a kitchen for the medical staff, rooms for orderlies and a dispensary.

The end of the Roman Empire resembled the end of all great civilizations and little need be said about it. The Roman legions in the more exposed of the frontier posts were recalled to Rome and the posts abandoned because the frontier incidents had become more and more frequent and alarming. Then quite suddenly barbarism, which is ever on the watch for weakness, gathered her forces and swept like a flood across Europe. In a short time the culture of Greece and many of the splendid public works and buildings created by the industry and might of Rome were destroyed.

CHAPTER IV

The Middle Ages (1096–1438)

IT is fashionable to look upon that period of history which forms a bridge between ancient and modern times, in other words, the Middle Ages, as a period of decadence and of stagnation, for which feudalism and the Church were entirely to blame. Now it is quite true that feudalism and ecclesiasticism were responsible for a great deal that was highly undesirable but it is unjust to blame them for the lack of liberty in Europe. It should not be forgotten that at this critical moment of history men actually preferred to bow to an autocratic authority rather than to be left without any form of government at all and these were the only alternatives at that time, iron rule or complete disorder. The downfall of the western Roman Empire had left Europe structureless, bereft of government, and at the mercy of marauding bands of barbarians. What was needed above all was a strong central government, an over-ruling authority under cover of whose protection some new form of social organization might eventually grow up, and it was the Church that made this growth of a new Europe possible. She alone was sufficiently strong to maintain order whilst this growth was taking place. For several centuries European history consisted mainly of the slow welding together of tribal units to form larger and larger groups so that out of them might eventually emerge something resembling a nation. In this difficult and tedious work of reconstruction the Christian Church, with its excellent organization, its strong central authority and its harsh discipline, played the leading part. So also did that child of the Church, the Crusades, help in this creative work by fomenting a feeling of brotherhood amongst men and by binding the quarrelling barons together in a common cause. In the great struggle between collectivism and anarchy taking place in Europe the

intellectual independence of the individual had to be sacrificed whenever it came into serious conflict with authority, and in this case authority meant the Church.

For some eight centuries, that is to say from about A.D. 400 to about A.D. 1200, such classical learning and science as had managed to survive the break-up of the Roman Empire passed into the Church's keeping and it was indeed fortunate that this conserving force still existed. Life and property were very insecure in those troubled times and nowhere else except within the stout walls of monasteries could manuscripts be written, annotated and preserved. The utmost that could be done during this period of unrest was to conserve what already existed and the fact must be accepted that little or no progress could have been made in that specialized and comparatively young branch of learning known as medicine. The monks were not really interested in it and all that they were concerned about was the entirely practical matter of how best to relieve sick persons coming to them for help. Medical research was at an end, the little knowledge of anatomy and physiology that had existed was forgotten and the new art of prognosis, on which Hippocrates had placed such store, was reduced to rule of thumb. And, with the disappearance of science, superstition crept back again into medicine so that incantations and magical charms resumed their former place in the treatment of diseases.

Sick men and women have always sought advice and remedies for their illnesses, and it was inevitable that in the absence of a medical profession they should apply to the priests for treatment. So customary did this become that Bishops, Abbots, and even Abbesses were forced to prescribe some form of treatment for those who sought their help. And it was a strange mixture of physical remedies, magic and ritual that these ecclesiastics dispensed— the remedies described in the works of Galen, a pinch of alchemy perhaps, a trifle filched from the Cabbalists and one or two sacred charms and amulets. Yet so popular did these ecclesiastical mixtures become and so much time did the dignitaries of the Church have to spend on their amateur excursions into medicine that in 1139 Pope Innocent III, fearing lest they might neglect their spiritual vocations for the sake of more lucrative medical practices, convened a Council at which the dispensing of medicines was sternly forbidden to

priests, and a more diligent pursuit of theology enjoined. Yet even a Papal Edict proved insufficient to stamp out this unauthorized doctoring and thirty years later Pope Alexander III was forced to forbid priests from attending medical lectures, with excommunication as a punishment should they be disobedient to this command. Still the priests continued to show too great an interest in medicine and finally a compromise was accepted by the papal authority. Henceforth the clergy were to be allowed to dispense medicines but they must relinquish all surgery.

Hippocrates had freed medicine from religion and taught men that illness was not a punishment sent by the gods but a natural phenomenon to be studied as any other natural phenomenon was studied. Now, under the Church's rule the older views of the supernatural origin of disease were revived. Even those monks who did not insist on all illnesses as being punishments for sin looked upon them as disciplines to be endured with patience and to be mitigated by constant prayer. Other changes besides this new attitude to illness were required, in order to bring medical ideas into line with the teaching of the Church. The older text-books on medicine were sometimes illustrated with diagrams showing how the signs of the zodiac controlled the various organs of the body, but now these pagan signs were eliminated from medical treatises and replaced by the names of saints. Saint Blaise was said to preside over the functions of the throat, Saint Appollonea over the teeth, Saint Lawrence over the back, Saint Bernadine over the lungs, and Saint Erasmus over the abdomen. Saintly patrons were also found for the various illnesses as well as for the working of the organs, and yet other saints were named who possessed the power to cure certain diseases, saints to whom the sick man would be wise to address his prayers. A great many alterations had to be made in medical terminology in order that it might conform to the requirements of Mother Church. (*See* Plate 25.)

Some of these difficulties could have been avoided had the level of culture of the rank and file of the Church been a little higher. But many of the monks were ignorant men and no people are more intolerant of other people's views than the ignorant. So low was the level of education within the monasteries that a decree had to be issued in the seventh century to the effect that nobody should be raised to the

priesthood unless he were able to read at least the Psalms and the Order of Baptism. So also do we find King Alfred complaining of the monks of his time that there were "few who could understand their service books in English . . . so few were there of them that I cannot remember even a single one South of the Thames when I succeeded to the kingdom". (Coulton.) The monks knew little or nothing about the healing arts but they held it to be their duty to relieve illness so far as it was within their ability to do this on the grounds that Christ had enjoined His disciples to minister to the sick. But as has been seen, it was for a long time contrary to Church rules for priests to have anything to do with physical remedies, and St. Bernard, the founder of the Cistercian Order in the eleventh century, not only forbade his own monks to study medical books but required of them that they should refuse all remedies other than prayer when they were sick themselves. "To buy drugs," he wrote, "to consult physicians, to take medicines, befits not religion." This prohibition of all medical remedies did not extend to all orders as is shown by the fact that the great Carolingian Monastery at St. Gall possessed a well-planned hospital and a garden in which were grown a number of medicinal herbs.

It is also true that a number of charity hospitals were founded by the Church at this time but they were refuges for the destitute rather than places where the sick could obtain expert medical care. Those who were admitted to these institutions might receive treatment but it would be of a religious and not of a medical nature. This was in keeping with the Church's attitude to illness which was summed up by St. Augustine in the fifth century in these words: "All diseases of Christians are to be ascribed to demons, chiefly do they torment the fresh baptized, yea even the guiltless, new-born infant." The infant mortality at that time was terribly high but it is curious that a man so intelligent as St. Augustine should have attributed this to the partiality of demons for young children and not to the neglect and ignorance of man. Christ cast out devils but from adults and not from young children, and surely St. Augustine might have noted this significant fact.

Under the firm belief that diseases were caused by demonic possession the sick were treated by the Church by such means as prayers, exorcism, the laying on of hands, and the exhibition of

holy relics. Since eighty to ninety per cent of patients will recover from their illnesses without any remedies at all, the great majority of those treated in these ways recovered, to the glory of the Church. The reputation of the Abbey at which the cure had been effected grew with the publication of these favourable results, and more and more patients would arrive there for treatment. Considerable rivalry existed between different monasteries and churches with respect to the merits of the various holy relics they possessed. In the twelfth century the shrine of the cathedral at Cologne claimed that it had acquired the skulls of the three Magi who came from the East to worship at the manger of the infant Jesus. The church of St. Gereon responded immediately by publicizing its possession of the relics of St. Gereon and his band of martyrs. The most cherished relic of all was, of course, either a small piece of the cross on which Jesus was crucified, or else one of the nails which had pierced his feet or hands, and a very large number of these relics were purchased from obliging dealers living in the Holy Land.

The saints of the Church employed curative measures similar to those used by Christ himself, such as the laying on of hands, and often with very good results. Because psychogenic factors exist in most cases of illness, the laying on of hands or the carrying out of some impressive religious ceremony were excellent methods of treatment in an age in which the great majority of the sick were devout members of the Church.

THE ROYAL TOUCH

The "royal touch" was a special ritual practised by the king in the Middle Ages, but it was a method of treatment that was applicable to two diseases only, epilepsy and the "King's evil". The "King's evil" was scrofula or a tuberculous swelling of the glands of the neck and, according to tradition, the practice of treating it with the "royal touch" began long previously in the time of Edward the Confessor. The account of its first being used runs as follows: "A young woman had married a husband of her own age, but having no issue by union, the humours collected abundantly in her neck, she contracted a sore disorder and the glands swelled in a dreadful manner. Admonished in a dream to have the part affected washed by the King, she entered the palace, and the King himself fulfilled

the labour of love by rubbing the young woman's neck with his fingers dipped in water. Joyous health followed his healing hand; the lurid skin opened so that worms flowed out with the purulent matter, and the tumour subsided. But as the orifice of the ulcer was large and unsightly, he commanded her to be supported at royal expense until she should be perfectly cured. However before a week had expired a fair new skin returned and hid the scars so completely that nothing of the original wound could be discovered; and within a year, becoming the mother of twins, she increased the admiration of Edward's holiness."

The practice which Edward the Confessor had initiated was carried on at first only by his descendants, but at a later date the "royal touch" was regarded as being a part of the divine right of all kings. Because by now there were many applicants to be touched, the ceremony had to be organized on a very large scale. Patients seeking treatment were first examined by court physicians and all who were deemed unsuitable were turned away. Next, certificates were demanded of those who had been accepted declaring that they had never previously been "touched" by the king for the disease. Finally the patients were blessed, their sores were touched by their sovereign and small golden coins were hung round their necks.

In France the custom of the royal touch dates back to the reign of Clovis the Frank (A.D. 496) and it was as popular there as in England. Louis XIV is said to have "touched" between two and three thousand people. This was considerably less than the Stuart Kings of England managed to do when the fashion was at its zenith in England. Richard Wiseman, one of the ablest surgeons of his day, gives an account of the ceremony as carried out in the reign of Charles II and states: "I have myself been an eye-witness of hundreds of cures performed by His Majesty's Touch alone, without any assistance of Chirurgery." Scrofula was very common in those days and if sufficient time be given spontaneous cures of this disease are quite usual. Each patient admitted to the royal presence received a small gold token or "touchstone", whether benefited or not, and Queen Elizabeth, with an eye to cutting down court expenses, ordered the size of these coins to be reduced. King William III had very little faith in his own powers as a miraculous healer, and when he was persuaded to try his hand at it, he is reputed to

have murmured over the applicant's head these words: "God grant you better health and more sense." Queen Anne, however, encouraged scrofulous patients to come to her palace and amongst those whom she "touched" was Samuel Johnson, a scrofulous infant of two years old at the time. After Queen Anne's death the ceremony of the royal touch fell into disuse.

THE MEDICAL SCHOOL AT SALERNO

Fortunately there survived during the whole of this bleak period of the Middle Ages a small centre in Europe in which the lamps of Greek culture still continued to burn brightly and where medical progress was occasionally made. It was in the tiny town of Salerno, not very far from Naples. In Roman times Salerno had been a fashionable health resort and after the fall of the Roman Empire it had served as a convenient meeting-ground for people of culture. There are two legends concerning the origin of the medical school in Salerno: one, that it was founded by Charlemagne, and another, that it was started by "four masters", Elinus the Jew, Pontus the Greek, Adale the Arab, and Salernus the Latin. The latter legend, whether true or not, is at any rate in keeping with two of the chief characteristics of the Salernitan School: that it was open to men of all languages and of all nationalities and even to women; that it was a lay foundation and not a by-product of the neighbouring great monastery of Cassino. Not that there was any enmity between Salerno and the Church. On the contrary, there is every reason to believe that the physicians studying medicine at Salerno and the Benedictine Monks at Cassino were very friendly, and it is quite likely that the former were allowed to make use of the monastery's fine library.

The Medical School of Salerno came into being during the ninth century, was at its zenith at the beginning of the eleventh century and then slowly declined during the thirteenth century. It was famous throughout Europe and at one time to have studied at Salerno was sufficient to establish the medical reputation of any young physician. Salerno was also the first medical school to urge that people who practised medicine should hold some qualification for doing so. The decree setting this forth was issued in A.D. 1140 by Roger II of Sicily. "Whosoever will henceforth practise medicine,

let him present himself to our officials and judges to be examined by them; but if he presume of his own temerity, let him be imprisoned and all his goods be sold by auction. The object of this is to prevent the subjects of our kingdom incurring peril through the ignorance of physicians."

The Medical School of Salerno gave useful instruction not only in medicine but in the ethics of medical practice. The following extract is taken from *De Adventu Medici*, written by Archimathaeus, a Salernitan professor, in the year 1140.

"When called to a patient commend yourself to God and to the angel who guided Tobias. On the way learn as much as possible from the messenger, so that if you discover nothing from the patient's pulse or water, you may still astonish him and gain his confidence by your knowledge of the case. On arrival ask the friends whether the patient has confessed, for if you bid him do so after the examination it will frighten him. Then sit down, take a drink and praise the beauty of the country and the house, if they deserve it, or extol the liberality of the family.

"Next proceed to feel the pulse, remembering that it may be affected by your arrival, or, the patient being a miser, by his thinking of the fee. . . . Do not be in a hurry to give an opinion, for the friends will be more grateful for your judgement if they have to wait for it. Tell the patient you will cure him, with God's help, but inform his friends that the case is a most serious one.

"Look not desirously on the man's wife, daughter, or handmaid, for this blinds the eyes of the physician, deprives him of the divine assistance, and disturbs the patient's mind.

"If according to custom, you are asked to dinner, do not hasten to take the first place, unless as is usual for the priest and the physician, it is offered you.

"Often send to enquire how the patient is, that he may see you do not neglect him for the pleasures of the table, and on leaving, express your thanks for the attention shown you, for this will please him much."

There follows then a dissertation on the medical treatment of various illnesses of a simple nature and instructions on that subject

which the beginner in medical practice finds to be a very difficult one, the rendering of the medical account. As will be seen, the whole matter is handled most delicately, the fact that a fee is now due to the doctor being implied rather than directly asserted.

"When the patient is nearly well, address the head of the family, or the sick man's nearest relative, thus: God Almighty having deigned by our aid to restore him whom you asked us to visit, we pray that He will maintain his health, and that you will now give us an honourable dismissal. Should any other member of your family desire our aid, we should, in grateful remembrance of our former dealings with you, leave all else and hurry to serve him."

During the first two centuries of its existence the hospital at Salerno succoured many wounded Crusaders before they continued their journey home, across Europe. Amongst the wounded Crusaders treated was Robert, son of William the Conqueror and now Duke of Normandy. Robert's prolonged absence from home at the Crusades lost him the throne of England and led later to his imprisonment by his usurping brother. It is said that the most popular of all the medical works emanating from Salerno, the handbook of medicine entitled *Regimen Sanitatis Salernitanum*, was specially written for Duke Robert's guidance. Like many medical works of that time it was written in Latin verse and it contains such excellent advice that, had he followed it and also been fortunate enough to have secured the English throne, Duke Robert might well have been the wisest of all our monarchs. No king could have been given clearer guidance.

> "The Salerne School doth by these lines impart
> All health to England's King and doth advise
> From care his head to keep, from wrath his heart.
> Drink not much wine, sup light and soon arise."

Then follows much excellent advice on the subject of diet.

> "A King that cannot rule him his diet,
> Will hardly rule his Realm in peace and quiet."

"Cow's milk and sheep's do well, but yet an ass's
Is best of all and all the others passes."

. . . . .

"Good sport to see a Mallard killed,
But with their flesh your flesh should not be filled."

. . . . .

"For healthy men may cheese be wholesome food
But for the weak and sickly 'tis not good."

"White *Muskadell* and *Candie Wine*, and, *Greek*
Do make men's wits and bodies grosse and fat;
Red wine doth make the voyce oft-time to seeke,
And hath a binding quality to that;
Canarie, Madera both are like
To make one leane indeed; (but wot you what)
Who say they make one leane, would make one laffe
They meane, they make one leane upon a staffe
Wine, Women, Baths, by Art of Nature warme,
Us'd or abus'd do men much good or harme."

"Some live to drinke new wine not fully fin'd
But for your health we wish that you drink none,
For such to dangerous fluxes are inclin'd,
Besides, the lees of wine doe breed the stone,
But such by our consent shall drink alone.
For water and small biere we make no question,
Are enemies to health and good digestion;
And *Horace* in a verse of his rehearses,
That *water-drinkers* never make good verses."

One of the earliest translations to be made of *Regimen Sanitatis Salernitanum* into English was made by Sir John Harington and presented by him to his godmother Queen Elizabeth. Sir John Harington gave his translation the somewhat cumbersome title *The Englishman's Doctor or the School of Salerno or Physical observations for the perfect Preserving of the body of Man in Continuall Health.* We have no way of learning Elizabeth's opinion of the health notes

she received from her godson or of knowing whether she applied the advice to herself or not.

The writings of some of the later Salernitans on the subject of medical practice and its management suggests that, as the years passed by, a certain deterioration occurred in professional conduct. *De Cantelis Medici* (Hints to Doctors) gives the following advice to beginners in medical practice:

"When you go to a patient always try and do something *new* every day, lest they say you are good at nothing but books."

"If you unfortunately visit a patient and find him dead, and they ask you why you are come, say you knew he would die that night, but want to know at what hour he died."

It is obvious that the writer of this useful work knew a great deal about the pitfalls and difficulties of general practice, but he would have been wiser perhaps to be a little less outspoken about them. So also must another Salernitan writer on the same subject be considered a little indiscreet when he gives the following advice to beginners. He suggests to them that if a patient shows a strong disinclination to pay his account, then they should "contrive that he shall take alum instead of salt with his meat; this will not fail to make him come out all over spots".

THE WOMEN STUDENTS OF SALERNO

Salerno was astonishingly liberal in its outlook, for whereas our great teaching hospitals in London only opened their medical schools to women students during the last two decades, Salerno was prepared to admit them centuries ago during the Dark Ages. In his *Lehrbuch des Geschichte der Medecin* Dr. H. Haeser records the names of the five women studying medicine at Salerno and states that Constantia Calenda made a great reputation for herself there. In order that young women resident at Salerno should be properly looked after it was obligatory that the director of studies should be a married man, since part of his professional duties was to keep a paternal eye on the lady students. Rudolph the monk also tells us that when he visited Salerno in 1059 he found there only one person who could meet him in argument: "a certain learned matron" who is

believed to have been called Trota or Trotula, and who is presumed
to be the authoress of the book, *On Diseases of Women*. This gynaecological work contains two excellent chapters on the management of
the new-born baby, but evidently the learned authoress did not lose
all interest in beauty culture for we find in her book a section
devoted to that subject. "To make the hair golden take of elder
bark, flowers of broom, yolk of egg and saffron equal parts; boil
them in water; skin off what floats on the surface and use as pomada."

Withington records the history of Sichelgarta, another of the
Salernitan ladies, who afterwards married Duke Robert Guiscard.
Her gifts were different from those of her two fellow students, the
ladies Calenda and Trotula, and much more heroic and spectacular.
The amazonian feats she performed at the side of her gallant husband
will be familiar to readers of the works of Gibbon and Sir Walter
Scott, but neither of these writers tell us anything about Sichelgarta's domestic history. Withington states that when a student
at Salerno she had shown particular interest in the study of Toxi-
cology and that later on in life she found her expert knowledge
of poisons very useful. As a fond mother she was naturally anxious
that her own son Roger should manage to acquire the birthright of
his half-brother, the famous Crusader Bohemund. On hearing that
the latter had gone to Salerno to recruit his health, she sent to his
medical attendant there, who happened to be none other than one
of her old teachers, a box containing a slow but very effectual
poison. Her former tutor "took the hint and administered the drug;
but Duke Robert somehow became suspicious of what was going on
and calling for the Bible and his sword he swore on the former that
he would plunge the latter into his wife's heart the day he heard
of his son's death. Sichelgarta was equal to the occasion; she at once
sent another trusty messenger to Salerno with a never failing antidote, and 'by the blessing of God, who had ordained Bohemund to
be a scourge of the infidel' he recovered". Yet apparently it was
only to be a temporary reprieve for some years later Sichelgarta
"succeeded in poisoning her husband and in making her son Roger
his successor". For the credit of the Duchess and the physician,
her former tutor, it should be added that the whole of this story
rests only on the testimony of the monk Ordericus Vitalis who wrote
it fifty years after these events are supposed to have happened. We

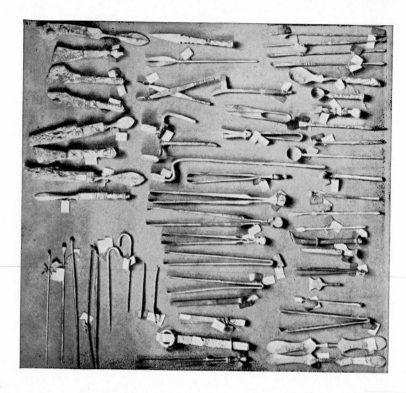

Surgical instruments found at Pompeii
(From the Naples Museum)

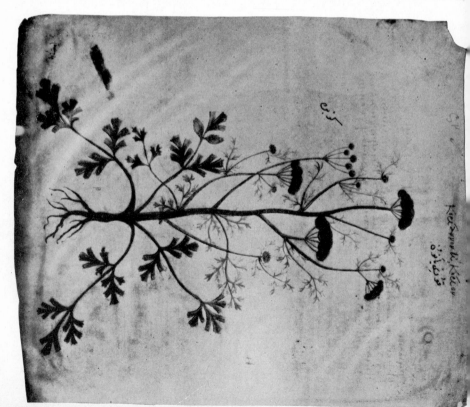

Coriander
(A drawing from the 6th century Vienna Codex of Dioscorides)

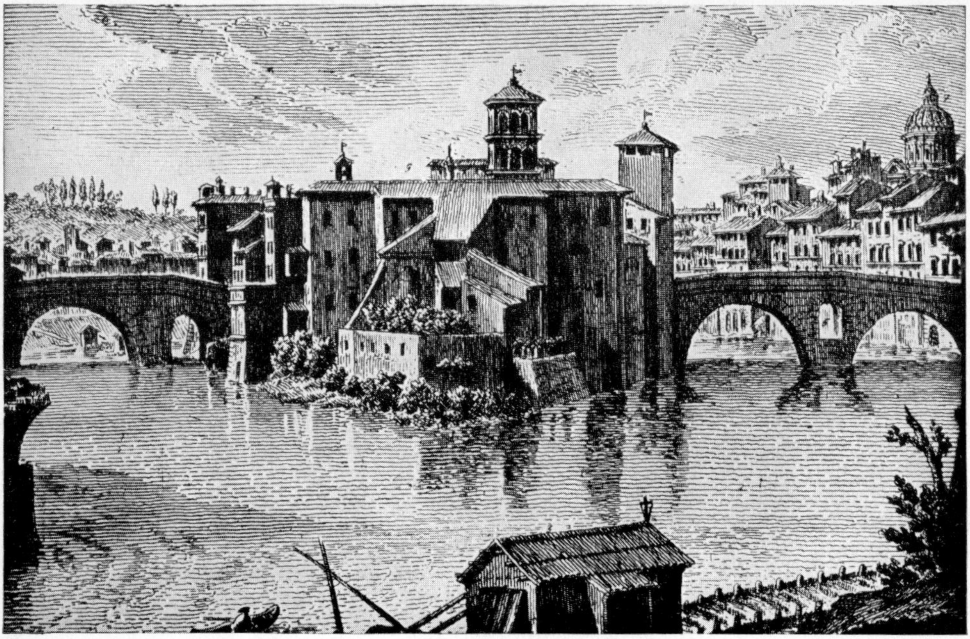

The Temple of Æsculapius on an island in the Tiber, later used as
a hospital for sick and abandoned slaves

Cauterizing the sores of a leper

(From a Persian work of the 13th century)

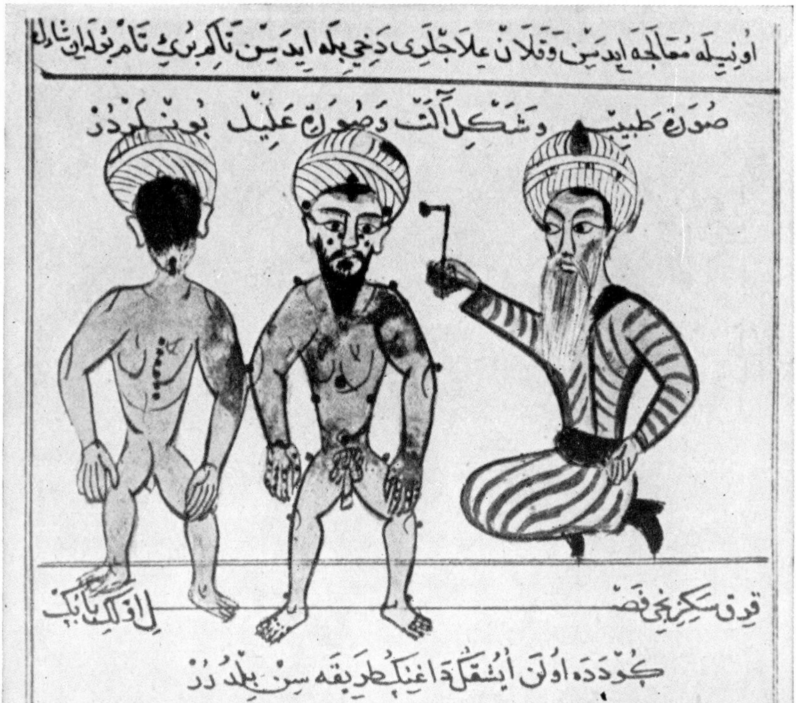

all know what brilliant work the imagination can do in the absence of any facts to hinder it, and it is more than likely that the account of events given by Ordericus Vitalis is not an entirely reliable one.

Men are always critical of the work done by women after they have irrupted into professions hitherto open only to the male sex and it would be interesting to know the opinion of contemporary medical men on the subject of the medical women of Salerno. Fortunately Guy de Chauliac (1300–1367) writes about the lady doctors of Salerno in his *Grande Chirurgie*, placing them in the fifth and lowest class of operator. He makes no adverse comment on their technical skill, his sole complaint against them being that they are too ready "to give over patients suffering from all kinds of maladies to the will of Heaven, founding their practice on the maxim, 'The Lord has given as He has pleased; the Lord will take away when He pleases, may the name of the Lord be blessed' ". Guy de Chauliac's criticism is quite understandable. A too prompt resignation to the Divine Will on the part of the surgeon is a little disconcerting to the nervous patient.

THE MEDICAL SCHOOLS OF MONTPELLIER, BOLOGNA AND PADUA

As the prestige enjoyed by Salerno began to decline, Montpellier became the headquarters of medical learning in Europe. Montpellier was also a health resort and, geographically speaking, it was conveniently placed for students coming to it from France, Spain, Italy and Southern Europe. The fame and popularity of all these mediaeval schools rose and fell in accordance with the ability and the renown of the scholars, physicians and surgeons on their teaching staffs. A history of the medical schools of Montpellier, Bologna and Padua would therefore resolve itself into a list of honourable names and an account of the works for which these men had become famous. As it is not the aim of this book to be a complete history of medicine, only a few of the men to whom these mediaeval centres of learning owed their reputation will be mentioned.

ARNOLD OF VILLANOVA (1235–1312)

Arnold of Villanova, a Portuguese physician who taught at Montpellier, is certainly worthy of mention, if for no other reason than that his life history shows how carefully it was necessary for

teachers of medicine to tread during the Middle Ages if they were to avoid persecution at the hands of the Church. Arnold of Villanova was a man of great attainments, a graduate in theology and law as well as in medicine. He was also fortunate enough to possess powerful friends, amongst others no less exalted a person than Pope Boniface VIII himself who, at a critical moment of his career, gave him the excellent advice that in future he would be much wiser to stick to medicine and to leave the subject of theology severely alone. Arnold of Villanova had enough sense to act on this excellent advice, and he made no more public excursions into theology. He practised both as a surgeon and as a physician and he was the first man to make tinctures by extracting roots and dried leaves with alcohol. It was whilst searching for the Elixir of Life that he hit upon the virtues of an excellent preparation called brandy, a medicine to which he gave the name "aqua vitae". Fortunately his non-medical books were not read until after his death so that it was only then that the full measure of his heresy was discovered. The ecclesiastical authorities felt so strongly on the subject that they announced to the world that Arnold of Villanova had been in league with the Devil and they ordered that the worst of his treatises should be publicly burnt. A less biased scrutiny of Arnold of Villanova's works shows that his sole error.was that he had often been guided by his own judgement in an age in which no man was expected or allowed to think for himself. Nor was it only Church doctrines that he had doubted for he was as sceptical of many of the statements of Galen as he was sceptical of certain theological dogmas. The times being what they were, he may be counted fortunate to have died in bed and not to have been burnt with his philosophical treatises.

GUY DE CHAULIAC (1300–1367)

No account of the later mediaeval period would be complete that did not mention Guy de Chauliac. He was the son of a French peasant and he studied theology and medicine at Montpellier and Bologna, eventually becoming physician and chaplain to His Holiness, Clement VI. And not only to the one pope for he lived long enough to act in the same capacity to Clement VI's two successors at the Vatican.

Guy de Chauliac was a man of wide culture as well as a skilled

physician and surgeon. The literary work which earned him widespread professional recognition was *Chirurgie Magna*, and some of the inventions he describes in this book are still to be found in hospitals at the present day. It was Guy de Chauliac who introduced the practice of applying extensions to fractured limbs by means of weights and pulleys. He was the first to describe the Trendelenberg position in surgery, and the chain and handles by means of which bed-ridden patients are able to raise themselves into a sitting position was also his invention. He was a great scholar and at the same time a man of a practical turn of mind. His comments on the Salernitan women surgeons have previously been mentioned.

GILBERTUS ANGLICUS AND JOHN OF GADDESDEN

The only Englishmen of any note who studied at Montpellier were Gilbertus Anglicus (died 1250) and John of Gaddesden (1280–1361). The first of these Englishmen became a very competent doctor but the compendium of medicine for which he was responsible is a very dull work. John of Gaddesden is much more interesting and it is said that Chaucer, his contemporary, knew and used him as a model for the "very parfit practisour" in *Canterbury Tales*. This description of him is at any rate an apt one, for he acquired a very fashionable practice and developed all those refinements of medical treatment which are *de rigueur* when a doctor has to deal with such an exalted clientele as that catered for by John of Gaddesden. It is recorded that he looked after the son of Edward II during an attack of smallpox and that he prevented the prince from becoming permanently disfigured by wrapping him up in a red cloth and arranging that the bed hangings and the window curtains in his room should be of the same red colour. If the story of the red curtains be true—and it is usually accepted as such—then we must regard John of Gaddesden as a pioneer in the field of light therapy. Guthrie quotes the following description of him taken from Freind's *History of Physick*, which was published in the year 1725. "Nothing came amiss to him. He could dissolve the Stone, draw out the humour of Gout with an ointment, conquer Epileptic fits with a necklace, and cure a Palsy with Aqua Vitae." But Freind frankly admits that John of Gaddesden was by no means negligent of his own profit in the ordering of his

practice. "He was very artful," he writes, "in laying baits for the Delicate, for the Ladies, for the Rich; for the former he had such a tenderness that he condescends to instruct them even in Perfumes and washes; especially some to dye their hair; and such a respect for the latter that he is always studying to invent some of the most select and dearest medicine for them; and of these is a very good thing indeed, for he orders twice the quantity for them as he does for the poor."

Men of the type of John of Gaddesden have existed in every age and in spite of their foibles they will always be needed in the medical profession. We may laugh at their bedside manners, at the refinements they have made in the art of medicine, at their devising of red bed-hangings, at their necklaces specially designed to prevent the occurrence of epileptiform convulsions and at their perfumed ointments, but a world of many different kinds of men and women requires a medical fraternity of many kinds of doctors. John of Gaddesden is a well-known medical type that, despite the passing of the Health Act and of the modern passion for reducing all men to the same level, still manages to survive and, within its limits, to do excellent work.

MONTPELLIER AND PARIS

Montpellier's fame was far shorter lived than that of its great predecessor Salerno, and in course of time medical preference was transferred to Paris and Padua. These were the fashionable schools of the thirteenth and fourteenth centuries to which medical students from every country flocked. And without any doubt Paris had great names with which to draw to herself foreign visitors. The names of two monks were amongst the most brilliant, if not the most brilliant, of all those connected with the Paris Medical School, to wit, Roger Bacon (1214–1294), an English Franciscan, and Albertus Magnus (1192–1280), a German Dominican. Both of these monks were men of encyclopaedic knowledge, as learned in the Natural Sciences as they were in philosophy and theology, but whereas the great Dominican was content to rely on authority for his knowledge, the great Franciscan was that highly dangerous thing, an original thinker. Roger Bacon is said to have spent large sums of his own money on his scientific experiments and he is credited with having made almost as

many scientific discoveries as Leonardo da Vinci did. He is reputed to have invented the telescope, the microscope, spectacles, and a diving bell, and to have prophesied that one day men would be able to fly.

Because Roger Bacon had deferred too little to Church rulings in his scientific books, the general of the Franciscan Order interrupted his lectures and placed him under strict supervision in Paris. He was instructed to remain there even although this entailed for him much suffering and many privations. The publishing of any more scientific books was also prohibited but fortunately the new Pope Clement IV had heard of Roger Bacon's immense ability and he sent word to him privately ordering him, notwithstanding any injunctions he had previously received from his superiors in the Order, to forward to him, the Holy Father, his scientific treatises. After this intervention on the part of the Pope, Roger Bacon was allowed a little more liberty in Paris but this lasted only for a time. In 1278 his books were again condemned by yet another general of the Franciscan Order, and still later, when that general had in turn become Pope, Roger Bacon found himself back again in prison. This time he had done what no man could be allowed to do with impunity: he had attacked the ignorance of the clergy, and had called attention to the insufficiency of their education. It was all too true, but truth is a dangerous commodity to deal in and Roger Bacon was now in permanent disgrace with the Church.

The great stature of this Franciscan was not appreciated during his life-time because he was too far ahead of his contemporaries to be understood. He had as fine a mind as had the great St. Thomas Aquinas, but as he happened to be a modern thinker instead of a good schoolman he was forced to spend a large part of his life in prison. Even now few people realize how great a man he was or appreciate the fact that it was Roger and not Francis Bacon who was the first to champion the experimental method of research, the method by which all our scientific progress has been achieved.

THE MOSLEM EMPIRE

In the seventh century Islam gathered together its growing strength and swept across lands that had formerly belonged to the Emperor of the East. By the ninth century a vast and, on the whole,

tolerant Mohammedan Empire had been established with its centre at Baghdad. From the point of view of medicine this was a satisfactory event, for the Mohammedan Empire was far more liberally minded in its attitude to learning than its great competitor, the Christian Church. It extended a welcome to all great scholars from wherever they came, irrespective of their birth-place and their religion. When therefore the word Arab or Arabian is placed in the chapter in front of the word medicine it refers only to the language in which the physicians of that particular school of medicine happened to speak or write, for the teachers at Islamic centres of education were by no means necessarily Arab by birth. Included among the exponents of Arab medicine were Syrians, Persians, Hebrews, Turks, Greeks and even Spaniards. Nor was it even essential that they should be followers of Mahomet, for some of the representatives of this Arabian school remained Jews and others continued to be Christians.

The Moslem rule established in Southern Europe was a benevolent and tolerant one and most countries prospered under it. Cordoba in Southern Spain became the capital of the Western Caliphate and grew into a great city of about two hundred thousand houses and about a million inhabitants. The material, educational and spiritual needs of these inhabitants were adequately supplied by 600 inns, 900 public baths, and 600 mosques, each with a free school attached to it. In the province of Cordoba there were 17 universities and 70 public libraries, the largest of these—Al-Hakem —containing nearly a quarter of a million volumes. A civilization as cultured as this could not fail to produce able physicians and philosophers, and great men of the calibre of Avenzoar and Averroes appeared to grace it.

Magnificent Moslem hospitals were also built, the finest being those of Damascus and of Cairo. We possess a description of the former in an account given by a contemporary writer, Ibn Al-Alhir, of a personal visit he paid to it. He relates that during his return journey from a visit to Jerusalem in 1184 he fell ill and, disliking the local doctor who had been called in, he dismissed him. "Then I rode into the city (Damascus) and asking the address of a physician, was directed to the great hospital. On my entrance, the superintendent came to me and inquired most affably into my case. Then he wrote a

prescription, saying: 'Your attendant will bring you what is written on this paper.' 'But Sir,' said I, 'thanks be to God, I am rich enough to pay for my drugs without trespassing on the property of the poor.' He replied: 'Sir, I doubt not that you can do without our medicine, but here no one despises Nureddin's benefits. In the name of God, I assure you that Sultan Saladin's sons and their whole families send here for medicines and never pay.' I answered that I could not approve of that. 'It was Nureddin's desire,' he continued, 'to be useful to all believers, rich or poor.' "

The hospital appears to have been run regardless of cost and it was an extremely comfortable place in which to stay, as is shown by the following story told by another contemporary writer, Khalil. "While making the pilgrimage to Mecca in 851" (1427), writes Khalil, "I stayed at Damascus, and had with me a certain Persian, a man of wit and intelligence, who followed the rites of the four orthodox sects, performing them all at the same time. When he went over the hospital and saw the patients' diet and all their comforts and advantages, which are without number, he pretended to be ill and stayed three days there. The physician having felt his pulse, recognized his case and prescribed any diet that he liked, so he was fed upon young chickens, cakes and sherbet, and all manner of fruits. But after two days the doctor wrote a prescription implying that a guest should not stay beyond the third day." So this clever Persian, a man of such intelligence and wit that he was able to resolve all theological differences by performing the rites of four orthodox sects simultaneously, took the hint given by the house physician and left the hospital.

If it be true, as it seems to be, that the Arabs were responsible for the burning of the great library at Alexandria, they certainly did their best now to atone for this barbarity. The rule of the Caliphate in Europe was far more cultured, tolerant and benign than that of the Church had been, but it was destined soon to be destroyed. In 1236 St. Ferdinand of Castile captured Cordoba and twenty years later Baghdad was razed to the ground by the Mongols. Both of these conquerors, Christian and pagan, were ruthless in their destruction of the previous Moslem culture. The Mongols are said to have used the remains of the great library at Baghdad as material with which to build a bridge over the Tigris, whilst the Holy Office claimed to have

destroyed at least a million Arabic volumes in Southern Spain. Cardinal Ximines worked so hard at this exhilarating work of burning books that he was able to boast afterwards that he had been personally responsible for casting 5000 copies of the Koran into the flames.

THE ARABIAN SCHOOL OF MEDICINE

When the Moslems began to rescue medicine from the stagnation of the Middle Ages they realized that the first thing that they had to do was to make good translations into Arabic of all the old Greek scientific and medical works that had fallen into disuse. They set about this task at once and soon, as the result of their industry, Greek science and medicine spread throughout the whole of the Moslem world. But the Arabic scholars of the day were not content merely to produce translations of. other people's works. They began to write also commentaries on the old Greek texts and later they started to publish new and original medical treatises. Now, for the first time for many centuries, creative thinkers were to be found in a Europe which a little while previously had seemed to have lost for good all capacity to think. Great men of the calibre of Rhazes of Basra (860–932) and of the Persian physician Avicenna (980–1036) now made their presence felt.

RHAZES OF BASRA

The first of these two justly celebrated physicians was a man of many parts. He published a medical work in which there appears for the first time a detailed description of measles together with an account of the method by which the rash of measles can be distinguished from other kinds of eruption. Rhazes was a man of wide interests and he wrote books which bore such varied titles as: *Advice on Buying a Slave, Bites from Venomous Beasts* and *Medical Hints for Travellers*.

AVICENNA

But Avicenna was by far the greater of these two Arabian physicians and he is now accepted as being the most brilliant of all the Islamic doctors. He was born in Bokhara, where he started life as an infant prodigy capable of reciting the whole of the Koran at

the tender age of ten. By eighteen his ability was so obvious to everybody that he was appointed court physician, a position which conferred on him the great privilege of being allowed to make use of the royal library. Avicenna was a man who lived life to the fullest, working as hard as it is possible for any man to work and at the same time enjoying good company, witty conversation, wine and music. Although Paracelsus did not recognize this fact Avicenna had much in common with himself so that it was a mistake on his part to have inaugurated his course of medical lectures by a public burning of Avicenna's medical works. Avicenna, like Paracelsus, was a wanderer moving on from one city to another, so that we find him first practising medicine at Khiva, then at Jurjan, next in Ispahan, and finally at Hamadan. He was a prototype of a by no means rare kind of physician, a highly cultured man who is not only an excellent doctor but also a writer, teacher and philosopher.

Avicenna gained a great reputation in his life-time as a poet and some of his verse has been likened to that of Omar Khayyám, whom he antedated by a century. And it is quite true that the following verse might equally well have been taken from Avicenna or the Rubá'iyát.

"From Earth's dark centre unto Saturn's Gate
I've solved all problems of the world's Estate,
From every snare of Plot and Guile set free,
Each bond resolved, saving alone Death's Fate."

Sir William Osler compares him with Plato. He writes: "The touch of the man never reached me until I read some of his mystical and philosophical writings, translated by Mehren. It is Plato over again. The beautiful allegory in which men are likened to birds snared and caged until set free by the Angel of Death might be anywhere in the immortal Dialogues" (*Evolution of Modern Medicine*).

It is said that Avicenna over-stepped the bounds of prudence and that he shortened his life by becoming dissipated. This belief is supported by a contemporary saying to the effect that "all his philosophy could not make him moral, nor all his physic teach him to preserve his health". Avicenna died in his fifty-eighth year and his death was in keeping with his life. When he realized that no

treatment could cure him he resigned himself to the inevitable, sold his goods and distributed the proceeds amongst the poor, read the Koran through from beginning to end every three days and died in the holy month of Ramadan. The tomb of this great healer is an object of pilgrimage and many cures are said still to be effected there.

Only two other Islamic physicians of this period need be mentioned, Avenzoar (1072–1162) and his pupil and friend Averroes (1126–1198). The latter was more influential as a philosopher than as a physician and, having criticized as I have the Christian Church, it is only fair that I should add that Averroes' unorthodox religious views eventually landed him also in prison.

SUMMARY OF THE STATE OF MEDICINE IN THE MIDDLE AGES

If we except the medical research carried out at such centres of Islamic culture as Salerno, it would be true to say that very little or no progress at all was made in physiology, anatomy or medicine during the first half of the Middle Ages. The physiology and the medicine of that time was identical with Galen's physiology and with his medical doctrine of the four humours. Few doctors had the courage to question the teaching of the great authority whose opinions had been accepted for so many centuries and fewer still possessed enough initiative to embark on fresh clinical observations of their own. In some departments of medicine, such as in hygiene and public health, the doctors of the Middle Ages had lost ground since the fall of the Roman Empire and were seemingly content to have lost it. Rome had at least taught doctors the importance of drainage and the need for providing towns with a good water supply, but the towns of this period were completely deficient in both of these. They possessed no drains, and had no water supply; the houses were ill-ventilated and filthy, the streets narrow and foulsmelling. The only advance that can be recorded during these centuries of scientific and medical inertia was the further development of the hospital system.

THE HOSPITALS OF THE MIDDLE AGES

The Romans had brought the hospitals to a certain stage of development when they established large buildings for the treatment

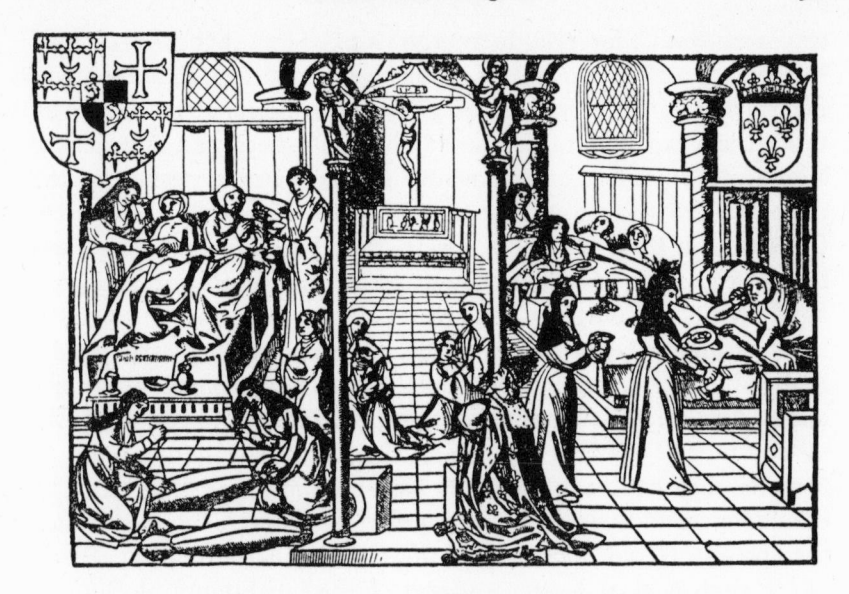

FIG. 3.—Hospital Ward in the Middle Ages (the Hôtel Dieu)

of troops stationed on distant frontiers and when they opened Valetudinaria for the care of sick civilians. Now, in the Middle Ages, the idea of the hospital was carried a little further forward by the Church when she built "hospitalia" or guest-houses for the accommodation of pilgrims. These were set up in many parts of Britain, at first only along the routes travelled by pilgrims, but later elsewhere. Still later hospitalia of a somewhat similar kind were opened for the care of orphans and for the "succouring" of the aged and the blind. (*See* Fig. 3.) Praiseworthy though these efforts to alleviate the lot of the poor and the sick undoubtedly were, there was a limit to what the Church was able to do for the lame, the sick and the blind and it was inevitable that many unfortunate people should be left without any help at all. This was particularly true of the lepers. Leprosy was a specially difficult problem with which to deal and the chief effort made by the Church lay in the direction of segregating everybody attacked by what was obviously a contagious disease. In bygone ages the disfiguring disease of leprosy had existed only in the East but during the earlier centuries of the Christian era it slowly crept along the Mediterranean coasts and then made its

way northwards. Everybody appreciated the fact that it was spread by contact and in consequence of this knowledge the leper was banished from all human society and even declared to be legally dead. Excluded from taking part in church services, all that he was allowed to do, if he were a devout Christian, was to peep in at the celebration of the mass through the leper's window of the church. Cruel though these regulations were, they began to take effect and in course of time they were so successful that leprosy disappeared to all intents and purposes from Europe.

It is impossible to write of the medical history of the Middle Ages without referring to the terrible visitations of periodic epidemics and particularly to the visitations of the plague that became known at that time as the Black Death. Such epidemics were by no means new, for they had been known in classical times (*see* Plate 11), but the living conditions in all the great towns were now ideal for the spread of epidemics and in the fourteenth century the Black Death destroyed at least a quarter of the inhabitants of Europe. There can be little doubt that it was imported into Europe from the East, reaching Sicily in 1346, and Constantinople, Greece and parts of Italy early in 1347. In 1348 it reached Spain, Northern Italy, Rome, Germany, France and England. So devastating was its assault and so tremendous the toll of victims exacted that the Pope found it necessary to consecrate the Rhone in order that this river might be utilized as a means of disposing more rapidly of the dead. But this subject is of such importance and throws so much light on the medical knowledge and customs of the Middle Ages that it will be dealt with more fully in the next chapter.

CHAPTER V

Mediaeval Epidemics

EUROPE has never witnessed sickness on a larger scale than it did during the Middle Ages, and since the course of medicine is affected by great epidemics it will be useful to say something about the mediaeval plagues. By studying what happened at that time we shall learn also a great deal about mediaeval Europe and be in a better position to appreciate the state of medicine and of the medical profession at that period of history. I am indebted for much that is to follow to Johannes Nohl's book *The Black Death*, which gives us contemporary accounts of the ravages of the plague in Italy during the great epidemics of 1345 and 1350. Florence lost from a third to a half of its inhabitants from the plague and the total death-roll in Europe, although it was much less densely populated than it is at present, must have run into hundreds of thousands.

The Black Death was said to have reached Europe from China *via* the trade routes running through Persia, Russia and Turkey, and this is likely to have been true. Michael of Piazza, a Franciscan friar, gives a vivid description of its arrival in Sicily. "At the beginning of October, in the year of the incarnation of the Son of God 1347, twelve Genoese galleys were fleeing from the vengeance which our Lord was taking on account of their nefarious deeds and entered the harbour of Messina. In their bones they bore so virulent a disease that anyone who spoke to them was seized by a mortal illness and in no manner could evade death. . . . Those infected felt themselves penetrated by a pain throughout their whole bodies, and, so to say, undermined. Then they developed on their thighs or on their upper arms a boil about the size of a lentil which the people called 'burn boil'. This infected the whole body and penetrated it so that the patient violently vomited blood. This vomiting continued

93

. . . three days, there being no means of healing it and then the patient expired. . . . When the inhabitants of Messina discovered that this sudden death emanated from the Genoese ships they hurriedly expulsed them from their harbour and town. But the evil remained with them and caused a fearful outbreak of death. Soon men hated each other so much that if a son was attacked by the disease, his father would not tend him. If, in spite of all he dared to approach him, he was immediately infected and could by no means escape death, but was bound to expire, within three days. Nor was that all: all those belonging to him, dwelling in the same house as him, even the cats and other domestic animals, followed him in death."

Michael of Piazza goes on to say that the victims of the Black Death died without the last rites being administered to them and without having been able to settle their worldly affairs. Ecclesiastics and attorneys dared not come near to them and the "minor friars and Dominicans . . . who heard the confessions of the dying were themselves immediately overcome by death, so that some even remained in the rooms of the dying. . . ." When the catastrophe had reached its climax the Messinians resolved to leave their town. One portion of them settled in the vineyards and fields, but a larger portion sought refuge in the town of Catania, "trusting that the holy virgin, Agatha of Catania, would deliver them from their evil".

And so the Black Death spread pitilessly, inexorably and without intermission through Italy. Two freight ships carried it to Pisa. "And thereupon there began a great dying in Pisa, and from there spread over the whole of Tuscany." The description of the spread of the plague is apt to become monotonous, for everywhere there occurred the same grim sequence of events, sickness, death, terror, panic and demoralization. Boccaccio, who lost his own father in the epidemic, stresses what other Italian writers also emphasize—the desertion of the plague victims by their friends and their relatives. "Let us admit that one citizen fled after another, and one neighbour had not any care for another, parents nor kindred ever visiting them, but utterly they were forsaken on all sides; this tribulation pierced into the hearts of men, and with such a dreadfull terror that one brother forsooke another, the Uncle the

Nephew, the Sister the Brother, and the Wife the Husband: nay, a matter much greater, and almost incredible; Fathers and Mothers fled away from their own Children."

MEDICINE AND THE BLACK DEATH

The physicians were fully conscious of their complete helplessness in the face of this vast contagion. Guy de Chauliac, the celebrated physician in ordinary to Clement VI, expresses their feelings on this subject. "The disease was most humiliating for the physicians, who were unable to render any assistance, all the more as for fear of infection they did not venture to visit their patients; and if they could do no good and consequently earn no fees, for all infected died with the exception of some towards the end of the epidemic; who escaped as the boils had been able to mature." The physicians, therefore, confined their efforts to instituting certain feeble so-called prophylactic measures and to repenting of their own medical sins for "by this means the venomous astral arrows may be averted".

The prophylactic measures advised by the physicians were admittedly poor, if not to say utterly ridiculous. The medical faculty in Paris relied for prophylaxis on dieting, declaring "cold, moist and watery foods to be harmful". Also fish, presumably on the same grounds that they had come from a watery environment. "Excesses of abstinence, excitement, anger and drunkenness are dangerous." So it was declared, but everything at that time was dangerous. The Italian medical men were all for encouraging quietude of mind, a prophylactic measure which in these trying circumstances was none too easy to adopt. "In the first instance no man should think of death; nor should he conceive any passion for any man. Nothing should distress him, but all his thoughts should be directed to pleasing, agreeable and delicious things. . . . In times of plague light women should be entirely dispensed with, as well as all intercourse with drunkards. Thirst should not be suffered, but only temperate drinking indulged in. Listening to beautiful melodious songs is wholesome, as is also to enjoy the joys of the season in the company of agreeable people. The contemplation of gold and silver and other precious stones is comforting to the heart." (Marsilio and Garbo quoted in *The Black Death* by J. Nohl.)

Because it was believed that the air was filled with plague contagion, those doctors who did dare to attend plague patients wore a cloth helmet and a respirator stuffed with aromatic herbs. (*See* Fig. 4.) This gave them the appearance of birds and the following doggerel lines are descriptive of the plague doctors in the Mediaeval and in later epidemics.

> "Their caps with glasses are designed,
> Their bills with antidotes are lined,
> That foulsome air may do no harm,
> Nor cause the doctor-man alarm.
> The staff in hand must serve to show
> Their noble trade, where'er they go."

A number of different antidotes to the foul air in the houses were experimented with. Dishes of fresh milk were left exposed to the air in the bedrooms, warm new bread was placed on the lips of the dying in the hope that it might absorb the plague poison, and herds of cows and oxen were driven through the streets so that their sweet breath might neutralize its action out of doors. In the Balkans the idea arose that the air could be changed by very powerful smells, and billy-goats suddenly found themselves comfortably quartered inside the farmers' bedrooms. The Chief Chancellor of Hungary for ever afterwards prided himself on having escaped the plague by his adoption of this highly-flavoured prophylactic measure. Gruling likewise reported that no one ever died who resided in a butcher's house in which a billy-goat was kept, but, as always happens when a medical man has made a useful observation like this, a sceptic immediately contradicted him. In an account of the plague's visit to Leipzig, Dr. Rivins states that people living in houses containing billy-goats frequently became infected with the Black Death in that city.

A certain philosopher recommended "bottled wind" as a useful antidote but he was unable to say how the bottling should be done. Another suggestion was to mix the individual's own urine with a little cuckold wort, wormwood and ironwort, to strain the mixture through a cloth and to drink a small quantity of it every morning. Nohl states that a great many protective amulets were sold at that

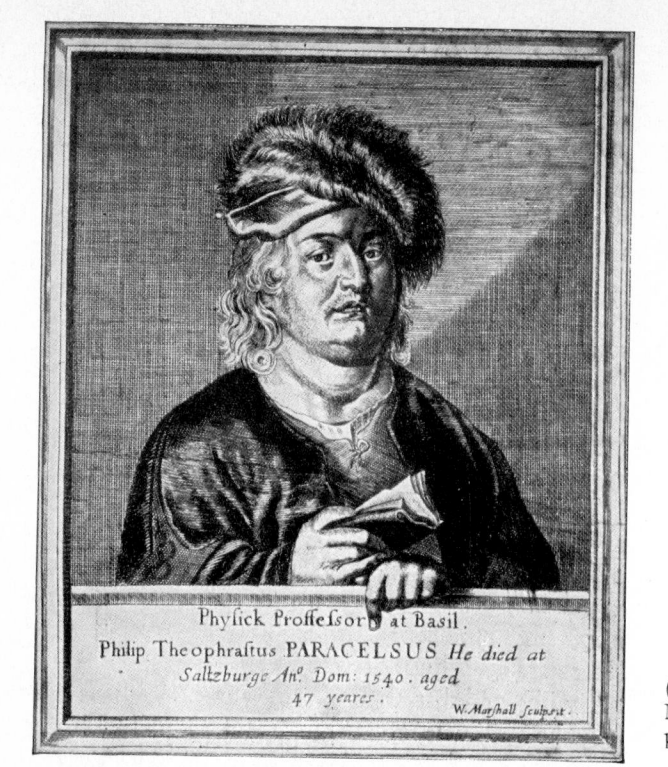

Phyſick Proffeſſorꝑ at Basil.
Philip Theophraſtus PARACELSUS *He died at*
Saltzburge An⁰. *Dom:* 1540. *aged*
47 *yeares*.
W.Marſhall ſculpſit.

Paracelsus
(Line engraving by W.
Marshall made from a
picture in the Louvre)

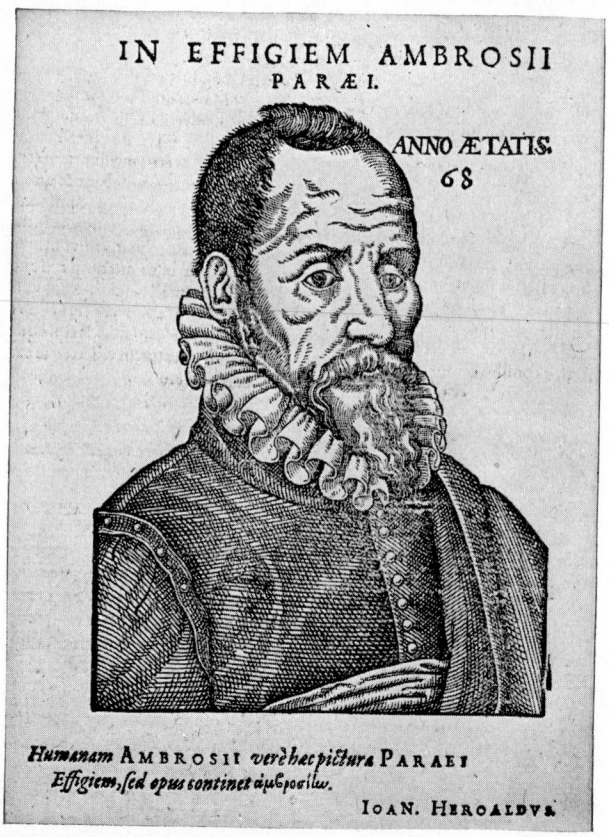

IN EFFIGIEM AMBROSII
PARÆI.

ANNO ÆTATIS.
68

Humanam AMBROSII *verè hæc pictura* PARAEI
Effigiem, ſed opus continet ἀμϐρoσίαν.
IOAN. HEROALDVS.

Ambroise Paré
Engraving from Am-
broise Paré, Opera,
Frankfurt, 1612)

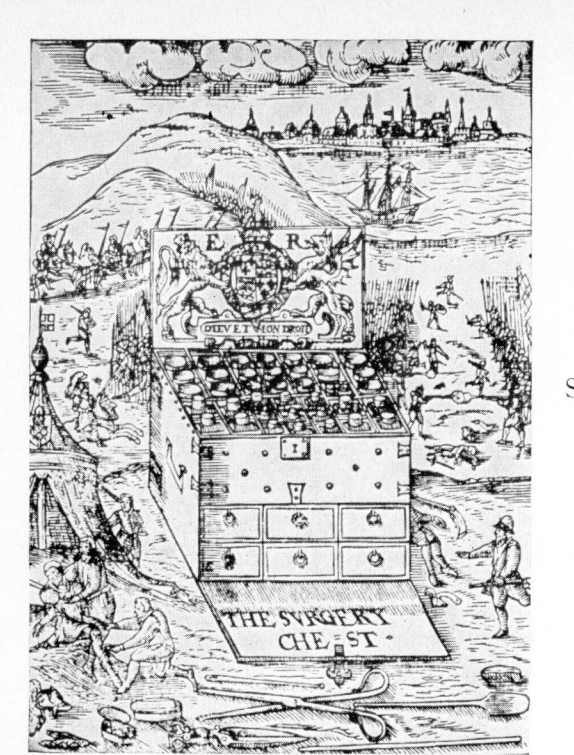

Surgery chest used at the time
the Armada

Mediaeval physician with apothecary and either a surgeon or a herb-gatherer
(From a 15th century French MS. in the *Bibliothèque Nationale*)

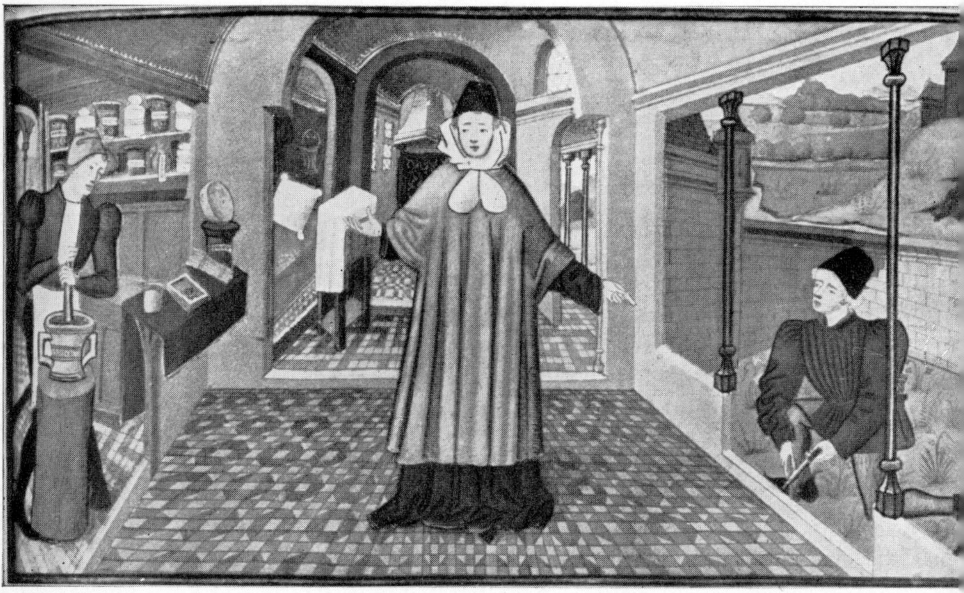

time, not only by quacks, old women and begging friars, but quite frequently by medical men. Even an intelligent man like Guy de Chauliac, who had long given up belief in sorcery and magic, now recommended people to follow the advice of Hermes. This advice

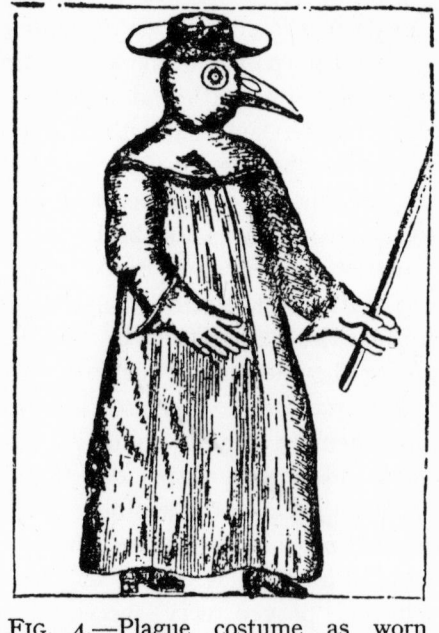

FIG. 4.—Plague costume as worn at the Marseilles outbreak in 1720

was to the effect that when the Sun was in the sign of the Lion and the Moon did not turn towards Saturn, they should "don a belt of lion skin, which, in pure gold and as clearly cut as possible, should bear the image of a lion".

QUARANTINE MEASURES AGAINST THE BLACK DEATH

Fortunately the rulers and administrators were in a slightly better position than the medical profession in that they could at least aim to limit the spread of the plague. The first Italian regulations against the disease were those drawn up at Reggio in 1374 by Viscomte Bernabo who had posted up the following enactments: "Everyone sick of the plague is to be brought out of the town into the

fields there to die or to recover. Those who have nursed plague patients
are to remain secluded for ten days before having intercourse with
their fellow men. The clergy are to examine the sick and report
to the authorities on pain of being burnt at the stake and con-
fiscation of their possessions. Those who introduce the plague shall
forfeit all their goods to the state. Finally, with the exception of
those set apart for the purpose, no one shall administer to those
sick of the plague on pain of death and forfeiture of their possessions." When we recall the fact that bubonic plague is conveyed
by the fleas living on rats, that the medical treatment of the day was
completely useless, and that close contact with other people in the
slums of overcrowded towns was the best way of spreading the
disease, these regulations of Viscomte Bernabo must be considered
excellent. Burning at the stake seems a severe penalty for failing
to report to the authorities a case of plague, but the situation was a
critical one, requiring the adoption of the sternest measures.

So also were the quarantine measures instituted in Italy remarkably efficient when we bear in mind how little was known
about the pathology and method of spread of the disease. The word
"quarantine" is itself a relic of the sanitary measures adopted at
that time by the small republic of Ragusa, on the eastern shores of
the Adriatic. The civil authorities of this tiny state issued certain
regulations which had proved very successful when they had
previously been employed in Venice. A landing stage was built at
a considerable distance from the city and the usual harbour and
all immigrants were ordered to land there. They were detained in
this spot outside the city, at first for a period of thirty days and
later, when this was found to be too short a time, for forty days.
From the Italian words for this period of forty days' isolation
("quarenta giorni") has been derived the modern term quarantine.
It reminds us of a valiant and very successful effort on the part of a
small republic to stop the spread of the Black Death during the
Middle Ages.

These Italian plague regulations served as models which were
later copied by many German states and towns. In Germany, a
country always amenable to an iron discipline, the sternest measures
against transgression were imposed, so stern that even death did
not exonerate from punishment those who had infringed its plague

regulations. The servant girl Barbara Thutin of Koenigsberg infected herself and her master with the plague by bringing into the home property belonging to people who had previously died of it. History records her punishment. "As by this she had grossly contravened the strict prohibition, an execution was carried on her *after* death, she being exhumed on March 21, 1710, in the new cemetery, where she had been buried, and on the 22nd hanged in her coffin on the gallows, and after a few days burnt at the foot of the gallows as an example for others."

THE ATTITUDE OF THE CHURCH TO THE BLACK DEATH

The Church taught that the pestilence had been ordained as a punishment for man's sins and this belief persisted as late as 1720 when the last great epidemic occurred at Marseilles. The Black Death had become for people the apocalyptic rider on the pale horse spoken of in the Bible, and everything seemed to point to the near advent of the judgement day, as had been proclaimed by Christ and His apostles. Having formulated the general nature of the trouble, each ecclesiastical authority was at liberty to specify the particular sin for which the plague rampant at that time was being used as a punishment. The Spanish clergy attributed it to the Opera, whereas the English bishops were in favour of its being a punishment for the Theatre. There were not a few clerics who firmly believed that the long pointed shoes which had come into fashion just prior to the outbreak of the Black Death had proved particularly irritating to the Divine Maker of this Universe, and that He had promptly responded by sending the plague. On the other hand, the inhabitants of Frammerbach, in the Spessart, had it on their consciences that the clothes they were wearing on Sundays and holidays were not always modest and seemly. They vowed therefore that henceforth the women would always wear only black blouses and black skirts and the men the plainest of grey suits. In France the disaster was attributed by many to King Philip's three sons having married within the prohibited degrees of consanguinity, and in Poland it was put down to the grave mistake of burying a sorcerer in consecrated ground. The Protestants saw in the plague of 1552 a clear vindication of their own reformed theological views. The plague, they said, had been caused "by the divergence of Church doctrine in many

supreme articles, particularly such bearing on the Holy Sacraments and the blood of our dear Lord Jesus Christ". After all, this attack by the Protestant on the Roman Church was only tit for tat for what the Roman Church had previously said. When the English sweating disease had invaded Germany in 1529 the Roman clergy had proclaimed everywhere and in no uncertain terms too that "a new religion must necessarily be followed by a new torment of villains".

But there were notable exceptions to the somewhat inglorious role played by the Church at this moment of European crisis. Whilst the epidemic was at its height at Marseilles, the Capuchins and Jesuits hastened from the surrounding country towards the stricken city in order that they might put themselves at the disposal of those attacked by the plague. Another band of heroic people about which little or nothing is now known, were the ecclesiastical fraternities of "fools", expressly founded for the purpose of combating the widespread fear of death.

The "Companies of the Fool" of Aarau were said to have the special blessing of the Virgin Mary and to be watched over by the patron saint of the pestilence, St. Sebastian. But the real saint of the Black Death in the Middle Ages was not St. Sebastian but that gentle youth St. Rochus, episodes of whose life have been depicted by Titian, Tintoretto, Rubens and other painters of less note. The story of Rochus is that he was born of elderly parents at Montpellier at about the end of the thirteenth century. As a youth he made a pilgrimage to Rome at a time at which the plague happened to be raging in that city and he immediately enrolled himself as an attendant at the hospital of Agaspendente. Finding himself assailed by the plague Rochus fled into a neighbouring forest, in order not to become a burden on his already overworked hospital colleagues. A fresh spring of water miraculously appeared where he lay stricken in the forest and at the same time the nobleman who lived in the large neighbouring house noticed strange behaviour on the part of his favourite hound. It frequently snatched pieces of bread from the table and then made off with them into the wood. The hound was followed one day and was seen to lay the bread at Rochus's feet. Henceforth the nobleman charged himself personally with the care of his forest guest and he was so markedly influenced by him that

eventually he also adopted the life of a recluse and, like Rochus, became a wanderer.

Having helped a great many plague victims on his journey, Rochus in his wanderings eventually reached Montpellier where he passed unrecognized. Then a new war broke out and Rochus was accused by someone in authority of being a spy and was thrown into prison. There he remained for five years, preparing himself for death with constant prayer and fasting. When at last death drew near to him he asked for and was granted the services of a priest. As the summoned confessor entered the dark cell he found it illuminated by a celestial light. This sign from heaven was recognized by the priest who immediately reported it to the authorities, and then hurried back with many other people to the cell. But when the door of the prison was opened to them and they entered the cell they found Rochus lying there dead. On one of the walls of his cell he had hurriedly scribbled these words, "He who is seized by the plague and seeks refuge in Rochus will gain relief in the disease." So runs the story of Rochus.

Nor was the Protestant Church without its own heroes of the plague years. Martin Luther elected to remain in Wittenberg during the epidemics of 1516, 1527, 1535, 1538 and 1539. "My place is here," he answered when pressed to leave, "and discipline forbids me flee until such time when the same discipline may command. I hope that the heavens will not fall down if Frater Martinus should happen to die."

Pestilence, like war, is a testing-ground which brings out both the best and the worst features in humanity. Unfortunately there were uglier things to be revealed by the Black Death than fear and the instinct for self-preservation even at the cost of other people's lives. There were men and women who believed that punishment for sin was by no means the sole reason for the plague and who put forward other explanations. Some attributed it to witchcraft and yet others put it down to the evil action of those who belonged to the opposite political party. There was talk also of poisoning of the wells, and there existed not a few who knew for certain that this public outrage was being perpetrated by the Jews. Here, at any rate, was something practical to be done, to round up the Jews and burn them. A pogrom was started and the

news that Jews had been found in the very act of poisoning the wells was circulated far and wide. The punitive burning of the Jews was carried out very thoroughly at Narbonne and Carcassone, and in Burgundy alone fifty thousand Jews were liquidated in this cruel way. There is nothing new under the sun and, as has happened more recently in totalitarian states, confessions were frequently extracted from innocent prisoners prior to their liquidation. Yet even in the blackest moments of history a few righteous men are always to be found, men who dare to move in the opposite direction to that in which the blind stampeded herd moves. Protests were raised against the killing of the Jews and amongst those who protested loudest and most courageously was Boccaccio, the author of that naughty work the *Decameron*.

THE SWEATING SICKNESS

As already stated, in the year 1485 a new scourge appeared in heavily stricken Europe. It was known both as the Sweating Disease and the English Sweat. People said that it had arisen in England on account of the strange nature both of the English climate and of the English people. Even in the Middle Ages English weather gave rise to many jokes and it was now being said that rain had fallen without cessation for five years prior to the first outbreak of the new disease. So also was it widely recognized on the Continent that the insanitary and uncleanly habits of the English were highly injurious to health. Hecker wrote of the English and of their habits as follows: "They were not accustomed to cleanliness, moderation in their diet, or even comfortable refinements. Gluttony was common amongst the nobility as well as among the lower classes; all were immoderately addicted to drinking the luscious Greek wines, especially Cretan wine, Malmsey and Muscat, and the manners of the age sanctioned this excess at their banquets and their festivities. If we consider that the disease mostly attacked strong and robust men—that portion of the people who abandoned themselves without restraint to all the pleasures of the table—while women, old men and children almost entirely escaped, it is obvious that a gross indulgence of the appetite must have had a considerable share in the production of this unparalleled plague." Hecker himself had no doubts on this subject.

In his *Chronicles of England* Grafton gives the following account of the 1485 epidemic of this new disease. "A new kynde of sickness came sodainly through the whole region . . . which was so sore, so paynefull and sharpe that the like was never hearde of, to any man's remembrance before that tyme. For sodainly a deadly and burning sweate invaded their bodies and vexed their blood, and with a most ardent heat, infested the stomacke and the head grievously, by the tormenting and vexacion of which sickness men were sore handled, and so painfully pangued that if they were laid in their bed, being not able to suffer the importunate heate they cast away the sheetes and all the clothes lying on the bed."

Other epidemics of the "English Sweate" occurred in 1506, 1517, 1528 and 1532, but very little about them is to be found in contemporary English medical literature. This is rather surprising and in his *History of Medicine* published in 1861 Meryon makes the following caustic comment on this lack of English reference to the disease. "The silence of English medical writers on the disease is perfectly inexplicable, unless we accept Hecker's reason, that, as they did not find it noticed by their revered masters the Greeks, they were generally too ignorant to give a satisfactory account of it, and so they left it untouched. Erasmus, a shrewd observer of the habits of the English during the sixteenth century, was, probably, not very far from the truth in imputing the frequent visitations of the plague, as well as of the sweating sickness, to the filthy condition of the houses generally; so bad were they that he was deterred from accepting the splendid offers of Henry VIII and Cardinal Wolsey to induce him to fix his residence in England." There is a further note by Meryon on this subject to the effect that: "A magnificent apartment, a yearly pension of 600 florins and a benefice which produced 100 marks yearly was not sufficient to counterbalance Erasmus' disgust . . . at the incommodious and bad exposition of the houses, the filthiness of the streets and the sluttishness within doors. The floors are commonly clay, strewn with rushes, under which lie unmolested a collection of lees, grease, fragments, bones, spittle, excrement of dogs and cats and everything that is nasty." If this is a true description of a better-class English home it is not surprising that the greatest scholar in Europe turned down the invitation to live in one.

MASS HYSTERIA

There is a limit to what men can endure and still manage to retain their mental balance and in the Middle Ages this limit was frequently exceeded. The periodic reappearance of the plague began to have a widespread emotional effect on the inhabitants of Europe. There were few who doubted that it was a visitation from God, a punishment for sins, and this belief evoked in many men and women a deep feeling of contrition. Repentant sinners filled the churches, and the towns and villages often resounded with lamentations. Fanatics were seen inflicting chastisement on themselves and calling on others to repent. Religious mania and mass hysteria spread. In Hungary there arose a company of flagellants, which took the name of the Brotherhood of the Cross. It sent forth missions composed of brothers robed in sombre garments and with large red crosses displayed on their chests. They carried triple-thonged scourges tipped with iron ends and they marched through the towns with their heads covered and their eyes on the ground. On reaching a new town they were generally welcomed by the ringing of bells and then the townsfolk would assemble in the square, to watch the public act of penance. This was enacted twice daily and, having made many "converts", the mission would continue its journey.

The mass hysteria sometimes took another form. It often led to the performing of a wild convulsive dance which was called either the dance of St. Vitus or else the dance of St. John. Like the act of penance of the Brotherhood of the Cross the dance was started in the town square and by a comparatively few people, who screamed, flung themselves about hysterically, and then continued their wild dance hour after hour, till in the end they fell to the ground utterly exhausted. Soon after the dance had started the assembled spectators responded to the mass suggestion and joined in the wild mêlée. In the year 1374 hundreds of men and women brought together in this manner danced at Aix la Chapelle and when they had recovered sufficiently from their exhaustion they visited other towns and repeated the mad performance in Cologne, Metz and Erfurt. Finally the clergy became so alarmed at this outbreak of hysteria that they organized special services for the expulsion of devils, and managed to arrest for a time the rapid progress of the dancing mania. (See Plate 11.)

The name St. Vitus's Dance has sometimes been given to this hysterical dancing. Saint Vitus was a Sicilian youth who, on the eve of his martyrdom by Diocletian, prayed that all who commemorated the day of his death might be protected from the dancing mania. But although the dancing mania was manifested on a specially large scale after the visitation of the Black Death, it was by no means a new phenomenon. Big outbreaks of it had occurred previously in the tenth century and it is likely that they occurred even earlier. In Italy they were attributed to the bite of the tarantula spider and because of this certain dances are now known as Tarantellas. In Germany they were put down to possession by a devil and treated by exorcism. Paracelsus was particularly interested in the phenomenon and he loudly protested against any disease being attributed to the action of devils or being named after a saint. Like Hippocrates he was insistent that all illnesses should be ascribed to natural causes.

Even at the present day the rhythmic movements of children suffering from chorea are still referred to as St. Vitus's Dance by the public and it would be a pity to discard this old-fashioned term for good, for into these three simple words can be read many an interesting page of European history.

CHAPTER VI

The Renaissance (1500–1700)

THE term Renaissance is being used here in its widest sense. It stands for that resurgence of energy which took place in Europe and which led to a greater freedom of man's creative faculties than had been possible during the preceding mediaeval period. The revival of classical learning associated with the Renaissance is being looked upon not as the cause of this awakening from intellectual lethargy but as one of its signs. The revival was, of course, an event of great importance, for man's rediscovery of the classic past restored his confidence in his own faculties by revealing to him the continuity of history and the identity of human nature beneath the many diversities of language, custom and creed. Circumstances were by now much more propitious to the return of culture, if for no other reason than that the barbarous Teutonic tribes that had overrun Europe had themselves been Christianized, civilized, and assimilated to the conquered races. Order was returning everywhere and there was a new sense of freedom in the air, an eagerness, a spirit of inquiry, and a quiet determination on the part of people, who had hitherto accepted blindly the rulings of the Church, to make a change and to start thinking for themselves.

This reaching out after new ideas was made articulate and spread by the invention of printing, and was encouraged also by the discovery of the New World and by the opening up of a sea route to the Indies. And with the revival of classical learning there came also a revival of all the arts. Those mighty geniuses of the Renaissance, Michelangelo, Raphael, Leonardo da Vinci and Dürer, were not only taking a delight again in the beauty of the human form but were studying that form more carefully. They had found, moreover, that in order to represent it faithfully on canvas or in marble, a

better knowledge of its anatomy was required and more especially knowledge of the anatomy of the bones, ligaments and muscles. Some of these great artists even began to dissect the human body and to make drawings of its deeper structures. Leonardo da Vinci in particular became interested in the study of anatomy and he did not confine his attention to the more superficial structure but acquired also a knowledge of the anatomy of the heart and of the large blood vessels. (*See* Plate 16.) After dissecting these organs carefully he discovered the descriptions of them given by Galen were gravely at fault. The branches or bronchioles or air tubes had no connection with the heart, as Galen had asserted they had, but diminished gradually in calibre and then ended blindly in the lungs. Leonardo da Vinci confirmed what his dissection had taught him by the additional experiment of inflating the lungs with air. He found that however much he increased the pressure of the air he could never manage to drive air from the bronchioles into the heart. He was unable to do this because these two structures were entirely separate and not connected with each other as Galen had stated.

Having proved Galen's theory wrong, Leonardo da Vinci made more dissections of the heart and paid special attention to the valves at the roots of the great blood vessels. Experiments with these valves showed him that they were so placed as to ensure that the blood should always flow only in one direction and not be able to regurgitate back into the heart. Yet the ancient idea that blood percolated from one side of the heart to the other through the intervening septum was so firmly fixed in everybody's mind that even so great a genius as Leonardo da Vinci was unable to get rid of it. As a consequence of this blind spot in his thinking he failed to anticipate Harvey's discovery made a century later of the circulation of the blood.

A very great anatomist arose about this time in the person of Andreas Vesalius of Brussels, a young man whose anatomical career was so astonishing that it can only be described by the word meteoric. As a student, first at Louvain and then at Paris, he grew so tired of hearing long passages being read by a professor out of the works of Galen that he went off to study anatomy at Padua, where a certain amount of actual dissection of the human body was being carried out. At Padua he made such a good impression on his seniors that he

was elected professor of anatomy at the tender age of twenty-four. His anatomical lectures soon became so popular that students flocked to Padua from all parts of Europe; so many arrived, indeed, that there was no room to accommodate any more. Five years after he had published a short preliminary guide to anatomy and physiology Vesalius brought out his *chef-d'œuvre*, a magnificently illustrated volume of anatomy entitled *The Structure of the Human Body*. Although many of the errors of Galen's teaching still found a place in this new work, it was hailed by the more enlightened of his contemporaries as a masterpiece and a masterpiece it undoubtedly was. It has been said—but this is very uncertain—that some of the illustrations for Vesalius's great work were contributed by Titian. (*See* Plate 15.)

Sir Michael Foster, the eminent Cambridge physiologist, writes of Vesalius as follows: "Five years he wrought, not weaving a web of fancied thoughts, but patiently disentangling the pattern of the texture of the human body, trusting to the word of no master, admitting nothing but that which he himself had seen: and at the end of five years, in 1542, while he was as yet not twenty-eight years of age, he was able to write the dedication to Charles V of a folio work entitled *The Structure of the Human Body*, adorned with many plates and woodcuts, which appeared at Basle, the following year, 1543."

Then, with the publication of his book, a storm broke over his head so shattering that its reverberations reached centres of learning all over Europe. The scholarly world was affronted and even his former teacher, Jacobus Sylvius, now turned against him and abused him roundly as a careerist and an upstart. The reason for all this noise was that Vesalius had been guilty of doing what no man had hitherto dared to do: he had contradicted the great Galen and had gone so far as to suggest that instead of only reading his books, students of medicine should go back to Nature and learn from her actual works. Columbus, Vesalius's own favourite pupil, also turned against his master and joined in the general outcry. Frightened lest some of Vesalius's unpopularity should fall on his own head, Columbus sought to deride and discredit the man he had formerly admired. All these ill-natured attacks were not without their effect on their victim. Vesalius was an impulsive man, unequipped with

the patience demanded of the martyr, and as he had arrived in Padua suddenly and unannounced, so did he depart suddenly and without warning. First he collected into a heap all his unpublished manuscripts and burnt them, and then shaking the dust of Padua off his feet, he left that city for good. He abandoned the study of anatomy and accepted instead the lucrative job of court physician to Charles V. He also took to himself a wife and became a good courtier, always making the safe remark. Thus ended abruptly the short career of a great anatomist. His retirement from anatomy was permanent, for, as Vesalius himself wrote long afterwards, the Church forbade the study of human anatomy so that he "could not lay his hand so much as on a dried skull, and much less have the chance of making a dissection".

But Vesalius's work had not been in vain. It had imparted a new vigour to the study of anatomy, and dissections were now being carried out in all of those countries in which the Church did not expressly forbid them. An Anatomy Act was passed in Great Britain which gave the Barber-Surgeons of London the right to dissect the bodies of four executed criminals every year. (*See* Plate 14.) Nor was this all that was accomplished to stimulate the study of anatomy in Great Britain. A reader in anatomy was appointed by the Guild of Barber-Surgeons and it was made obligatory that all the members of the Guild should attend his demonstrations regularly. Dr. John Caius, one of the founders of Gonville and Caius College, was appointed to this post of reader in anatomy on his return from Padua in 1546 and he continued to hold it until the year 1563. But Dr. Caius was not the only link binding London to the famous school of medicine in Padua. A large number of Englishmen were now enrolling as students in the University of Padua and amongst them was a certain young man named William Harvey, a name that was afterwards to become famous in the annals of British medicine.

AMBROISE PARÉ (1510–1590)

Surgery demands an exact knowledge of anatomy, and progress in one department of medicine is often followed by parallel progress in another. This was to happen now, for a man was born in the year 1510 who was destined to have as great an influence on surgery as Vesalius had had on anatomy. (*See* Plate 9.) It was an influence

acquired not so much through his having made startling new surgical discoveries as through the sheer force of his character. Not that Ambroise Paré's contributions to surgical technique are in any way negligible, for he was responsible for several notable and extremely useful advances. His greatest contribution was his teaching that haemorrhage after an amputation should be arrested by the exact method of ligature and not by the blind and brutal use of a red-hot cautery. He also introduced a method of turning a child within the womb of its mother in cases of mal-presentation. He devised a number of new surgical instruments, including artery-forceps, and he constructed some extremely ingenious artificial limbs. (*See* Fig. 5.) It would probably be true to say that not one of these contributions was entirely original but that it was Paré's name which brought them to the notice of his colleagues and induced them to examine and to adopt them. But by far the greatest of Paré's contributions to surgery was the shining example of his own life, a life which he devoted whole-heartedly to the perfecting of his art and to the alleviation of human suffering.

Ambroise Paré was born in 1510 at Lavalle in Moyenné. His father was a cabinet maker but also barber and *valet de chambre* to the local noble, the Sieur de Lavalle. The fact that his father was a barber, his elder brother a master barber-surgeon at Vitré, and his paternal uncle a barber-surgeon in Paris must have directed his attention from the very beginning to the family profession. Little is known of his early life, but it is believed that he started the study of surgery at Vitré with his elder brother and was then, in 1532, apprenticed to his uncle in Paris. He managed to free himself a few years later from the hair-cutting and shaving side of his uncle's business and devote himself entirely to the study of surgery. He obtained the appointment of resident surgeon, corresponding to that of house surgeon nowadays, in the Hôtel Diese, an ancient monastic foundation which was at that time the only public hospital in Paris. There he worked and gained experience for a period of three years.

Because his elementary schooling had been poor so that he knew neither Latin nor Greek he was debarred from entering the University of Paris, as was *de rigueur* with all better-class students. We know that this was the case from a characteristically honest

Portraict de la main artificielle. **A**

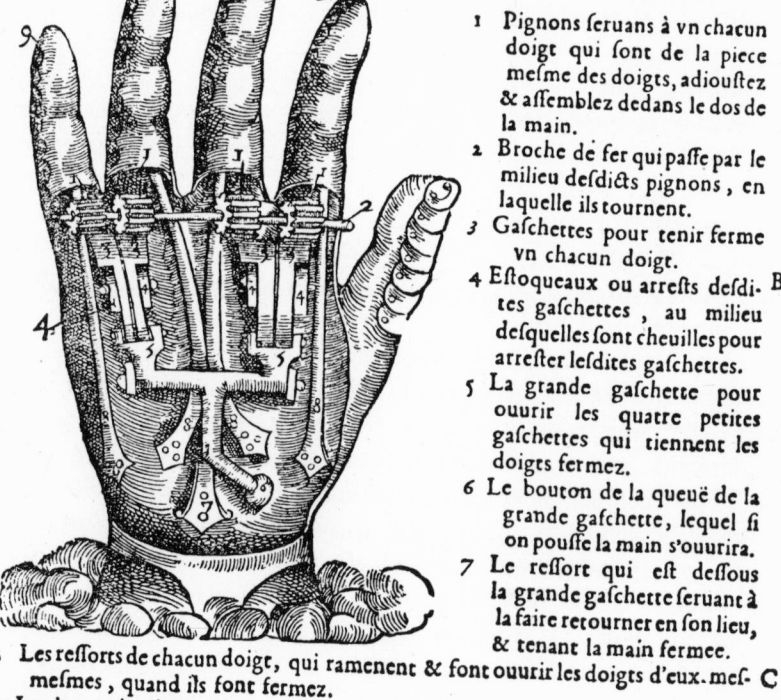

Description de la main de fer.

1 Pignons feruans à vn chacun doigt qui font de la piece mefme des doigts, adiouftez & affemblez dedans le dos de la main.

2 Broche de fer qui paffe par le milieu defdicts pignons, en laquelle ils tournent.

3 Gafchettes pour tenir ferme vn chacun doigt.

4 Eftoqueaux ou arrefts defdi- **B** tes gafchettes, au milieu defquelles font cheuilles pour arrefter lefdites gafchettes.

5 La grande gafchette pour ouurir les quatre petites gafchettes qui tiennent les doigts fermez.

6 Le bouton de la queuë de la grande gafchette, lequel fi on pouffe la main s'ouurira.

7 Le reffort qui eft deffous la grande gafchette feruant à la faire retourner en fon lieu, & tenant la main fermee.

8 Les refforts de chacun doigt, qui ramenent & font ouurir les doigts d'eux. mef- **C** mefmes, quand ils font fermez.

9 Les lames des doigts.

Fig. 5.—A sixteenth-century artificial hand (from Ambroise Paré, Oeuvres, 1614)

entry in his own journal in which he disclaims having had the grounding in the principles of surgery which his better-qualified colleagues possessed. "I desire not to arrogate to myself that I have read Galen, either in Greek or Latin; for it did not please God to be so gracious to my youth that it should be instructed either in the one tongue or in the other." In the end this supposed handicap was to prove an advantage to Paré for it preserved him from the too academic training to which his better-educated contemporaries were subjected. Instead of studying Latin books he was compelled to study Nature herself as the great Hippocrates had done, and

from Nature he learnt far more than he would have culled from the
Latin treatises of Galen. From the very beginning his knowledge
came to him from practice and not from learned works. Instead of
becoming a student at the University of Paris, he was articled to the
hard university of war, a school which has ever been a great teacher
of surgery. (*See* Plate 10.)

Ambroise Paré lived in troubled times. During the greater part
of his life France was engaged in war against Italy, Germany,
England, and finally against herself, that is to say in the disastrous
civil war waged between the Catholics and the Huguenots. It was
natural, therefore, that a newly qualified surgeon, in search of
experience, should enter the medical service of the army. There
was no organized army medical service in those days, but barber-
surgeons accompanied the troops during a campaign, attended to
the wounded and received a suitable reward for their professional
help. They were usually attached to the person of a general or noble
leader and Paré was now nominated surgeon to the Maréchal de
Montejan, colonel-general of the French Infantry. Paré tells us the
story of his long service with the army and of his many campaigns
in an entertaining book entitled *Apology and Treatise containing
the Voyages Made in Divers Places*, and something must be said
about this work. It was written long afterwards when Paré had
achieved fame and in answer to an attack made on him by an
academic professor of medicine in Paris, by name Dr. Etienne
Gourmelen. The professor had criticized Paré's use of ligatures for
the arresting of haemorrhage after amputation and had condemned
it as bad practice. After answering his opponent's objections, Paré
took the opportunity of giving an account of his surgical experience
in his various campaigns. He wished to drive home the fact that whilst
Dr. Gourmelen was relying for his surgical knowledge on books, he
was obtaining experience at first hand in the hard surgical school
of war and was actually witnessing the things he was talking about.
Every now and then he pauses in his story to address this scholar
critic and haunter of medical libraries rather scornfully as *"mon petite
maître"*. "Dare you teach me surgery?" he asks him, "you who
have never come out of your study. Surgery is learned by the eye
and hand. You, *mon petite maître*, know nothing else but how to
chatter in a chair." Paré was well able to look after himself. Yet

Hondius sculp 1642. Cum

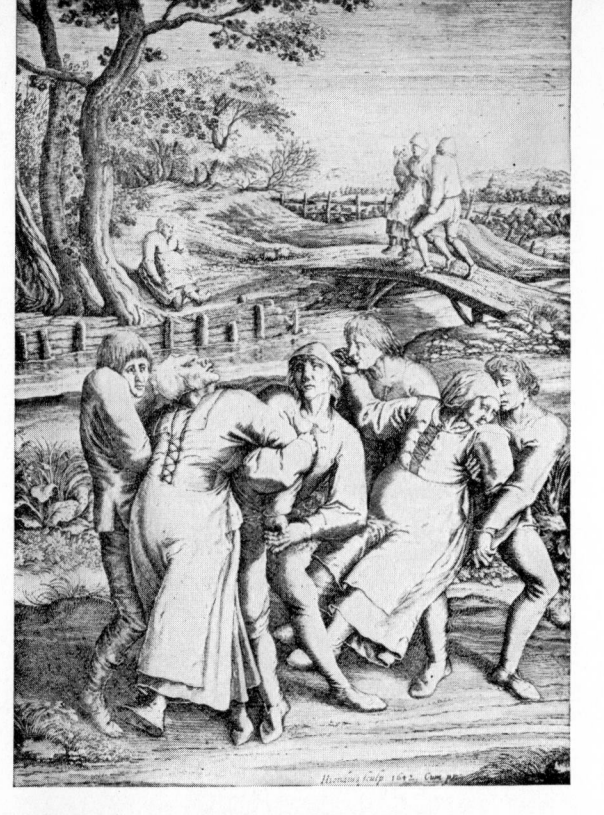

Dancing Mania following
the Black Death

The plague in Rome
(Engraving of a painting
by Poussin in the Louvre)

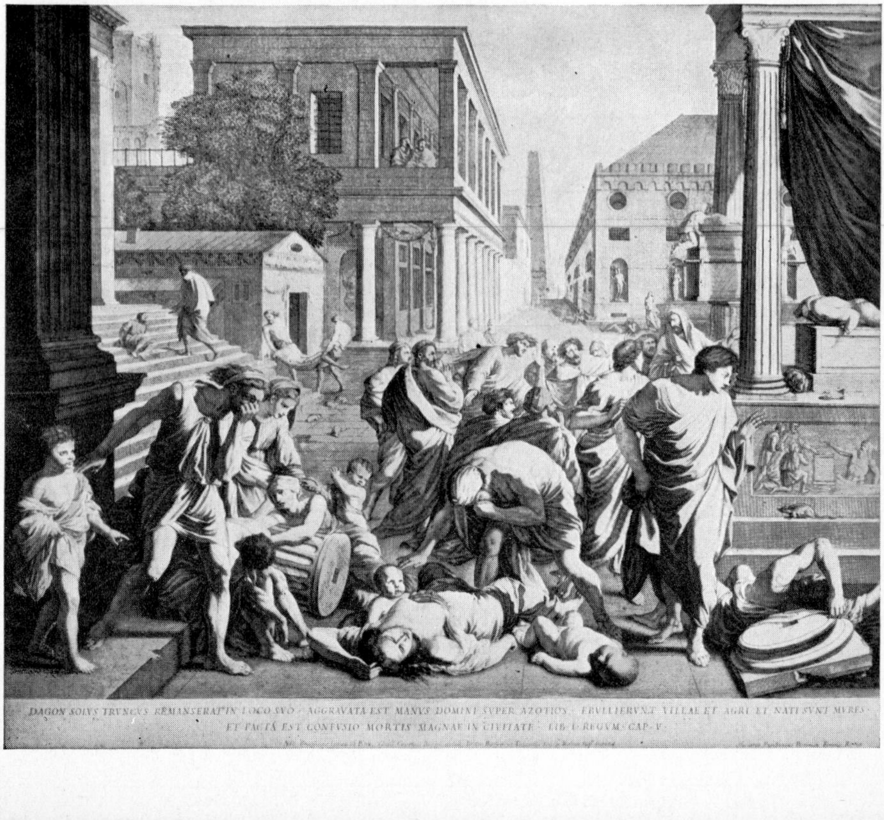
DAGON SOLVS TRVNCVS REMANSERAT IN LOCO SVO · AGGRAVATA EST MANVS DOMINI SVPER AZOTIOS · EBVLLIERVNT VILLAE ET AGRI ET NATI SVNT MVRES ·
ET FACTA EST CONFVSIO MORTIS MAGNAE IN CIVITATE · LIB · I · REGVM · CAP · V

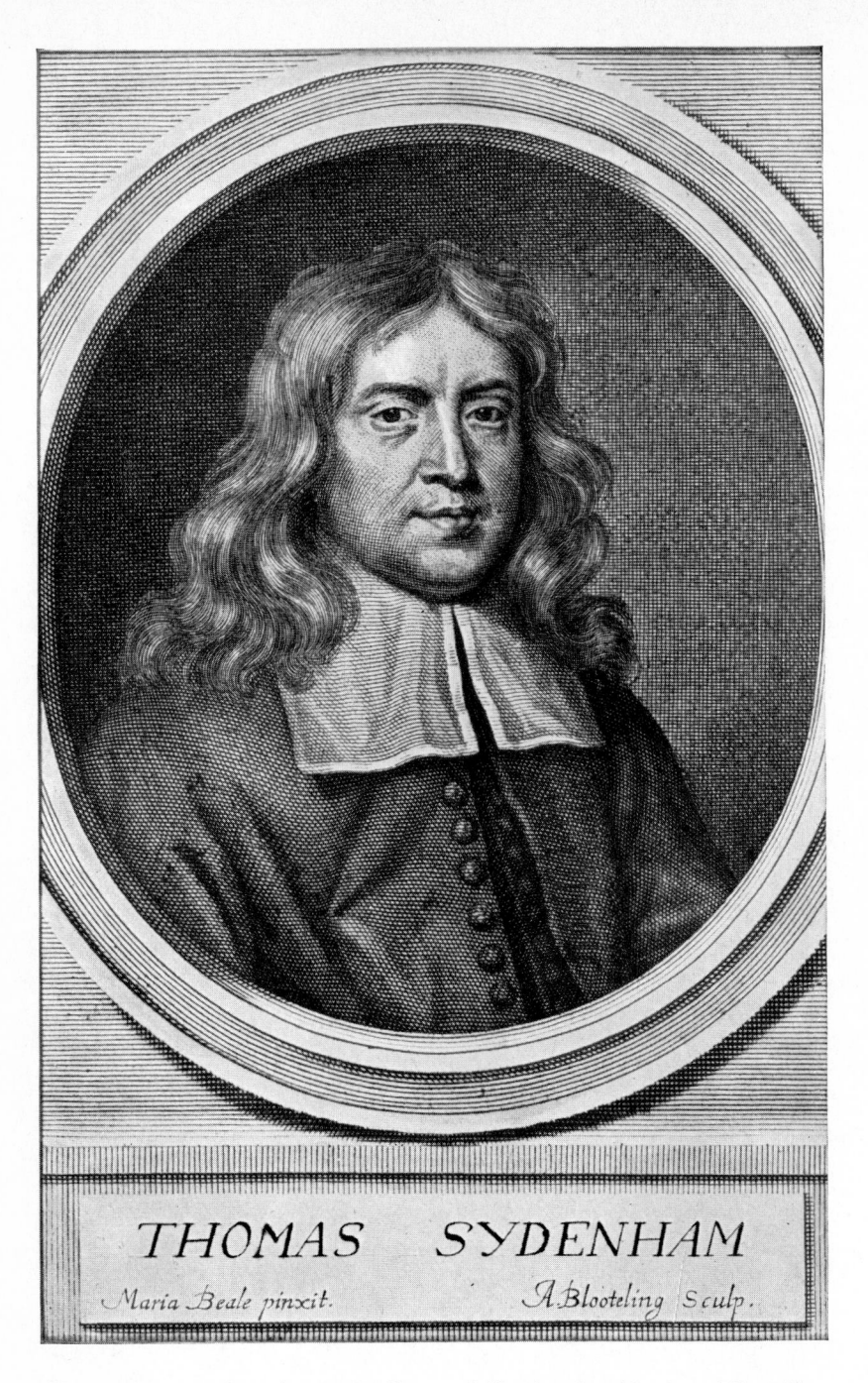

THOMAS SYDENHAM

Maria Beale pinxit.   A. Blooteling sculp.

(From the engraving in the Wellcome Collection by Abraham Blooteling
after Maria Beale)

we must be grateful to Dr. Etienne Gourmelen for having attacked Paré in his learned treatise *Chirurgicae artis, ex Hippocrates et aliorum veterum medicorum decretis*, for by doing so he provoked the writing of a fascinating and entertaining book.

Paré has a great deal to tell us for he spent thirty years on active service except for short rests in Paris in the intervals between campaigns. It was a hard life and from the very start of his army career he was brought up against the great problem of human suffering, a subject to which he was to devote much time and thought. Suffering was thrust in front of him with brutal abruptness when, as a young man and newly attached to the army, he took part in the capture of Turin. "We entered pell mell into . . . the city," he writes in this war journal of his, "and in a stable where we thought to lodge our horses we found four dead soldiers and three propped against the wall. . . . They neither saw, heard, nor spoke, and their clothes were still smouldering, burned with gunpowder. As I was looking on them with pity there came an old soldier who asked me if there were any way to cure them: I said, No. Then he went up to them and cut their throats, gently and without ill will. I told him he was a villain: he answered he prayed God, when he should be in such a plight, he might find someone to do the same for him, that he should not linger in misery."

It was here also at Turin that he made his first observation on the subject of the treatment of wounds. He had been taught, as all young surgeons at that time were taught, that as gunshot wounds were envenomed they must be soused promptly with scalding oils in order to "drive out" their essential poison. A fortunate accident was to show to him that what he had previously learnt was entirely wrong and that much harm was done to tissues by employing such brutal methods. His own account of his discovery that the classical method of treating wounds was entirely wrong is so graphic and is so revealing of Ambroise Paré's character that even although it has often been quoted, it must be given again in his own words.

"The soldiers within the castle, seeing our men come on them with great fury, did all they could to defend themselves, and killed and wounded many of our soldiers with pikes, arquebuses and stones,

whereby the surgeons had all their work cut out for them. Now I was
at this time a freshwater soldier; I had not yet seen gunshot wounds
at the first dressing. I had read in Jean de Vigo's book, *Of Wounds in
General*, chapter 8, that wounds made by firearms partake of venen-
osity, by reason of the gun-powder, and for their cure he bids you
cauterize them with oil of elder, scalding hot, mixed with a little
treacle. And to make no mistake, before I would use this said oil,
knowing that it was to bring great pain to the patient, I asked first,
before I applied it, what the other surgeons used for the first dressing;
which was, to put the said oil, boiling well, into wounds, and tents
and setons; wherefore I took courage to do as they did. At last my
oil ran short; and I was compelled, instead of it, to apply a digestive
made of yolk of eggs, oil of roses and turpentine. In the night, I
could not sleep in quiet, fearing some default in not cauterizing,
lest I should find those, to whom I had not applied the said oil,
dead from the poison of their wounds; which made me rise very
early to visit them; where, beyond my expectation, I found that
they to whom I had applied my digestive had suffered but little
pain and their wounds without inflammation or swelling, having
rested fairly well that night. The others, to whom the boiling oil was
applied, I found feverish, with great pain, and swelling round the
edges of their wounds. Then I resolved never more to burn these
cruelly poor men with gunshot wounds." (Ambroise Paré's *Journeys
in Divers Places, 1539–1569.*)

Paré, like Hippocrates, is continually protesting in his writings
against the use of remedies which are capable of harming the patients
and of interfering thus with the healing processes of Nature. His
phrase "*Je le pensait; Dieu le guarit*" (written thus in old French),
is frequently quoted and it occurs more than once in his journal.
For example, he recounts how, when an old soldier attempted to
obtain more victuals by force from some peasants, a mob of them set
upon him and maltreated him so brutally that when he eventually
managed to crawl back to camp his fellow soldiers regarded any
efforts on their part to succour him as foredoomed to failure and,
instead, started to dig a grave for him. Fortunately Paré was called
to see him and he set about the difficult work of trying to save the
poor man's life. "I did him the office of physician, apothecary,

surgeon and cook. I dressed him to the end of the case and *Dieu le guarit*."

Paré's fame increased and spread far beyond the army. Thirteen years after he had qualified as a barber-surgeon he was admitted, in spite of the fact that he knew no Latin, to the privileged circle of surgeons of the College of St. Come. He also bought, about the same time, a house in Paris situated close to the Pont St. Michel. In 1559 he retired from the army for good, lived permanently in Paris and soon acquired a large and fashionable practice amongst the most eminent men and women of France. In the course of his long professional life he was surgeon to at least four monarchs and his advice was often sought in desperate cases when other treatment had failed. The following extracts from his journal were written at a time when he was probably at the height of his fame and the occasion was as follows. The King had despatched him to look after M. le Marquis d'Aurel, who for seven months had been going from bad to worse as the result of a compound fracture of the thigh. It was now obvious to everybody that the Marquis d'Aurel's medical attendants had given up all hope of saving his life and it was after news to this effect had reached the King that he decided to call in the help of the foremost surgeon of the day. Paré starts his account by giving us a thumb-nail sketch of the deplorable state in which he found his new patient and it is clearly the picture of a man poisoned by the toxins of prolonged sepsis:

"I found him," he writes, "in high fever, his eyes deep sunken, with a moribund and yellowish face, his tongue dry and parched, and the whole body wasted and lean, the voice low, as of a man very near death."

Then follows the careful clinical study of the primary cause of the poisoning, namely, the infected and fractured femur, complicated by septic involvement of the knee joint.

"I found his thigh much inflamed, suppurating, and ulcerated, discharging a greenish and very offensive sanies. I probed it with a silver probe, wherewith I found a large cavity in the middle of the thigh and others round the knee . . . also several scales of bone, some loose, others not. . . . There was a large bed-sore; he could rest neither day nor night; and had no appetite to eat, but very thirsty.

. . . Seeing and considering all these great complications, and the vital powers thus broken down, truly I was very sorry I had come to him, because it seemed to me there was very little hope he could escape death. All the same, to give him courage and good hope, I told him I would soon set him on his legs, by the grace of God and the help of his physicians and surgeons."

Here we have evidence of Paré's psychological insight and professional tact. He realized how slender was the hope of being able to save his patient, but he knew that nothing at all could be attempted unless he secured his confidence and inspired him with hope. He was equally aware of the fact that those who had previously been looking after the Marquis had neglected to drain the wound and had thus contravened a first principle in surgery. Yet he was gracious enough to say to the Marquis that with the help of his former medical attendants he, the Marquis, "would soon be set on his legs".

"Having seen him, I went for a walk in a garden, and prayed God to show me this grace, that he should recover, and to bless our hands and our mendicants to cure such a complication of disease. I turned in my mind what measures I must take to this end. They called me to dinner. I came into the kitchen, and there I saw, taken out of a great pot, half a sheep, a quarter of veal, three great pieces of beef, two fowls, and a very large piece of bacon, with abundance of good herbs. Then I said to myself that the broth of the pot would be full of juices and very nourishing. After dinner, we began our conversation, all the physicians and surgeons together, in the presence of M. le Duc d'Ascot and some gentlemen who were with him. I began to say to the surgeons that I was astonished that they had not made incisions in the patient's thigh, seeing that it was all suppurating, and the thick matter in it very fetid and offensive, showing that it had long been pent-up there; and I had found with the probe caries of the bone, and scales of bone already loose. They answered me, Never would he consent to it; indeed, that it was near two months, since they had been able to get leave to put clean sheets on the bed, and that one scarce dared touch the coverlet, so great was his pain. Then I said, To cure him, we must touch

something else than the coverlet of his bed. Each said what he
thought of the malady of the patient, and, in conclusion, they all
held it hopeless. I told them that there was still some hope, because
he was young, and God and Nature sometimes do what seems to
physicians and surgeons impossible."

Paré then outlines the treatment he proposed to give, which
included free incisions for drainage, fomentations, lifting the patient
into a clean bed, hot-water bottles, a pillow so adjusted as to relieve
pressure on the bedsore, dusting-powders, an opiate to ensure good
sleep at night and a moderate allowance of wine. To help sleep
artificial rain must be made, by pouring water from a height into a
cauldron, so that it made the soothing sound of falling rain. The
generous diet included raw eggs, plums stewed in wine and sugar,
the good broth Paré had noticed—he noticed everything—as he
passed through the kitchen, white meat of fowls and other roast
meats easy to digest. The medicines prescribed must be properly
flavoured and good bread that was neither too stale nor too new
must be obtained from the farmhouse.

"This my discourse was well approved by the physicians and
surgeons. The consultation ended, and we went back to the patient,
and I made three openings in his thigh. . . . Two or three hours
later, I got a bed made near his old one, with clean white sheets on
it; then a strong man put him into it, and he was thankful to be
taken out of his foul stinking bed. Soon afterwards, he asked to
sleep; which he did for nearly four hours; and everybody in the
house began to feel happy, and especially his brother."

Slowly, but without any serious setbacks, the young man
recovered, and the period of convalescence was reached. Paré
made as detailed arrangements for this as he had made for the more
serious phase of the illness.

"Then, when I saw him beginning to get well, I told him that he
must have viols and violins, and a buffoon to make him laugh:
which he did. In a month, we got him into a chair; and he had

himself carried about his garden, and to the door of his chateau, to watch people passing. The villagers for two or three leagues round, now that they could see him, came on holidays to sing and dance, a regular crowd of light-hearted country folk, rejoicing in his convalescence, all glad to see him, not without plenty of laughter and plenty of drink. He always gave them a hogshead of beer: and they all drank his health with a will. . . . In six weeks he began to stand a little on crutches, and to put on flesh and to get a good natural colour. He wanted to go to Beaumont, his brother's place: and was taken thither in a carrying-chair, by eight men at a time. And the peasants, in the villages through which we passed, when they knew it was M. le Marquis, fought who should carry him, and insisted that he should drink with them: and it was only beer but they would have given him Hippocras, if there had been any, and all were glad to see him, and prayed God for him."

Paré's description of the course of this young man's illness reveals the exactness of observation and the attention to detail for which he was famous. Nothing escaped his notice: he observed that the pus coming from the wound had a particularly foul odour and on inserting a probe he found that the bone was both bare and movable. This strongly suggested the presence of a loose piece of dead bone, in other words of a sequestrum, and emphasized also the urgent need for good drainage. His colleagues declared that their exhausted patient would never consent to an operation, but Paré was confident that, properly handled, he could be induced to change his mind. He knew that it was essential that they should treat not merely a broken and suppurating leg but a complete man made up of body, mind and spirit. In a desperate case such as this, even the merest trifle, everything, was important, so everything had to be considered beforehand and planned. In his preliminary survey he foresaw the need for the removal of the patient into a clean bed, the provision of satisfactory nursing, a suitable diet, and finally, but not least, proper surgical treatment of the leg. He even prepared for that time in convalescence when his patient would become irritable and bored, and suggested methods of keeping him amused. Paré assisted Nature in every way possible and with his help, Nature eventually cured his patient. *"Dieu le guarit."*

Although Paré's long association with the army made him particularly expert in the treatment of wounds, his medical interest was far too wide to brook confinement to this one subject. He suggested, and was right in coming to this conclusion, that syphilis was a common cause of aneurism. He perfected his own method of version of the child within the womb, and he took an unusual interest in everything pertaining to the important art of nursing. He even planned a great work on a subject so removed from surgery as the plague, and actually published an article protesting against the folly of physicians who prescribed for this disease exotic remedies like powdered mummy and unicorn's horn.

In 1541 Paré retired from the army and for a time settled down in Paris, acquiring also a vineyard in Meudon. But in 1542 we find him hurrying off again to take part in the siege of Perpignan in the company of the Vicomte de Rohan. There he gained great kudos by locating the position of an arquebus ball in the shoulder of Monsieur de Brissac, Grand Master of Artillery. Nobody had been able to find where it had lodged, but by instructing the patient to assume the exact position in which he was at the moment of being wounded the ball could be palpated lying under the muscles in the region of the shoulder-blade.

It has often been debated whether Paré was a Catholic or a Protestant and the truth probably is that he was the former but that he preferred to remain aloof from all religious and political controversies in order to devote himself entirely to his profession. In spite of this, his life was in considerable danger on August 24th, 1572, the night of the St. Bartholomew's massacre. Two days previously he had been called in to examine Admiral Coligny who had been mortally wounded, and doubtless this fact that he had been in attendance on the Admiral became widely known. But fortunately the King took good care of his surgeon on that memorable and terrible night, sending for him to "come that night into his chamber, commanding him not to stir out of it; and said it was not reasonable that one who was worth a whole world of men should be murdered, and he would not urge him, no more than he would urge his old nurse, to change his religion". (Brantôme.)

During his long life-time Paré had been surgeon to four Kings and in August 1589 the last of his royal patrons, Henry III, was

fatally stabbed by a monk, but when Paré was not in attendance on him. After Henry's death the citizens of Paris revolted against his unpopular successor and this led to renewed civil war and bloodshed. Paris was besieged and for thè last time Paré, now an old man and retired from surgery, makes his appearance on the stage of history. We can picture for ourselves this final scene. The Parisians are starving and in despair and they are clamouring for surrender, but the Commander of the city, the Archbishop of Lyons, refuses to give way. Instead of surrendering he increases the severity of the penalities for civil disobedience. Paré meets him in the street and addresses him in public. The old surgeon's name carries so much weight that the Commander stops and listens, is brought by Paré's word to realize that it is useless for him to persist in the face of so much suffering. He capitulates and the Parisians hail the old surgeon as their saviour. A few months later Ambroise Paré dies at the age of eighty and is buried in the church of St. André des Arts.

If Paré portrays the Renaissance of surgery, then the man who called himself Paracelsus can be taken as the representative of Renaissant Medicine. Neither of these great men could have accomplished his task at an earlier period of history without incurring serious risk of imprisonment by the Church. They are representative of a different age, symbols of the resurgent energy which was invigorating European thought and driving men of every calling, art and profession to question old values and to re-examine things afresh. Osler has called Paracelsus the Luther of Medicine, the very incarnation of the spirit of revolt, and in many ways he resembles that tempestuous and intemperate reformer of the Church. Other writers have dismissed him as a braggart and a drunkard who made a great deal of noise but who contributed nothing of real value to the progress of medicine. It was the same during Paracelsus' life-time, that few men, except the many patients he had cured, could decide whether he was a charlatan or a great physician. He was always the centre of a dispute, a topic on which but few men could reach agreement.

The trouble is that we know only the barest outline of this strange man's life. It is true that he wrote an immense number of books but we possess very few of the original manuscripts that he left behind

him. Even those manuscripts which survive are exceedingly difficult to decipher, for Paracelsus's "handwriting" was truly abominable and his manuscripts were full of errors. The majority of his books were dictated and in the words of one of his students, Oporinus, they were dictated at such a speed that "you'd think that the devil was speaking in him". With so little in the way of incontrovertible fact to guide one and with so much in the way of legend and imaginative embellishment it is very difficult to be sure about any of the statements made concerning this remarkable man.

PHILIPPUS AUREOLUS BOMBASTUS VON HOHENHEIM (1490–1541)

The individual who inherited this name but who called himself Paracelsus for short was born in 1490 at the Swiss place of pilgrimage Einsiedeln. (*See* Plate 9.) He was the only child of a nobleman of the house of the Bombasts and on the early death of his mother his father moved with him to Villach in Carinthia. There his father established a practice as a physician and began to interest his small son in the natural sciences and in the art he was himself practising, that of the doctor. We know very little about his earlier education beyond the fact that whilst still a youth he was initiated into the mysteries of metallurgy, chemistry and alchemy by Sigmund Fuger of Schwaz in the Tyrol. Then he became a medical student in Vienna.

From his earliest years Paracelsus displayed a passion for wandering and after he had qualified in Vienna he visited several of the Italian universities in order to take part in post-graduate studies. He was now well equipped to settle down and in time acquire a practice, but instead he set out on travels which were destined to continue almost without cessation for the whole of his life. Of one thing Paracelsus was convinced, that wisdom was not to be found in books; it could come only from experience, and from conversing with all sorts of men. According to his own statements—and whatever we may doubt in his writings there is no reason to doubt what he says about his own travels—he journeyed through Spain, Portugal, France, Italy, Germany, Scandinavia, Russia, Poland, Croatia and Turkey. It is known also that he visited the tin mines of Cornwall, inspected other mines in Sweden, worked either as a student or a teacher in all of the more important centres of learning in Europe, and saw military service in the Netherlands.

During all these years of incessant journeying he took extensive notes, gave lectures, wrote and dictated books, quarrelled with the authorities, made equally ardent friends and enemies, and engaged in private practice.

At last in 1525, after more than ten years of ceaseless journeying, he felt disposed to settle down to practise in the city of Salzburg; but it was not to be. He was accused—and perhaps on good evidence —of having had dealings with the ringleaders of the Peasant War, and was forced to leave the city in a hurry in order to escape arrest.

In 1526 Fate seemed to have intervened in his favour by making him, perhaps for the first time in his life, popular with the civil authorities. In that year Johannes Froben or Frobenius, the famous humanist, publisher and printer of Basle, became bedridden due to an infection of the foot, which in time became so serious that his physician declared that the only way of saving his life was to amputate his leg. It was at this moment that Paracelsus was called in to give a second opinion on the case. He was also invited to stay in his patient's house so that he could superintend the treatment he had prescribed. This treatment was remarkably successful and in the course of a week or two Frobenius was up and about again. Whether Paracelsus knew or not that in the house of his patient there had lodged, and perhaps at that very moment was lodging, a man of still greater fame than Frobenius, is doubtful. Yet such was the case, for the eminent European scholar Erasmus was not only a close friend of Frobenius but frequently stayed with him. Soon after Frobenius's recovery Paracelsus received a letter from the famous scholar. In it Erasmus gave an account of certain symptoms and asked for guidance with regard to his own health. Paracelsus replied, made certain suggestions and in due course received another letter from Erasmus. The letter ended thus: "I cannot offer a fee equal to thy art and thy learning but certainly a grateful spirit. Thou hast called Frobenius from the Shades, who is my other half and if thou restorest me thou restorest two in one. . . . Farewell. Erasmus Rotterdamus."

The news of Frobenius's recovery added to Paracelsus's fame and in the same year the Municipal Council of Basle decided to appoint him physician to the town, a post which carried with it a

professorial chair at Basle University. His prospects seemed excellent. He would now be relieved of all anxiety concerning his future; his exceptional gifts had been at last recognized, he had an excellent rostrum from which to proclaim his teaching on the subject of medicine, and he could have as many patients as he liked. All that was now required of him was that he should exercise a little more tact, patience and discretion than he had previously shown. But this was the last thing that Paracelsus was prepared to offer the world, patience and discretion. Even the way in which he announced his coming lectures was calculated to irritate his colleagues. "It is not title and eloquence," the notice began, "nor the knowledge of the language, nor the reading of books, however ornamental, that are the requirements of a physician, but the deepest knowledge of things themselves and of nature's secrets and this knowledge outweighs all else. . . . The physician's business is to know the different kinds of disease, to understand their causes and symptoms, furthermore to prescribe remedies with discernment and perseverance and according to the special circumstances to help everyone as much as possible. . . . By the way of introducing the students to my own methods, I shall now be able, thanks to the generous appointment of the Basle authorities, to explain for two hours daily the manual of practical and theoretical therapeutics . . . of which I myself am the author, with the highest diligence and to the great benefit of my listeners." This was scarcely the manner for a new professor to adopt in announcing his arrival to colleagues who had never prescribed any treatment of their own but had always followed blindly the rules laid down in the books of Galen. But still worse was to follow.

His second affront was to insist on lecturing in German instead of, as was always customary, Latin. "I cannot boast of any rhetoric or subtleties," he said, "but I must speak the language of my native country, for I was born in Einsiedeln, a Swiss by nationality." Next he signalized his revolt against the dead hand of authority which had for so long stopped all progress in medicine by a public burning of the works of Galen and Avicenna. "This," he announced to his scandalized colleagues, "is the cause of the misery of this world, that your science is founded upon lies. You are not professors of the truth, but professors of falsehood. It is not the opinions which

a person holds, but the work which he performs that constitutes a physician. This doctorship—this *true* understanding—is not conferred by emperors or popes, or high schools, but is the gift of God. I am protecting my kingdom, not with empty talk, but with the power of the *arcana* (mysteries); not with such as are bought in apothecary's shops but with the *arcana* of Nature such as have been revealed to me by Nature herself." Paracelsus had an unshakable confidence in the knowledge that had been revealed to him and he did not hesitate to claim its superiority to that possessed by the academic type of physician. "My beard knows more than you and your writers," he proclaimed to the old gang at the University and to his students, "my shoe-buckles are more learned than Galen or Avicenna. . . . Me! Me! I say you will follow—you, Avicenna, Galen, Rhazes, Montagna and Mesues, I shall not be your follower but you shall be mine."

This manner of inaugurating a new lectureship was not conducive to a peaceful life at Basle University. So we need not be surprised that within two years of this strange beginning Paracelsus was shaking off the dust of the city of Basle from his feet and hurrying along the road again. He was not in the least fitted for an academic life and he had no real desire to be fitted for it. Life to him was always to be a pilgrimage, a never-ending quest. He afterwards wrote: "I went in search of my art, often incurring danger of my life. I have not been ashamed to learn that which seemed to be useful from vagabonds, executioners and barbers. We know that a lover will go a long way to meet the woman he adores; how much more will the lover of wisdom be tempted to go in search of his divine mistress."

So Paracelsus, who might well have served Goethe as a model for his Faust—a devil dwelt in him as well as a saint—set forth again on his travels. We hear of him in Colmar, then in St. Gallen and finally in Zurich, practising in each city with marked success, acquiring everywhere a reputation for bringing about astonishing cures, loved by his patients and invariably detested and finally driven away by those who were in positions of authority. "I pleased no one," he wrote of this later period of his life, "except the sick whom I treated." His statements about himself are as outspoken as are his statements about other people and he was

fully aware of how bitterly he was hated by the great majority of medical men. His ceaseless journeying eventually came to an end at Salzburg, a town which he reached completely worn out by his exertions and his sufferings. It was there that he had once, many years ago, thought of settling down, and it was there that he died, in the year 1541, at the age of fifty-one. He had predicted long previously what was actually to happen, that his message would not be understood for at least twenty years after his death.

But he underestimated the time needed for a proper appreciation of his teaching, for it is very little understood even at the present day. What did he teach? In his own account of the principles of medicine he taught that the healing arts rested on four pillars or columns, which he called philosophy, astronomy, alchemy and sapientia. He regarded philosophy as the gateway through which a man must enter in order to begin the study of medicine; astronomy, and by astronomy he implied astrology—a "science" still popular at that time—was also necessary to a doctor; alchemy would also prove helpful both in understanding certain cosmic principles and in the preparation of some of his remedies; but sapientia or wisdom was the most needful of all four of these requirements. There were many physicians, he added, who entirely failed to acquire wisdom. "The greatest and highest of all qualifications which a physician can possess," he wrote, "is sapientia and without this qualification all his learning will amount to little or nothing, so far as any benefit or usefulness to humanity is concerned. He alone is in possession of wisdom who is the possessor of reason and knows how to use it without error or doubt. . . . We cannot find wisdom in a book nor in any external thing; we can only find it within ourselves. . . . A physician must seek for his knowledge and power within the divine spirit; if he seeks it in external things he will be a pseudo-medicus and an ignoramus. . . . A physician should exercise his art not for his own benefit but for the sake of his patient."

At this distance of time we can only judge Paracelsus by what he has left behind in his writings, and as has already been said the counfsion in which his manuscripts were left makes it very uncertain what he actually wrote and what was written by some of his imitators. But whoever were the authors of these various works attributed to Paracelsus, many of them are of a very high order and

are infused with a similar spirit to that found in the works of Hippocrates. Paracelsus made no attempt in his writings to appeal to a large audience, and he was always contemptuous of popularity. In his book *Concerning Long Life* he freely admits that his method and his practice will not be intelligible to the great majority of people and that he writes only for men of greater understanding. The following epigrams are taken from writings usually attributed to Paracelsus.

"The patient must not be out of the physician's mind day and night. He must put his whole power of reasoning and his judgement deliberately in the service of his patient."

"The best of our popular physicians are the ones who do the least harm. But unfortunately some poison their patients with mercury, and others purge or bleed them to death. There are some who have learned so much that their learning has driven out all common sense, and there are others who care a great deal more for their own profit than for the health of their patients. . . . A physician should be the servant of Nature, not his enemy; he should be able to guide and direct her in her struggle for life, and not throw, by his unreasonable influence, fresh obstacles in the way of recovery."

"If you wish to be a true physician you must be able to do your own thinking and not merely enjoy the thought of others."

"To be an alchemist is to understand the chemistry of life. Medicine is not merely a science but an art; it does not consist in compounding pills and plasters and drugs of all kinds, but it deals with the processes of life, which must be understood before they can be guided. A powerful will may cure, where a doubt will end in failure. The character of the physician may act more powerfully upon the patient than all the drugs employed."

Paracelsus was a follower of the old philosophy which taught that man was a microcosm in a macrocosm. Everything that was in the universe from a stone up to God was to be found in man and he was bound by the same cosmic laws. Hence the saying: "As above so below." "How marvellously man is made and formed," wrote Paracelsus, "if one penetrates into his true nature . . . and it is a great thing . . . that there is nothing in heaven or in earth that is not also in man. . . . In him is God who is also in heaven; and all the forces of heaven operate likewise in man. Where else can heaven

be rediscovered if not in man? Since it acts from us, it must also be in us. Therefore it knows our prayer even before we have uttered it, for it is closer to our hearts than to our words."

"Man is born of the earth, therefore he also has in him the nature of the earth. But later, in his new birth, he is God and in this form receives divine nature. Just as man in nature is illuminated by the sidereal light that he may know nature, so he is illuminated by the Holy Ghost that he may know God in His Essence. For no one can know God unless he is of divine nature and no one can know nature unless he is of nature. Everyone is bound to that in which he originates and to which he must at some time return."

His statements about medicine are as revealing as are his statements about philosophy and religion.

"No disease comes from the physician, nor any medicine. But he can aggravate the course of the disease, and he can also improve it. What teacher can be better in this respect than nature itself? Nature possesses the knowledge and makes the meaning of all things visible; it is nature that teaches the physician. Since nature alone possesses the knowledge, it must be nature that compounds the recipe. . . . The art of healing comes from nature, not from the physician. Therefore the physician must start from nature, with an open mind."

"Theory and practice should together form one and should remain undivided. For every theory is also a kind of speculative practice."

"Practice should not be based on speculative theory; theory should be derived from practice."

"These are the qualifications of a good surgeon:
Regarding his innate temper
A clear conscience,
Desire to learn and to gather experience,
A gentle heart and a cheerful spirit,
Moral manner of life and sobriety in all things.
Greater regard for his honour than for money,
Greater interest in being useful to his patient
    than to himself,
He must not be married to a bigot."

A rather slightly built man with sensitive, nervous hands, a man with a relatively large, bald skull framed in unruly hair, with blazing eyes, deep set and very serious; a man of an "irritable temper"—such is the picture of Paracelsus that Joland Jacobe has painted for us in his book, *Paracelsus—Selected Writings* (Routledge & Kegan Paul, 1951.) We may ask, and it is an interesting point, "Where did he obtain his knowledge and who were his teachers?" We may ask but we shall never know the answer to this question. In the literature concerned with Paracelsus a number of names have been given of men whom he met on his travels and who may have influenced him, the names of philosophers, alchemists, wandering scholars, priests and abbots. It is quite possible that he learnt something from all of these and from others who are not mentioned, but, above all, he learnt from that never-failing and hidden spring of knowledge which welled up from deep within him. In spite of the denial of certain schools of Western philosophy there is more than one way of arriving at truth.

Paré and Paracelsus were very different types of men but they had this in common, that they were both giants. Everything in them was on a large scale, their faults as well as their virtues, and, however carefully we search, there is nothing mean or niggardly to be found in their natures. They are the two greatest figures of the medical Renaissance and any other man who comes after them in this story of medicine must of necessity seem mediocre and ordinary in comparison with them. Yet two great Englishmen of the Renaissance have to be mentioned if that story is to be in any way complete.

They must be mentioned, not only on account of their professional merits but also because they played an active part in the establishment of the first great authoritative body in the history of medicine, the Royal College of Physicians. Their names are Thomas Linacre and John Caius.

THOMAS LINACRE (1460–1524)

He was born at Canterbury and very little is known of his parents. But this scarcely matters, for it was his great friend William Tilling of Selbing, a small town near Hythe, and not his parents who exerted the chief influence on Linacre's earlier years. Tilling was a gentleman of private means who had gone up to Oxford in his youth and had

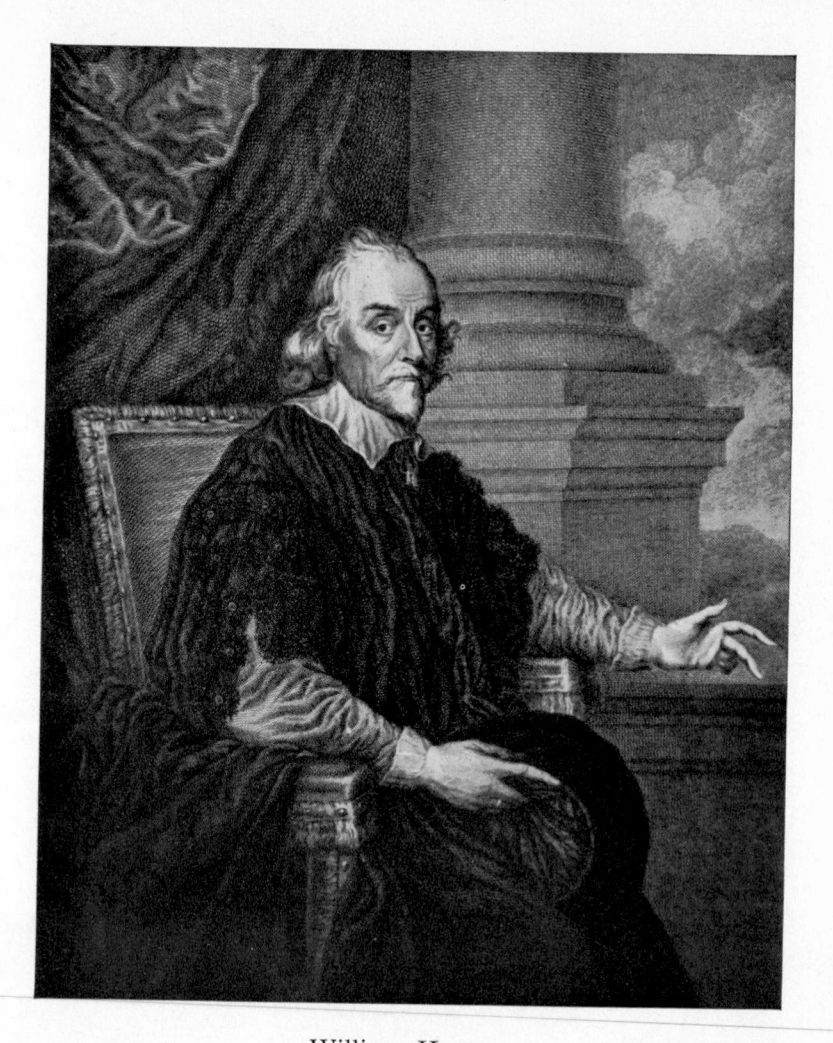

William Harvey

(From the line engraving by J. Hall after the picture in the Royal College
of Physicians)

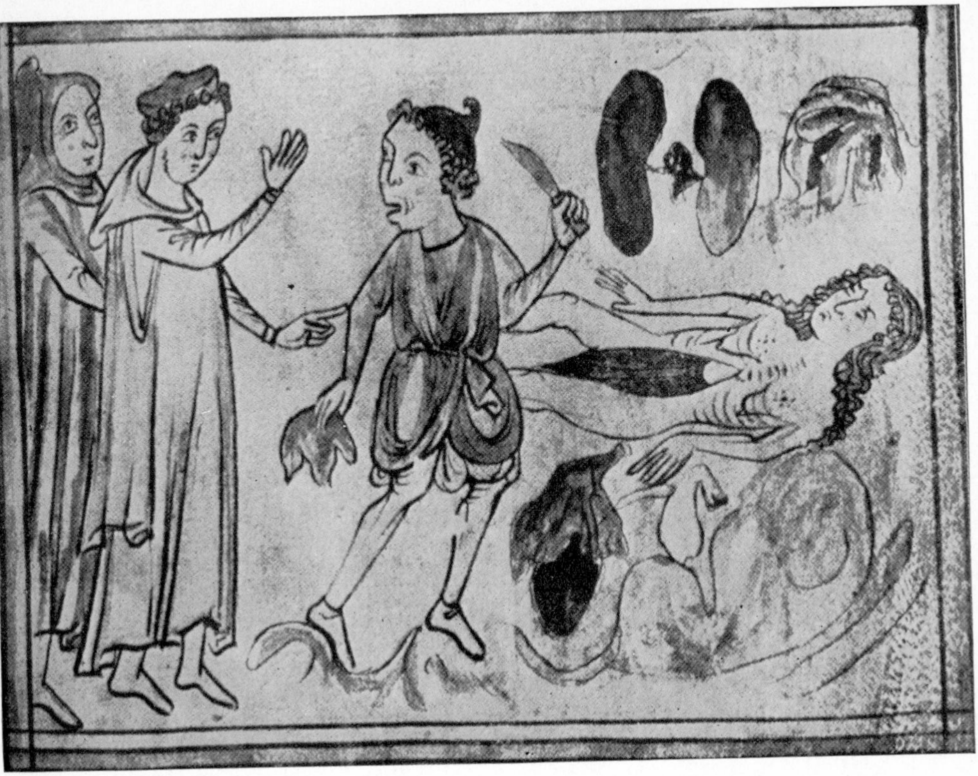

Dissection scene in the 13th century Bodleian MS. Ashmole 399

Henry VIII granting a charter to the Barber-Surgeons

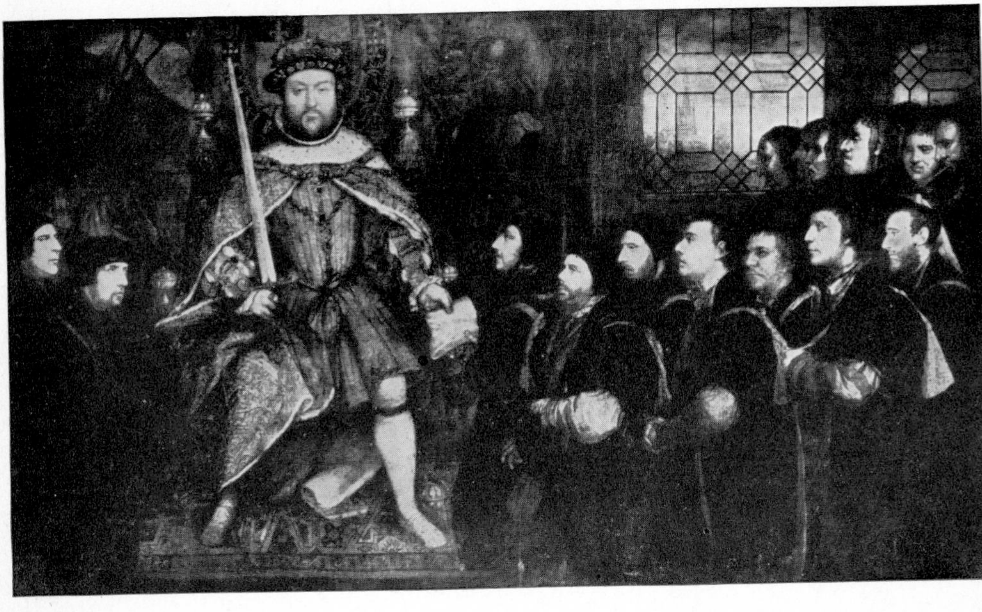

realized there how important it was for anyone who sought to be properly educated to study Greek. It was probably from Tilling that the young Linacre had his first lessons in Greek and there can be no doubt that it was on Tilling's advice, and possibly with his financial assistance, that Linacre went up to Canterbury Hall, Oxford, a college afterwards known as Christchurch. At the age of twenty-four Linacre made a trip to Italy with his friend and counsellor Tilling who had been specially selected by Henry VII to lead a mission to the Vatican. Having discharged his obligations to the mission, of which he was an unimportant member, Linacre visited Florence and there he had the good fortune to be entertained at the court of Lorenzo the Magnificent. He met there many of the famous men of the day and amongst others old Dr. Nicholas Leonicernis, a notable Greek scholar and also a lecturer in medicine. At his advice Linacre left Italy and returned to Oxford, this time as a senior student in the school of medicine. There in 1497 he fell in with that great European genius and scholar Erasmus, who happened then to be in residence at Oxford, and who apparently thought very highly of that university town. "The air," wrote Erasmus of Oxford, "is soft. The men are sensible and intelligent. Many of them are learned and not superficial either. They know their classics and so accurately that I have lost little in not going to Italy. When Colet speaks I might be listening to Plato. Linacre is as deep and acute a thinker as I have ever met with. Grocyn is a mine of knowledge, and Nature never found a sweeter and happier disposition than that of Thomas Moore."

Linacre became in time a very good classical scholar as well as a well-qualified medical man and Henry VII appointed him tutor and physician to his ill-fated son Prince Arthur when the latter went up to the University. In later years Linacre became physician to his charge's royal father and it was thanks to his strong links with the King rather than to any particular professional ability that he was now able to further the interests of his profession. Linacre noted with alarm the number of ill-equipped men, often of very doubtful character, who were practising medicine; illiterate monks, apothecaries, quack doctors, both home bred and from abroad, all these men were doing untold harm to the public and at the same time were bringing medicine into disrepute. Linacre managed to obtain from

Henry VIII letters patent for the establishment of a corpus of acknowledged medical men, a carefully picked medical body which later became the Royal College of Physicians of London. This College was empowered by royal charter to examine and to license physicians and to decide who should be allowed to practise medicine in the City of London and its immediate neighbourhood and who not. The College also possessed the right to inflict fines on those practising medicine without having obtained the necessary licence. (*See* also page 329.) The first President of the Royal College was Thomas Linacre himself and no better man could have been chosen for this position. He was the leading classical scholar of the day, and was trusted and highly esteemed by the whole of the medical profession. He died in 1524 and was buried in St. Paul's Cathedral.

JOHN CAIUS (1510–1573)

Caius was elected to a Fellowship at Gonville Hall, Cambridge, at a very early age and then he went off to Padua to study medicine. On his return to England he practised first at Norwich and then at Shrewsbury, where he made such a name for himself that he was given a court appointment in Henry the Eighth's life-time. He afterwards became physician in turn to Edward VI, Mary and Elizabeth. Caius succeeded Linacre as President of the Royal College of Physicians and rebuilt his old college, Gonville Hall, which in gratitude to his munificence now became Gonville and Caius College. Later, as an elderly bachelor, and, like most elderly bachelors, rather set in his ways, he became Master of Gonville and Caius. But again like many elderly men, he found the changes at Cambridge not to his taste. With the rise of Protestantism the old quiet monastic atmosphere of Cambridge had disappeared and had been replaced by a great deal of irreverence, lack of discipline and noise. The studious, poor, short-haired and long-gowned student of Caius' own days at Cambridge and still more of Linacre's days at Oxford, had been replaced by undergraduates of an utterly different kind. Dr. Caius also noted a general deterioration in the rising generation elsewhere and wrote about it: "Even the children"—and as physician to Edward VI, Mary and Elizabeth in her younger days, he had been given every opportunity to see this—"are being so brought

up that if they be not all day by the fire with a toast and butter and in their furs they be straight sick." (Quoted by H. Bashford.)

Caius was a prolific writer and, although nobody really knew anything about it, he was the chief British authority on the mysterious disease called either the Sweat or the Sweating Sickness. But medical posterity is indebted to him far more for what he did to raise the status of the medical profession—and more especially the status of the surgeon—than for his contributions to literature. It is noteworthy that John Caius, the man who consented to act as the first reader in anatomy to the newly formed Guild of Barber-Surgeons, was not a surgeon but an eminent physician. And physicians at that time had very little truck with anything so vulgar as a common Barber-Surgeon.

CHAPTER VII

The Seventeenth Century of Genius

AS the sixteenth century was outstanding for art and letters, so was the seventeenth century a golden one for European science. Whitehead labels it the century of genius. "A mere catalogue of some names," he writes, "will be sufficient, names of men who published to the world important work within these limits of time: Francis Bacon, Harvey, Kepler, Galileo, Descartes, Pascal, Huyghens, Boyle, Newton, Locke, Spinoza, Leibniz. I have limited the list to the sacred number of twelve, a number much too small to be truly representative."

Whitehead rightly places Francis Bacon at the head of this galaxy of genius for Bacon acted as a scientific scout by setting forth the method which others were to use in advancing the frontiers of science. Francis Bacon must certainly be credited with having brought the experimental method to the notice of his contemporaries, but he was by no means its first advocate. His namesake, Roger Bacon (1214–1294), a much greater man than he, had written on this subject three hundred years previously. Nothing could have been more to the point than the message contained in this single sentence of Roger Bacon's: "Experimental science has three great prerogatives over other sciences; it verifies conclusions by direct experiment; it discovers truth which they otherwise would never reach; it investigates the course of nature and opens to us a knowledge of the past and of the future." But Roger Bacon was unfortunately in holy orders and as he repeatedly incurred the displeasure of the Church on account of his clarity of thought and expression, he spent fourteen years of his life in prison. Great though his contributions to science were, they would have been considerably greater had it not been for the Church's persecution.

132

Francis Bacon was a person of great learning and a vigorous preacher of this same gospel of the experimental method. He urged his fellow men to forsake the four "idols" to which they had bowed down during the previous centuries, called authority, popular opinion, legal bias, and personal prejudice, and to replace them by the inductive method of reasoning from experience. Bacon pictured the world as a vast labyrinth of phenomena, in which the mind of man would be irretrievably lost unless the thinker held on to some thread by which to guide his footsteps. The thread which would lead him to the goal of knowledge and would prevent him from being lost in all the surrounding false passages was the inductive method of reasoning. But this new method could of course only be used when the necessary facts had been collected and assorted. "Man, the servant and interpreter of Nature, can do and understand so much, and so much only, as he has observed in fact or in thought of the course of nature; beyond this he neither knows anything nor can do anything." In this preliminary collecting of facts it was necessary that the mind should be emptied as much as possible of all preconceived ideas and should remain in a receptive state. "All depends on keeping the eye steadily fixed upon the facts of nature, and so receiving the images simply as they are; for God forbid that we should give out a dream of our imagination for a pattern of the world."

No message to men could have been more salutary at that time than this of the Lord Chancellor's. For the last five centuries thought had been forced to conform to authority, popular opinion and personal prejudice, and in no department of thought was this error more in evidence than in that of medicine. Medical men had ceased to observe Nature as Hippocrates had taught them to observe her and had become entirely subservient to two authorities: to the Church so far as philosophy was concerned, and to Galen with regard to all that appertained to medical diagnosis and treatment.

So medicine was badly in need of Bacon's advice and although doctors did not immediately accept it, in course of time it had its effect. Professor Guthrie writes of Francis Bacon that he "was content to point the way and to leave scientific verification to others. The legal training of a Lord Chancellor, which admitted of no imagination, was not the best preparation for a scientist.

Consequently Francis Bacon was well content to 'ring the bell which called the wits together'." This is, perhaps, a little unfair to a man so fully occupied with affairs of state, politics and intrigue as Francis Bacon was. But that he was keenly interested in science and that he would have devoted much more of his time to it had he enjoyed more freedom is strongly suggested by many things. It must be remembered that James the First of England was far from being a liberal patron, so cheese-paring indeed about expense that towards the close of his life Bacon was continually in trouble for lack of money. It was shortness of cash which drove him to write and publish so many books. That Bacon's interest in the experimental method was more than a theoretical one is shown by an event which occurred shortly before his death. In March 1626 he came to London and whilst driving in the neighbourhood of Highgate Hill he noted many snowdrifts on the heath. This started a train of thought in the ex-Chancellor's mind and he began to speculate as to whether snow was a means of preserving flesh from putrefaction. He decided to put this immediately to a practical test, stopped his carriage near to a cottage, alighted and bought from the cottager a fowl. After ordering it to be killed he assisted, with his own hands, the cold work of stuffing the eviscerated body of the fowl with snow. Shortly after doing this he was seized with a sudden chill, and became so rapidly unwell that he had to be driven straight to Lord Arundel's house which happened to be near at hand. There he died of pneumonia a few days later, his death hastened perhaps by the experiment he had carried out that cold day on Highgate Hill.

GALILEO (1564–1642)

The work of Galileo Galilei had an indirect influence on medicine, mainly on account of the stress he had placed on exact measurement. This led in time to the use of careful measurement in medicine both as a help to diagnosis, and as a means of research. Galileo actually started his brilliant career as a medical student but later he abandoned medicine in favour of mathematics. As a boy he had been so strongly attracted to the religious life that he wanted to become a novitiate, but his father had other designs for him and, taking advantage of his son's suffering from an attack of ophthalmia, he withdrew him from the monastery and sent him to Pisa to study

medicine. The young Galileo Galilei was an extremely gifted young man with a very wide range of interests, the type of man who would have made a name for himself in any calling he had cared to follow. He was as talented as a musician as he was as a painter, and he was also of a mathematical turn of mind. Whilst attending services in the cathedral he used to watch a lamp swinging on a long chain from the roof and he measured the time of its swing in terms of the beating of his pulse. It was in this way that he discovered the principle of the pendulum which he turned to good account fifty years later in his construction of an astronomer's clock. His interests veered more and more strongly in the direction of mathematics and with the help of his teachers he obtained his father's permission to abandon his medical studies. His subsequent career as a mathematician and astronomer and his trouble with the Inquisition are sufficiently well known not to need recording. The two reasons why Galileo has been given a place in the story of medicine are, first because it was he who emphasized the need for exact measurement in medical research, and second because, whilst engaged in constructing his telescopes, he produced, as a kind of by-product of his main work, a primitive microscope, an instrument which, a little later, was to become of great importance to medicine.

One of the earliest fruits of the use of exact measurement in medicine was the invention by Sanctorius of the first clinical thermometer. Sanctorius (1561–1636) taught at the most renowned medical school of the day, Padua, and having invented a means of measuring the temperature of the body, he next introduced an apparatus for recording the beat of the pulse. Actually Galileo was the original inventor of both of these new medical instruments but Sanctorius modified Galileo's designs and was responsible for introducing them into medical circles.

Robert Boyle (1627–1691) was another scientist whose research in the broader fields of chemistry and physics had important repercussions on medicine. He was a member of a small and extremely gifted band of young men who were enthusiastic advocates of exact measurement in experimental research. They formed themselves into a society known at first as the Invisible College, which met at Oxford. At a later date Charles II granted this group of brilliant young men a royal charter and they became the Royal Society,

with headquarters in London. Boyle was the first man to demonstrate that air was material and possessed mass, and he formulated the laws which determine its compressibility and volume. These laws which apply to all gases are still known by his name.

Inspired by Boyle's work, John Mayow (1645–1679), a lawyer by profession but a scientist by inclination, began to investigate the nature of the atmosphere and he was able to show that it contained an active principle which played an all-important part in the processes of combustion and respiration. He also succeeded in making oxygen by heating oxides, and came very near to the idea, even if he did not actually arrive at it, that it was oxygen that was responsible for the conversion of venous into arterial blood. By this valuable preliminary work Mayow laid foundations on which a very much better understanding of respiration was afterwards based.

It was through the work of such gifted men as Boyle and Mayow that a complete break was made with the past and that chemistry was placed on an entirely new footing. One by one the sciences were being rescued from the stagnant state in which they had sunk during the Middle Ages. Anatomy and physiology had already been freed from the dead hand of Galen by Vesalius and the Padua school of physiologists. So also had astronomy severed itself from astrology under the guidance of Galileo and Kepler. Brilliant though the achievements of Boyle and Mayow were in explaining the behaviour of gases, it was not this that mattered so much as the fact that they had infused an entirely new spirit into the study of chemistry. In their hands and in those of their colleagues chemistry was becoming an independent science, the principles of which could be discovered by the experimental method and its truths pursued for their own sake, quite apart from any light these chemical discoveries might throw on other departments of science.

WILLIAM HARVEY (1578–1657)

It was during this time of intense activity in many departments of science ancillary to medicine that William Harvey was born. (See Plate 13.) He was educated at the Grammar School at Canterbury and went up to Caius College, Cambridge, where he began his study of medicine. The medical school of the University at Padua had at this time an immense reputation amongst medical students in every

country and it was the place to which any ambitious and keen young man would go for advanced studies had he the means of doing this. Fortunately Harvey was fairly well off as regards money and, after leaving Cambridge, he spent four years at Padua, graduating there in medicine with first-class honours in the year 1602. Then he returned to England in order that he might start practice in London.

He was fortunate enough to be elected to the staff of St. Bartholomew's Hospital and also to be nominated Lumleian Lecturer in Anatomy and Surgery. The latter appointment gave him an excellent opportunity for continuing his researches in the anatomy of the vascular system, in which he had always been keenly interested. Fabricius, the successor of the great Vesalius and Harvey's own teacher at Padua, had some years previously published a work, "De venarium ostiolis" (the doors of the veins), which Harvey had studied very carefully. But Fabricius failed to see the true significance of the tiny valves found in the veins and regarded them merely as local mechanisms by which an over distension of the veins was avoided.

It is strange how near to discovering the circulation of the blood many of Harvey's predecessors had come, failing only to take that essential last step which would have made the whole matter clear to them. Even so long ago as the time of Hippocrates it had been realized that all the blood vessels communicated with, and ran into, one another. "The vessels which spread themselves over the whole body, filling it with spirit, juice and motion, are all of them but branches of an original vessel." Hippocrates then continues: "I protest I know not where it begins or where it ends for in a *circle* there is neither beginning nor end." Hippocrates actually used the term "the circulation of the blood". Vesalius had also examined carefully the valves in the veins and had made the additional and highly suggestive observation that every important artery supplying an organ was accompanied by its vein, yet all that he inferred from this companionship between arteries and veins was that it provided a means by which a "mutual flux of materials" could take place. Vesalius even proved to his own satisfaction that the very large valves situated at the junction of the great vessels with the heart insured that the blood should travel only in one direction, and yet having made this all-important observation he failed to take the

next step in his chain of reasoning. He was prevented from seeing that the blood must circulate because he still held to the old doctrine taught for hundreds of years, the idea that blood passed from one side of the heart to the other through the median septum. Fabricius, Harvey's teacher at Padua, had made the same mistake. Although he had demonstrated the fact that the valves in the veins were all constructed so as to direct the blood heart-wards, he clung to the idea that they were pockets to catch blood which otherwise might have collected in the extremities. It was a plausible enough idea and what commended it to the medical profession was that it was an idea which fitted in with the ebb and flow of the blood doctrine taught by Galen.

So it fell to Dr. William Harvey, late of Padua and now of St. Bartholomew's Hospital in London, to do what nobody else had yet succeeded in doing, namely, to complete the chain of inferences and to announce that the movement of the blood was a circular one and not, as his predecessors had imagined, a slow tidal movement of ebb and flow. For fourteen years Harvey's attention had been directed to this all-absorbing subject and he had dissected the vascular system of no less than eighty different species of animal. He had also examined carefully the valves and had noted, as his predecessors had done, that these veins ensured the flow of blood towards the heart and that the valves placed at the beginnings of the great arteries forced the blood to move in precisely the opposite direction, away from the heart. Two other things were clear to him: the first, that the median septum was impervious to blood; and the second, that if the left side of the heart expelled from itself at least two ounces each time it beat, the blood must undoubtedly move onwards somewhere in order to make room for more. Where did it go? It could only make room for more blood by going round and round.

Harvey announced his great discovery at his Lumleian lecture on April 16th, 1616. He began his lecture by recapitulating the steps by which he had reached two firm conclusions, first that the heart was an organ for the propulsion of blood, and second that the valves were so arranged that it was possible for the blood to travel only in one direction. He had now reached the dramatic moment in his lecture, so dramatic that his exact words must be recorded.

"But what remains to be said upon the quantity and source of the blood which passes, is of a character so novel and unheard of that I not only fear injury to myself from the envy of a few, but I tremble lest I have mankind at large for my enemies, so much doth wont and custom become a second nature. Doctrine once sown strikes deeply its root, and respect for authority influences all men. Still the die is cast, and my trust is in my love of truth, and in the candour of cultivated minds. . . .

"I began to think whether there might not be a *movement as it were in a circle*. Now this I afterwards found to be true; and I finally saw that the blood, forced by the action of the left ventricle into the arteries, was distributed to the body at large, and its several parts, in the same manner as it is sent to the lungs, impelled by the right ventricle into the pulmonary artery, and that it then passed through the veins and along the *vena cava*, and so round to the left ventricle in the manner already indicated."

Harvey published his great discovery in his book *Exercitatio Anatomica de Motu Cordis et Sanguinis in Animalibus* and, contrary to his expectations, it was accepted by the great majority of medical men. There was the usual minority that refused to abandon obsolete views and attempted to refute his arguments, but this minority was of small account. Such personal attacks as were made on him were as much due to his close association with the Stuarts as to his theory about the circulation of the blood. Honours quickly followed the publication of his great work. Harvey was appointed Physician Extraordinary to James I in 1618 and henceforth he moved largely in court circles. He spent the year after the publication of his work *de Motu Cordis* travelling on the Continent with the young Duke of Lennox and went to Scotland in 1633 for the crowning of Charles I at Holyrood. His connection with the unhappy House of Stuart was to become an even closer one. He was with the King when he raised his standard against the Parliament at Nottingham, but he managed to slip away to Derby for a day or two in order to discuss diseases of the womb with a Derby practitioner. It was whilst he was engaged in this professional conversation that the mob broke into his London rooms and destroyed most of his medical and anatomical specimens.

He was present at the Battle of Edgehill in 1642 and was given

charge of the two royal princes whilst the battle was in progress. There is a story that he spent his time during the battle sitting behind a hedge deeply engrossed in a book, but that the passage of a cannon ball close overhead reminded him of his duty to his young charges. Yet it would seem certain that he did not neglect his duties to the wounded on the battlefield for it is related that a certain Adrain Scrope, left on the field of battle and presumed to be dead, was "recovered by the immortal Dr. Will Harvey".

Harvey became keenly interested in the new science of embryology and was now busy studying the development of the chick. Sir Henry Bashford gives us a delightful sketch of Harvey in his later years in his book *The Harley Street Calendar*. "But he was probably at his happiest," he writes, "besieged with the King at Oxford, where he lodged at Merton for three years, working at his chicks and going over to Trinity to confer with the Reverend George Bathurst 'who had a hen' we are told 'to hatch eggs in his chambers, which he opened daily to see the progress'. Later, in the absence of the Warden on the Parliamentary side, he was appointed to succeed him. But after the King in disguise had crept over Magdalen Bridge to his ultimate surrender and death at Whitehall, Harvey returned to London, though never again, it would seem, to a permanent home of his own."

In London he lived in semi-retirement, seeing very few patients but maintaining a lively interest in the Royal College of Physicians for which he built and equipped a library and museum. The opening of these was inaugurated with a sumptuous banquet at which he entertained all the Fellows and Officers of the College. He was offered the Presidency of the College but he declined that honour on the grounds of his advanced years and his poor health. And there was no doubt that the defeat of the Royalist party, the execution of the King and the death of his wife had all taken their toll of him so that he was now older than his years. Dr. George Ent describes a meeting with Harvey in his retirement in a letter to the President of the College: "I found him, Democritus like, busy with the study of natural things, his countenance cheerful, his mind serene, embracing all within its sphere. . . . I forthwith saluted him and asked him if all were well with him. 'How can it be,' said he, 'whilst the Commonwealth is full of distractions and I myself in the open sea?

And truly did I not find solace in my studies and a balm for my spirit in the memory of my observations of former years, I should feel little desire for longer life. But so it has been, that this life of obscurity, this vacation from public business, which causes tedium and disgust to so many, has proved a sovereign remedy to me. . . . It is true the examination of the bodies of animals has always been my delight, and I have thought that we might thence not only obtain an insight into the higher mysteries of nature, but there perceive a kind of image or reflex of the omnipotent Creator himself.' "

Aubrey refers in his diary to the deterioration which occurred in Harvey's practice after the publication of his book. He states that he had heard Harvey say "that after his book on the circulation of the blood came out he fell mightily in his practice; 'twas believed by the vulgar that he was crack-brained and all the physicians were against him. . . . Though all of the profession would allow him to be an excellent anatomist," continues Aubrey, "I never heard anyone that admired his therapeutic way. I knew several practitioners in the town that would not have given threepence for one of his bills (prescriptions) and who said that a man could hardly tell by his bills what he did aim at." And Harvey's critics may have had good grounds for their adverse comments. His writing was abominable and his prescriptions may well have been as confusing as Aubrey suggests. Moreover, if his treatment of his patients was as drastic and brutal as his treatment of himself, he was unlikely to acquire a large practice. Aubrey tells us that Harvey "was much and often troubled with the gout and his way of cure was thus: he would sit with his legs bare, though it was frosty on the leads of Cockaine House (in Broad Street), put them into a pail of water till he was almost dead with cold, then betake himself to the stove, and so 'twas gone".

Ability in scientific research and skill in medical practice are two entirely different things and success in the one does not necessarily mean success in the other. Harvey's great discovery had little immediate effect on clinical medicine, for the latter frequently lags far behind medical research. It is quite understandable that the discussion of high questions at the meetings of the Royal Society in London and at conferences of Gresham College at Oxford did very

little to improve the treatment of the common ills. Peering through microscopes, making careful dissections, studying learned books and writing them in the queer mixture of dog Latin and English used by Harvey is one thing, and relieving humanity's pains, aches and indispositions is yet another.

Aubrey's description of him in his journal gives us a far more vivid impression of his personality and appearance than do his official portraits. He describes Harvey as follows: "He was as all his brothers very choleric, and in his younger days wore a dagger (as the fashion then was—nay, I remember my old school-master Mr. Latimer at 70 wore a dudgeon, with a knife and bodkin, as also my old grandfather Lisle and Alderman Whitson of Bristowe, which, I suppose was the common fashion in those days), but the doctor would be apt to draw out his dagger upon every slight occasion. He was not tall, but of the lowest stature, round, very black, full of spirit, his hair was black as a raven but quite white twenty years before he died."

THOMAS SYDENHAM (1624–1689)

Different types of men render different services and as William Harvey arrived on the medical scene at a particular moment of time to further medical research, so was Thomas Sydenham destined, four decades later, to raise the general level of medical practice. (*See* Plate 12.) Harvey and Sydenham were men whose temperaments differed as markedly as did their politics and had they met—the difference in their ages made this unlikely—they might easily have fallen out. Sydenham and his family were deeply committed to the Parliamentary party and we first meet Thomas Sydenham in medical history as a young and enthusiastic soldier of Cromwell's army. Demobilized at the age of twenty-two, after the complete defeat of the Cavaliers, he made his way towards Oxford, not quite certain in his mind what he would do on arriving there. But fate, in the shape of a certain Dr. Cox, who was attending his elder brother professionally, intervened, and by the time that Sydenham reached Oxford he had decided to study medicine. His situation was very like that of the young men who were demobilized at the close of the recent World War. Special privileges were offered to a man who had served in the Parliamentary forces and after little more than a

year's study Sydenham became a Bachelor of Medicine. Within another year he had been awarded a Fellowship at All Souls, and a few months later he was elected Bursar to that same distinguished college.

Then came a serious interruption of his work. News came that Prince Charles had landed in Scotland and Sydenham was soon back again with his old regiment, now stationed somewhere on the Border. It is reported that in this campaign against the Scots and the Royalists he both "led and doctored his men". After what Cromwell termed the "Crowning Mercy of Worcester", meaning by this the complete defeat of the Royalists, Sydenham received a grant of six hundred pounds for his recent services and with this useful windfall he was able both to marry and to start practising in London.

There he settled down in King Street, just to the south of the future St. James's Square, and within easy walking distance of the open country. A few years later his life as a London physician was rendered more difficult on account of the Restoration. With the return of Charles II the influence of the Sydenham family rapidly declined and although Sydenham himself was protected by the general amnesty that had been granted by Charles, his professional prospects could not be regarded as being good. What made things worse for him was that he was not as yet officially licensed to practise medicine, but fortunately this was remedied two years later when he became a licentiate of the Royal College of Physicians. And in the end Sydenham's disadvantages worked in his favour by encouraging the development in him of his own special gifts. His medical philosophy was a very simple one and can be easily formulated. He looked upon the human mind as being an extremely limited and fallible instrument that was quite incapable of dealing with fundamental truths. This being so, he felt that scientific and medical theories were of very little service to the practising physician. What the doctor had to do was to observe his patient very carefully and study in him the process that is known as illness. Each disease belonged to a definite species, as clearly cut as are the species to which animals and plants are assigned.

There is a story which illustrates very clearly the suspicion with which Sydenham regarded academic science and all forms of

theoretical medicine. After he had attained a great reputation, and was in his way a celebrity, a young man who later was to become equally famous, Sir Hans Sloane, came to him with a letter of introduction. In this letter Sir Hans Sloane was described as "a ripe scholar, a good botanist, a skilful anatomist". Sydenham read the letter, threw it aside and, to his would-be disciple's surprise, exclaimed: "This is all very fine, but it won't do—anatomy, botany! Nonsense! Sir, I know an old woman in Covent Garden who understands botany better, and, as for anatomy, my butcher can dissect a joint full as well; no, young man, all this is stuff: you must go to the bedside, it is there alone you can learn disease." This speech is typical of Sydenham and of his attitude to medicine.

As a younger man he had been described by his contemporaries as "a trooper turned physician" and the description was probably an apt one. Sydenham was essentially a man of action and he cared very little for the works of such men as Vesalius, Harvey and Malpighi. According to him, there was only one book to which a physician need ever turn, and that was the work of Hippocrates. Sydenham modelled himself on Hippocrates and like that great master was always insisting that the doctor must become a student of Nature and learn from her the right way to cure diseases. "By these steps and helps," he writes, "the great Hippocrates arrived at the highest pitch of physick, who, after laying down this solid and fixed foundation to build the art upon, has clearly delivered the symptoms of every disease without deducing them from any hypothesis. . . . He has likewise left us some rule drawn from the observance of Nature's method of promoting and removing distemper; such are his prognostics, aphorisms, and other writings of this kind."

Sydenham's appearance at this particular moment in the history of medicine was most opportune, for medicine was again in need of being freed from the theories with which it had become entangled, this time by the mediaeval scholastics. As a thinker Sydenham made no new advances but as an observer of the signs and symptoms of disease he was without rival. His accounts of the "natural history" of disease are as vivid and as exact as those of his great master, the Father of Medicine. What could be more graphic than the following description of the early stages of an attack of gout. "The victim goes

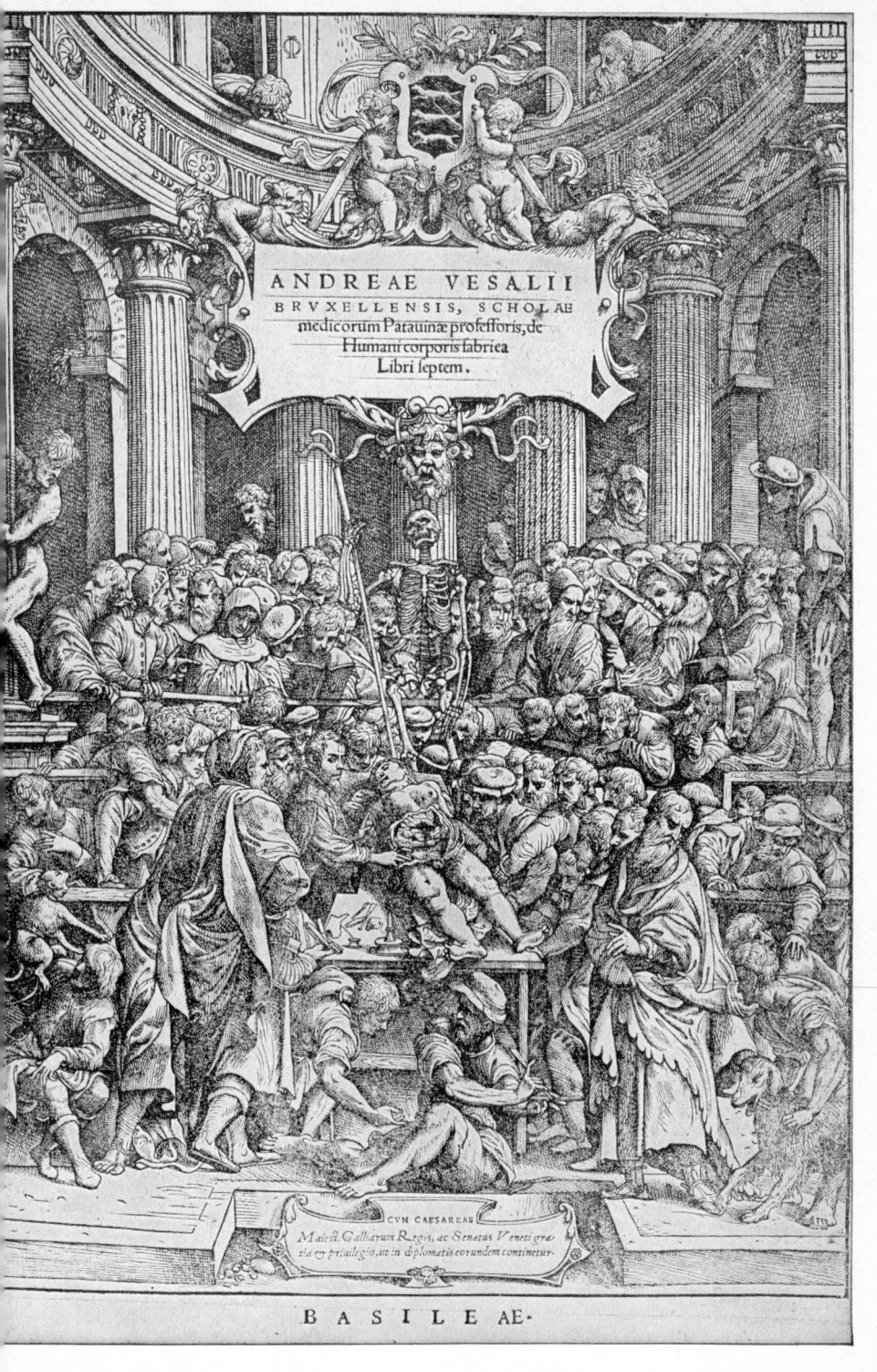

Andreas Vesalius: *De Humani Corporis Fabrica*
(Title-page of the 1st Edition, 1543)

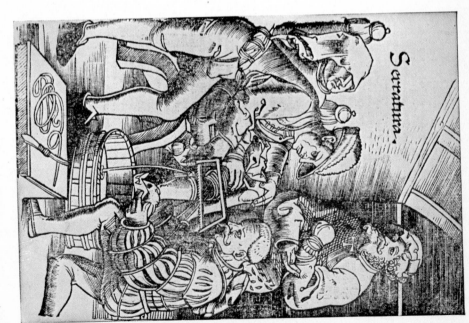

Blood vessels of the arm drawn by Leonardo da Vinci with notes in his well-known mirror writing

Operation in pre-anæsthetic days. The amputation of a leg in the 15th century

to bed and sleeps in good health. About two o'clock in the morning he is awakened by a severe pain in the great toe. . . . Then follow chills and shivers and a little fever. The pain becomes intense. Now it is a violent stretching and tearing of the ligaments, now it is a gnawing pain and now a pressure or tightening. . . . The night is passed in torture . . . and in vain effort by change of posture to obtain an abandonment of the pain. At last the patient has a respite. . . . In the morning he finds the part swollen. . . . A few days after the other foot swells and suffers the same pain."

The account strongly suggests that Sydenham had actually experienced what he is so skilfully describing and it is known from other sources in addition to Aubrey's journal that he suffered from gout and that in his later years he was also afflicted with stone. His clinical observations and descriptions of diseases from which he did not himself suffer are almost equally good. In treatment he always preferred the use of the simpler remedies or, where there existed some doubt as to what was wrong with the patient, an expectant attitude to the disease and no remedy at all. He practised the fashionable "blood letting" but always in moderation. He introduced the use of iron in cases of anaemia, popularized the giving of cinchona bark from Peru for malaria and treated syphilis with mercury. But by far his greatest contribution to medicine was his insistence on a return to Hippocratic principles at a time when medical men were losing themselves again in medical theories and philosophical speculations. As it turned out, the seventeenth century was to be a crucial and decisive century for medicine and Sydenham's influence at this moment of its history was of very great importance. His reputation with other physicians both in England and abroad was very considerable, and it is reported that whenever Sydenham's name was mentioned in his presence the great Boerhaave of Leyden uncovered his head. Boerhaave was acknowledged to be the finest teacher of medicine in Europe and it was no small testimony to have gained the respect of so great a man.

THE EARLY MICROSCOPISTS

Fresh advances in medicine and in science often await the invention of some new technique or scientific instrument and a whole series of discoveries of great importance to medicine followed

the appearance of the microscope. The microscope that had been invented by Galileo was very ineffective and it was not until the middle of the seventeenth century that a more satisfactory instrument with a compound system of lenses was introduced. Yet even before the invention of this more powerful microscope, excellent work was done with simple lenses by two researchers, namely, Malpighi and Leeuwenhoek. The discoveries which these two pioneers in histology made with their simple system of lenses are so important that more must be said about them.

MALPIGHI (1628–1694)

Marcello Malpighi, professor at Bologna University, is famous in the annals of medicine for his observations on the capillary circulation. He chose the lung of the frog as a suitable organ on which to demonstrate this because the frog's lung is a simple transparent organ on the surface of which blood vessels can easily be seen. Malpighi, like William Harvey, was also one of the earliest pioneers in the new department of biology known as embryology and he made valuable contributions to the subject of the development of the vascular and the central nervous systems. He was a tireless worker and was the first person to descibe the various layers of the human skin, the lymph nodes of the spleen and the glomeruli of the kidneys.

VAN LEEUWENHOEK (1632–1723)

Malpighi's fellow microscopist, Leeuwenhoek, was one of those amateur scientists to whom medicine owes so much. (*See* Plate 23.) The microscope is admittedly a poor instrument by which to earn a living and it was thanks to the prosperity of his drapery business at Delft that Leeuwenhoek was able to give sufficient time to his strange hobby. He was extremely expert at the difficult work of grinding lenses and is said to have made at least two hundred microscopes before he was satisfied with the results. The best magnification he could obtain was 160, but with this he was able to confirm Malpighi's observations on capillary circulation and to watch the movement of blood corpuscles in their passage through the capillary network of a tadpole's tail.

Almost all of Leeuwenhoek's important scientific discoveries were reported in letters to his friends and not, as is more usual,

in the form of scientific communications to learned journals. In these letters he had the knack of bringing out the drama of the occasion. He tells us how he first made trial of other biological material in the hope of being able to observe capillary circulation, such as the comb of a cock and the ear of a white rabbit, but without success. Then he tried the tail of a tadpole and succeeded in seeing what no man had ever witnessed before. Here are the actual words in which he reports his discovery. "Upon examining the tail of this creature, a sight presented itself more delightful than any my eyes had ever beheld; for here I discovered more than fifty circulations of the blood, in different places, while the animal lay quiet in water, and I could bring it before the microscope to my wish. For I saw, not only that the blood in many places was conveyed through exceedingly minute vessels from the middle of the tail towards the edges, but that each of these vessels had a curve or turning, and carried the blood back towards the middle of the tail in order to be conveyed to the heart. Here it plainly appeared to me, that the blood vessels I now saw in the animal and which bear the names of arteries and veins, are, in fact, one and the same, that they are properly termed arteries so long as they convey the blood to the farthest extremities of its vessels, and veins when they bring it back to the heart." (Hoole's Translation, 1798.)

Leeuwenhoek was introduced to members of the newly constituted Royal Society of London by a friend and we find him writing informal letters to the Society every now and then, in which he reports other observations made through his microscope. He was a man who had had no scientific education whatever but because he possessed unusual skill in the grinding of lenses his microscope was greatly superior to any previously made. He despatched to the Royal Society his drawings of blood corpuscles and of spermatozoa and muscle fibres and demonstrated in these drawings that the blood corpuscles of mammals were round whilst those of the amphibians were oval. But by far the most important of all his discoveries from the medical point of view was his discovery of bacteria and protozoa. This came about in the following manner. He examined under his microscope films of moisture that he had taken from between his teeth and to his amazement he found in

these films "little animals, more numerous than all the people in the Netherlands, and moving about in the most delightful manner". Delightful though these "little animals" may have been to their discoverer, the news that they were everywhere to be found was far from delighting other people. It was felt that scientists took pleasure in humiliating mankind, and aimed one blow after another at human dignity. First, the astronomers had ousted man's home, the earth, from the central position in the Universe it had previously enjoyed and had declared it to be nothing more than an insignificant planet revolving round a second-grade star. And here now was a Dutchman cheapening life by declaring it to be everywhere. An opposition party arose amongst the scientists to prove that the Dutchman had been mistaken and in the following passages we find Leeuwenhoek defending his discoveries from these critics:

"I have often heard that many persons dispute the truth of what I advance in my writings, saying that my narrations concerning animaculae, or minute living creatures, are merely my own invention. And, it seems, some persons in France have even ventured to assert, that these are not living creatures, which I describe as discoverable to our sight, and allege that after water has been boiled those particles in it which I pronounce to be animalculae will still be observed to move. The contrary of this, however, I have demonstrated to many eminent men, and I will be so bold to say, these gentlemen who hold this language, have not attained to a degree of proficiency to observe such objects truly. For my own part, I will not scruple to assert that I can clearly place before my eye the smallest species of these animalculae concerning which I now write, and can plainly see them endued with life, as with the naked eye we behold small flies, or gnats sporting in the open air, though these animalcules are more than a million degrees less than a grain of sand. For I not only behold their motions in all directions, but I see them turn about, remain still, and sometimes expire; and the larger kinds of them I see as plainly running along as we do with the naked eye. Nay I see some of them open their mouths, and move the organs of parts within them; and I have discovered hairs at the mouth of some of these species though they were some thousand degrees less than a grain of sand." (Hoole's

Translation of Leeuwenhoek, quoted by Stubbs and Bligh in *Sixty Centuries of Health and Physick*.)

Leeuwenhoek's observations on the capillaries in a tadpole's tail and his discovery of micro-organisms show how the discoveries of one researcher link up with those of another to form so many threads to be eventually woven into the fine fabric of science. First we have Leeuwenhoek confirming Malpighi's observations on capillary circulation and then, tracing this same thread backwards, we note that by demonstrating the capillary circulation Malpighi is merely adding the missing item in Harvey's otherwise complete account of the circulation of the blood. Tracing the thread further back still, we find that Harvey's great discovery was merely the final incident in a long and patient research undertaken by many generations of men who had made all the necessary observations but who had somehow failed to draw from what they had found the, to us, obvious conclusion. Similarly, if we travel from Leeuwenhoek in a forward direction and anticipate future events, we find that his observations on animalculae will link up eventually with the brilliant researches of Pasteur and ultimately with the great bacteriological discoveries of the last and the present century. No one in science or medicine ever works alone. Behind him stretches a long line of researchers disappearing into the misty past, and in front of him lies a series of discoveries yet to be made. The scientific researcher is like a weaver contributing only a few of the strands to the design appearing on a carpet, on the making of which a great many workers are engaged.

CHAPTER VIII

The Period of Consolidation (1700–1825)

THE medical historian, Dr. Charles Singer, refers to the years between 1700 and 1825 as the period of consolidation in medicine and the name is a good one. An immense amount had happened in the preceding two and a half centuries and time was needed to consolidate what had been gained. So also had the mind to grow accustomed to many new modes of thought and to be given an opportunity to adjust itself to the rapid advances of science. Newton's discoveries in physics had been of a particularly revolutionary nature, so much so that they seemed to have destroyed the very foundations on which previous thought had rested. He had revealed a universe which seemed to be quite independent of the Divine Order in which men had so firmly believed since it worked automatically and in accordance to certain universal laws. The universe was indeed nothing more than an immense self-moving and self-governing machine. Being a devout churchman, Newton had been very careful to add that God was the Maker and the Maintainer of this machine, but many were now coming to the conclusion that it was no longer necessary to postulate the existence of a Maker or a Maintainer of machines. In their opinion the universe could get on quite well without anybody to look after it. The important thing was that Newton had proved the universality of a Natural Law and had even shown how the stars could be weighed and their courses foretold by knowledge of this law. The real maintainer of the universe was, therefore, the Natural Law itself.

After Newton's death, scientists were busy demonstrating the reign of law in every department of science and in Physics, Chemistry, Botany, Physiology, Comparative Anatomy and Microscopy astonishing advances were made by the use of the experimental

method. So rapid was progress that both the scientific and the non-scientific worlds were bewildered with the multitude of discoveries being made. Time was badly required for sorting out all these novel ideas and for putting them into some sort of order.

Nor was it only the new scientific and medical material at the disposal of the doctors which needed study and systematization. Something had to be done to bring about improvements in methods of medical education. Until the seventeenth century there had been no organized clinical teaching at any of the universities, medical degrees being granted merely on the basis of a spoken disputation by the candidate. A great deal therefore had to be done, during the second half of the seventeenth and the first half of the eighteenth century, in the way of organizing medical instruction at the universities. Leyden was the first University to undertake this survey of medical education and with great benefit to itself. Because better clinical instruction could be obtained there than anywhere else and because its doors had been thrown open to students of every religious denomination and nation, Leyden University became immensely popular, particularly amongst Protestant students. It offered to its visitors the two following attractions in addition to the welcome it extended to everybody; it possessed well-equipped laboratories, and its medical department was presided over by no less a person than Hermann Boerhaave. This Leyden professor of medicine was such a celebrated person in the eighteenth century that something must be said about him.

HERMANN BOERHAAVE (1668–1738)

Some physicians achieve fame through their discoveries, others on account of their clinical skill, and yet others through the force of their characters. Boerhaave must be placed in the third of these three categories. (*See* Plate 19.) He made no great discoveries, and his "Aphorisms" do not suggest that he was an outstandingly clever physician, yet his reputation as a man and as a teacher of medicine was such that his name was known as far afield as China. He was first appointed to the Chair of Medicine in 1701 and within a few years of his appointment Leyden University was attracting more students from abroad than even the famous University of Padua. As a teacher Boerhaave was unsurpassed. He gave chemical, botanical,

anatomical and clinical instruction to the students, and whenever a patient died he took them with him into the post-mortem room and demonstrated to them on the dead body the cause of the patient's death. He was, therefore, the initiator of the clinical method of instruction which is still in general use in all our teaching hospitals.

Boerhaave was a tall, robust man with a pleasant voice, a keen eye, and a dignified but unassuming manner. He was a great lover of music and he invited his students and his friends to his house for musical evenings. But his genius was displayed principally in his teaching, in his capacity to inspire younger men with enthusiasm, in his wide learning and in his ability to make connections between different fragments of knowledge. He was above all a man of outstanding sanity and the sort of person who would probably have been popular and successful in whatever career he had followed.

Boerhaave attracted to Leyden a great many young men who afterwards became famous and through these old pupils of his he established and maintained connections with most of the great European universities. One of the most eminent of his disciples was Albrecht von Haller (1708–1777) of Berne University, and another was Gerhard van Swieten (1700–1772) of Vienna. This spectacle of a Dutch physician attracting to his university young men from every country and speaking every tongue, inspiring them with enthusiasm for their work and still maintaining relations with them long after they had left his care and returned to their native lands, illustrates the truly international character of medicine. Doctors are as prone to petty jealousies, outbursts of temper, impatience, suspicion and egotism as are any other men, but the cleavages which divide them seldom run along lines of nationalism, religious beliefs, politics or social class. When doctors quarrel they quarrel as different individuals and not as members of coteries or upholders of different politics and creeds. To be a doctor *should* mean that one is international in one's outlook, a member of the human species and not of some subdivision of it. So also is it of primary importance that a doctor should recognize that medical knowledge belongs to all mankind. He can never give his sanction to such anomalies as medical secrets or remedies patented for profit. Everything that he finds to be beneficial to a patient must henceforth be at everybody's disposal.

The medical profession has, on the whole, remained loyal to these principles, but from time to time there have been defaulters who have offended against them. The Chambellan family is a flagrant example of this. A certain Huguenot physician of that name settled in England in the later years of the reign of Henry VIII and anglicized his name to Chamberlen. He had two sons who devoted themselves to the study of midwifery and these two younger Chamberlens eventually invented the obstetrical forceps. But they kept their invention to themselves and passed it on to their own sons, excusing their conduct by saying that they were always willing to deliver patients when other doctors had failed to do so. The secret of the forceps was thus kept within the family until Dr. Hugh Chamberlen died in 1728 without leaving any heir to inherit the family secret. Dr. Hugh Chamberlen, the last of these mean practitioners, does not seem to have suffered from any conscientious scruples on the subject of the family selfishness, for he sums up the situation in the following smug reflection. "My father, brother and myself (though none else in Europe as I know) have by God's blessing and our own industry attained to and long practised a way of delivering women in this case without prejudice to them and their infants." Piety and avarice often go together. After the death of the last medical member of the family the forceps were found and instruments of a similar pattern came into general use.

LEYDEN AND EDINBURGH

The medical student of the seventeenth century was more internationally minded than is the medical student of today and he very frequently completed his medical studies abroad. In the earlier decades of the seventeenth century Padua was the university favoured by British students but later in that century Leyden became a very great rival to it. In 1660 Sir Robert Sibbald, a Scottish student, spent nearly two years at Leyden University and on his return to Edinburgh he became one of the founders of the Royal College of Physicians of Edinburgh (1681). Another and even closer link between Leyden and Edinburgh was forged by Archibald Pitcairne (1652–1713). After studying at Edinburgh, Paris and Rheims, Pitcairne became one of the original fellows of the newly formed Royal College of Physicians of Edinburgh. His medical

writings obtained for him so great a reputation abroad that he was invited to go to Leyden and was appointed Professor of Medicine there in 1692, being Boerhaave's immediate predecessor at that University.

Pitcairne's chief importance in the story of medicine is that he not only forged a strong link between Edinburgh and Leyden but also, through his pupils, connected Edinburgh with Pennsylvania University in the United States of America. The founder of that well-known American medical school and indeed of all medical education in the United States was a certain John Morgan (1735–1789), of Pennsylvania, and also of Edinburgh University. Whilst Morgan was in Edinburgh he studied anatomy under Munro and also visited Padua, spending some five years altogether in Europe. The Munros were a well-known medical family in Edinburgh. The first of them was a certain John Munro who had an ambition to create a medical school at Edinburgh similar to the Leyden medical school at which he had previously studied. He educated his own son, Alexander Munro (1697–1767), specially to equip him for becoming the first Professor of Anatomy at that school. His ambition was realized and Alexander Munro was eventually appointed Professor of Anatomy at Edinburgh. He is usually referred to as Munro *primus* in medical histories to distinguish him from his son and his grandson, both of whom in turn succeeded him and are referred to as Munro *secundus* and *tertius*.

When John Morgan returned to Pennsylvania from Europe he was appointed to the Chair of Medicine and some years later, on the outbreak of war, he became Director-General of the American Medical Services.

Another connecting link is made between Edinburgh and American medicine by Benjamin Rush (1745–1813), the Quaker physician, who, after taking a medical degree at Edinburgh, succeeded Morgan as Professor of Medicine in Pennsylvania. Rush is sometimes referred to as the Sydenham of America and he became as famous for his opposition to slavery, war and alcohol as he was for his ability as a physician.

CONSOLIDATION IN THE DEPARTMENT OF PHYSIOLOGY

The great scientific advances of the seventeenth century had a stimulating effect on physiology which continued well into the

eighteenth century. As already stated, Robert Boyle had shown that air was a material substance and John Mayow that one of its two principal components was essential to life. He also demonstrated that this vital part of the air (now known by the name of oxygen) was exhausted in the two processes of respiration and of combustion. But, as so often happens in the history of science, no use was made of this valuable information for many years.

The next contribution to the understanding of the physiology of respiration was not made until 1774 when an English Unitarian Divine named Joseph Priestly (1733–1804) showed that air which had been vitiated by respiration or combustion could be renovated by plants so that it became respirable and combustible again. This versatile nonconformist minister, whose whole life was a struggle against ill-health and poverty, also succeeded in making oxygen by heating oxides. He came very near to the idea, even if he did not actually prove this, that it was this gas oxygen that converted venous into arterial blood. And he contrived to do all this in his spare time, even although his house and his chapel were destroyed by enemies who accused him of being in league with the French revolutionaries. It was left, however, to the French chemist, Antoine Lavoisier (1743–1794), to make the final experiments which cleared up the whole question of the chemistry of respiration. Lavoisier carried out a long series of quantitative experiments on the changes which take place in the air in the two processes of breathing and combustion, and from these he discovered the true composition of respired air. He showed that carbon dioxide and water vapour were exhaled by the lungs and he disposed for good of the idea, which had for so long misled chemists, known as the "phlogiston" theory of combustion. He also made improvements in agriculture and street lighting, but unfortunately he was disliked by the advocates of liberty, equality and fraternity, and he and his wife were arrested by the revolutionaries. An attempt was made to save them and Hallé submitted to the tribunal the report of the Bureau de Consultacion on the subject of Lavoisier's valuable contributions to science. Coffinhal's sole comment on this was: *"La République n'a pas besoin de savants; il faut que la justice suive sa course."* Lavoisier perished on May 8th, 1794. "Only a moment to cut off his head," whispered Lagrange to Delambre as they witnessed the execution—to speak

louder might have been dangerous—"and perhaps a hundred years will have to pass before we have another like it." Lagrange was right. Lavoisier is the "Father of modern chemistry" and a hundred years had to pass before a chemist of comparable brilliance appeared in France.

Medicine owes a great deal to its amateurs amongst the clergy. As Priestly added to our knowledge of the physiology of respiration, so also did the Rev. Stephen Hales (1677–1761), born half a century later, throw light on the physiology of the vascular system. Without any previous technical training or equipment he started out to investigate the very difficult problem of the dynamics of the circulation. In order to determine the blood pressure he inserted cannulae into the arteries and the veins of various animals (including a horse), and then connected up these cannulae with pressure gauges or manometers. By this means he was able to measure and to compare the blood-pressures in different parts of the vascular system. He also computed the circulation rate, measuring the velocity of the blood as it passed along the veins, arteries and capillaries. Finally he showed that the capillaries were subject to dilatation and constriction. All of these discoveries of a country clergyman were of great help to doctors in both the diagnosis and the treatment of disturbances of the circulation. The Rev. Stephen Hales was one of those restless, versatile men who take note of everything, and never miss an opportunity of bringing about some improvement in existing conditions. In addition to making these valuable contributions to physiology he designed a ventilator, working on a windmill principle, and he arranged for this to be fitted to the roof of Newgate prison. The improvement in ventilation it brought about in Newgate led to a marked reduction in the death-rate amongst the prisoners from "gaol-fever". Stephen Hales was full of enthusiasms and in the course of his long and busy life he espoused many causes. His researches, in whatever field of enquiry they were made, displayed those two characteristics of genius, simplicity and directness.

THE SCIENTIFIC BACKGROUND OF SEVENTEENTH- AND EIGHTEENTH-
   CENTURY MEDICINE

To understand the advances in physiology made during this

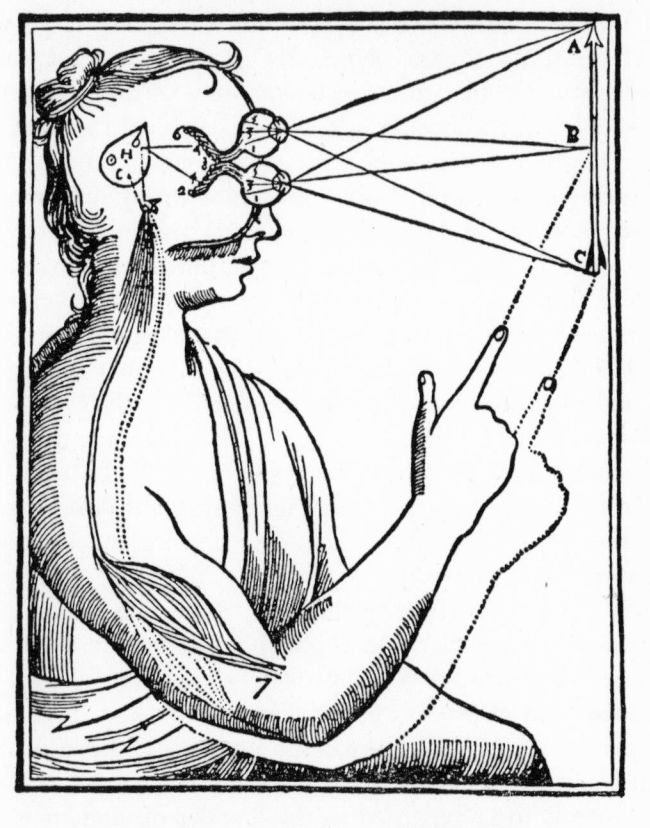

Fig. 6—Diagram from Descartes' posthumous work on Physiology. It is supposed to show how the image of the object A, B, C, thrown on to the retina, is transferred to the brain. Thence it passes to H, the pineal gland and seat of the soul. The manner in which it does so is wrapped up in the mystery of the soul

century we must view them in relation to the history of physiology in earlier times. As already shown, the great discoveries of Galileo and Newton led to the use of exact methods of measurement also in physiology and this encouraged the idea that all the workings of the body might eventually be explained along purely mechanical lines. Descartes, whose philosophy exerted a strong influence on all European thought, at this time supported this machine view of life. He regarded the human body as nothing but an extremely ingeniously contrived piece of machinery and as many agreed with this idea mechano-morphism became the official physiological creed. (*See* Fig. 6.) And, without any doubt, the idea that the body is a very complicated machine is an excellent working hypothesis which has yielded excellent practical results. There are many scientists indeed who maintain this machine view of the body, even at the present time, and who see no reason for changing it. They are of the opinion that the present-day inability of physics and chemistry to account for all vital events is no reason for doubting that they will eventually be accounted for in this way. Schrödinger, for example, regards the difference between the non-living and living as merely the difference between a comparatively simple and a very highly complicated kind of process. According to him—and there is much to be said for this view—there is no essential difference between living and non-living events.

If anyone is to be regarded as the founder of modern science it should be Isaac Newton. Before his time the movements of planets and heavenly bodies were regarded as being haphazard affairs under some special dispensation rather than determined by universal laws. But Newton showed that the three laws of motion together with the assumption of universal gravitation were sufficient to explain these movements. They also accounted for many other things besides this and Newton suspected that eventually they would prove applicable to the movements of the very small as well as to those of the very large. In other words, he believed that these laws would explain the behaviour of molecules and atoms. The French mathematician Laplace developed this idea of Newton's still further and taught that every particle in the universe obeyed the Newtonian laws of motion. Were there to exist a mind big enough to compre-hend the position and velocity of every particle in the universe, at a

given moment of time, then according to Laplace that mind would be able to foretell the motion of every particle to all eternity. This being so it would know in advance every future happening in the universe from the smallest to the greatest.

It was against this scientific background of determinism and materialism that eighteenth- and nineteenth-century physiology and medicine were developing. Since the advent of quantum physics we know, of course, that Laplace's deterministic views were based on a fundamental misconception. We are in a position to realize now that the all-powerful mind, postulated by Laplace, would not only be incapable of comprehending the position and velocity of *every* particle in the universe at a given moment, but would be incapable of comprehending *both* the position and the velocity of a single particle of the universe, at any given moment. It might be informed of one or of the other of these attributes, but never simultaneously of both. All movements and forces within the atom are subject to a different type of law, namely, the law of quantum mechanics, and modern scientists are far more modest on the subject of their capacities than was Laplace. They realize that many things are unknowable to them and will always be unknowable to them. In consequence of this they are far more aware than were their predecessors of the limitations and fallibility of human thought.

Having unburdened ourselves of these philosophical reflections we are in a better position to follow the development of physiology throughout the centuries.

THE EARLIER SCHOOLS OF PHYSIOLOGY

If Isaac Newton is the father of modern science, then Galileo can be looked on as being the father of that section of science known as physiology, for it was he who first laid stress on the importance of exact measurement to physiology, and progress was only made when more precise methods were introduced into its study. But Galileo was primarily a mathematician and astronomer and it was left to others to decide how exact measurement could best be used in experimental physiology. Much ingenuity was displayed and as a result of it the Iatro-physical School of Physiology appeared, a school which sought to explain all the workings of the human body, both in health and in disease, in terms of mechanism.

Sanctorius (1561–1636), professor at Padua University, was one
of the founders of this mechanical school. He invented a clinical thermometer, by which the temperature of the body could be taken, an
instrument he called a pulse clock, and also a large weighing apparatus on which he passed a great deal of the remainder of his life.
(*See* Fig. 7.) By means of this balance he was able to detect the loss
of body-weight which occurred through the process of invisible
perspiration. "The perspiration which is beneficial," he wrote,
"is not what goes off with the sweat, but that insensible steam
which exhales to the quantity of about fifty ounces in the space
of one day." He added that this insensible perspiration became
greater when one was asleep and that the nocturnal loss of body-
weight sustained in this way might reach as high a figure as forty
ounces a night. It is literally true to say that in his enthusiasm for
exact measurement in physiological research Sanctorius spent much
of his life seated on his own balance. He can therefore be regarded
as the founder of that modern department of physiology which is
concerned with the study of the body's chemistry, in other words
with metabolism.

Giovanni Alonso Borelli (1608–1679) was a personal friend of
Galileo's, a great mathematician, and also a member of this Iatro-
physical school of physiology. He investigated the mechanical
principles involved in muscular movement and incorporated his
findings in his great work *De Motu Animatum*. He attempted to
calculate the precise amount of energy expended in various muscular
movements and he studied the physical laws involved in animal
locomotion and in the flight of birds. But his inferences were all
based on the entirely erroneous assumption that muscles increased
in volume when they contracted and that this was due to their
becoming "inflated" with something reaching them through the
nerves. "Some corporeal substance," he wrote, "must be transmitted along the nerves to the muscles," and he called this hypo-
thetical substance "succus nervens". What was supposed to happen
then was that when this nerve fluid reached the muscle it mixed
with the blood of the muscle and produced a kind of explosion of
intense fermentation.

Giorgio Baglivi (1669–1707), Professor of Anatomy, started work
along the same lines as Borelli but he eventually came to the healthy

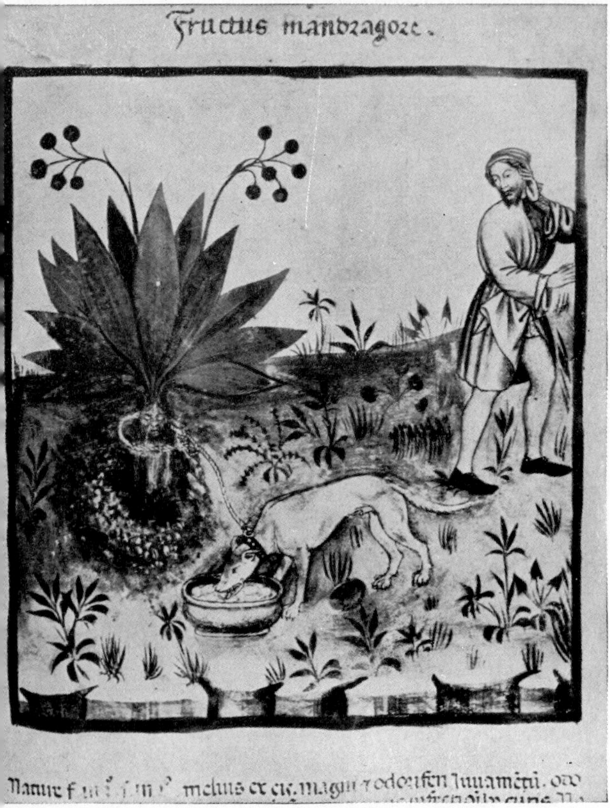

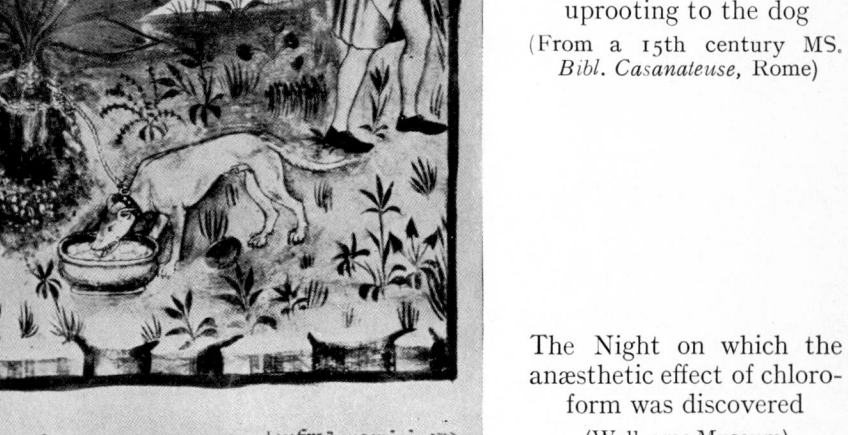

Fructus mandragore.

Uprooting a mandrake. The collector is hurrying out of earshot and leaving the uprooting to the dog

(From a 15th century MS. *Bibl. Casanateuse*, Rome)

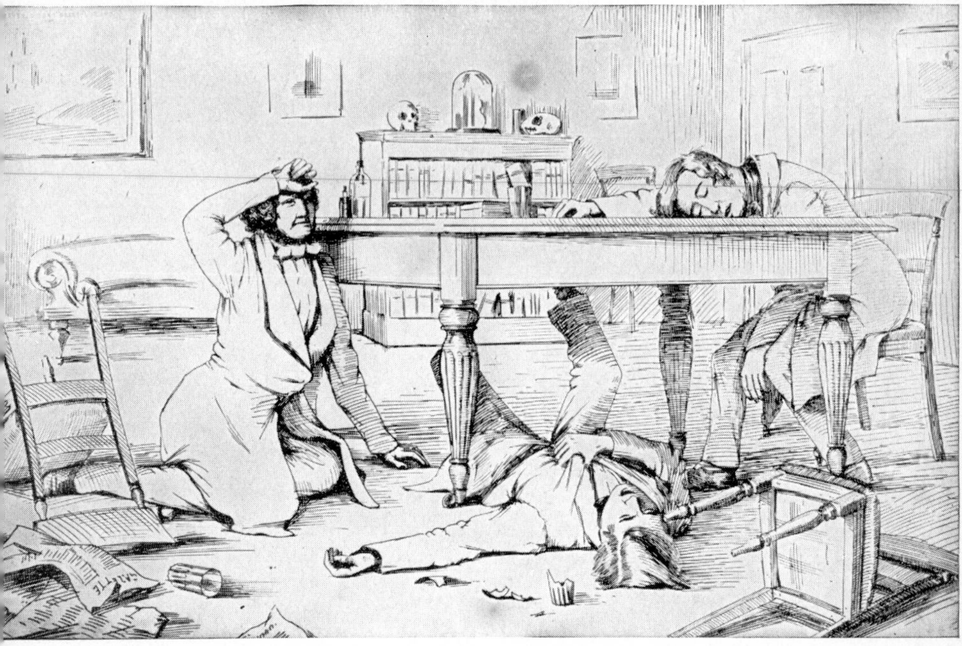

The Night on which the anæsthetic effect of chloroform was discovered

(Wellcome Museum)

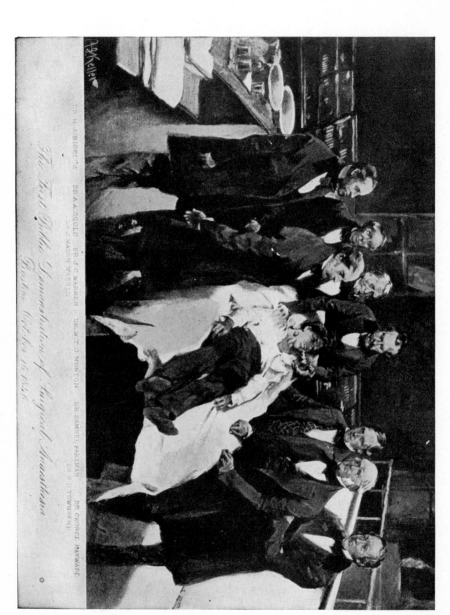

The first surgical operation under anaesthetic

The First Public Demonstration of Surgical Anaesthesia
Boston October 16 1846

DR. H. J. BIGELOW   DR. J. C. WARREN   DR. W. T. G. MORTON   DR. SAMUEL PARKMAN   DR. GEORGE HAYWARD
DR. A. A. GOULD   DR. J. MASON WARREN   DR. S. D. TOWNSEND

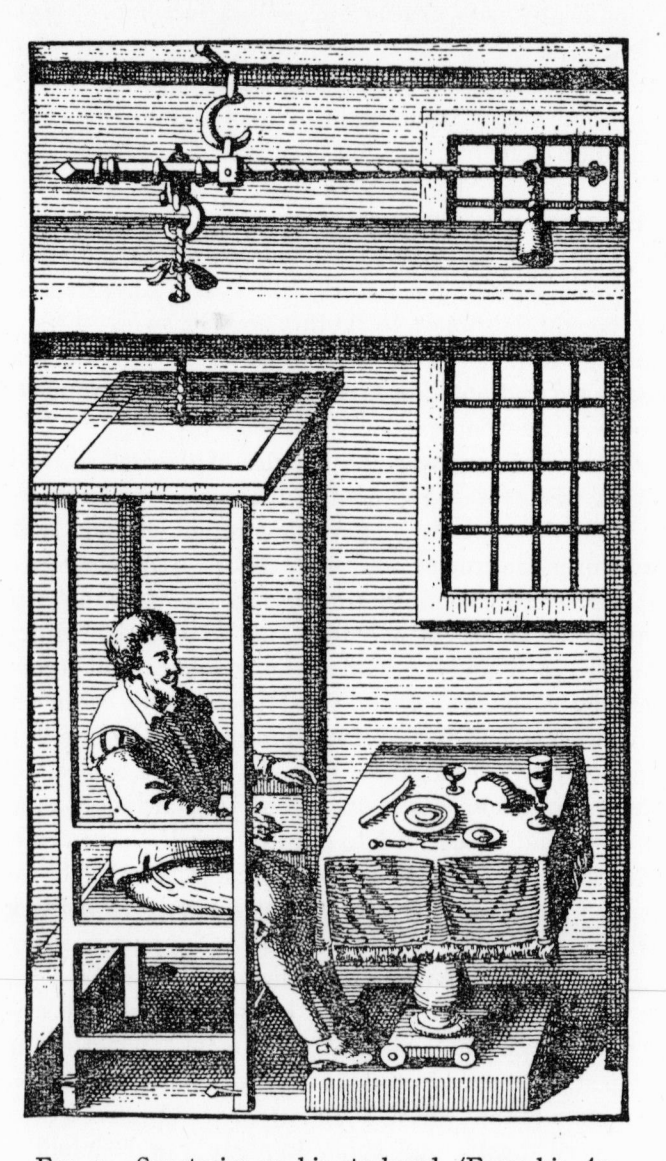

FIG. 7.—Sanctorius on his steelyard. (From his *Ars de Statica Medecine*. Leyden 1711)

conclusion that it was utterly useless to attempt to explain all the behaviour of the living body in terms of the one concept of movement. So also at a later date did many other physiologists agree with him that these efforts to maintain a school of physiology on mechanical principles alone had been unsuccessful.

JEAN BAPTISTE VAN HELMONT (1577–1644)

The Iatro-physical school of physiology was replaced by the Iatro-chemical school, for science, like every other department of human thought, is subject to rhythm and the swing of fashion. The Iatro-physicists had striven to explain life in terms of mechanics and had failed and now the Iatro-chemists set out to interpret it as a sequence of chemical reactions. It is generally considered that Jean Baptiste van Helmont was the founder of this school, and in histories of medicine van Helmont is often referred to as a Belgian mystic. Whether this is a good description of him is doubtful, but two things are true of him; first, that he was a devoted follower of Paracelsus, and second, that he was an exceptionally gifted man. He started his career as a student at Louvain University under Jesuit supervision, and it is said that one of his Jesuit tutors offered to teach him magic. The young van Helmont soon became sceptical of this instructor, and turned instead to the more profitable study of Stoic philosophy. Then, for a time, he became interested in the doctrines of St. Thomas à Kempis. Later his ardour for this writer cooled down and he decided to devote himself to medicine and to begin his study with the works of Galen. These deeply interested him but he happened one day to pick up a glove belonging to a lady who was suffering from the skin disease known as scabies or the itch. He was unfortunate enough to contract this disease from the gloves and proceeded to treat himself in accordance with the instructions given by Galen. That famous master of medicine looked upon the itch as being due to a "combustion of the bile" and a "saline state of the phlegm". Apparently the correct treatment for this was very drastic purgation. Baptiste van Helmont followed these instructions dutifully and weakened himself thereby not a little, without there being the slightest improvement in the state of his skin. Disgusted with the so-called healing art "he regretted that he had sacrificed both time and station in descending to it, gave

his library to students and affected sorrow afterwards that he had not rather burnt it, so angry was he with physic". (Meryon.)

He cured his "itch" eventually by means of remedies prescribed by Paracelsus, and filled with enthusiasm now for that great medical teacher, he determined to follow in his footsteps and, like him, to dedicate his life to the reform of medicine. He took therefore a doctor's degree in 1599 and, being a practical man, supplied himself with the financial assistance necessary for the carrying out of reforms by marrying a rich Brabantine lady. This gave him freedom from the need to earn a living and enabled him to travel, as Paracelsus had done, for the purpose of acquiring more knowledge. Helmont's personality is described tersely, in the following words, by his biographer Lobkowitz: "He was pious, learned, famous, a sworn enemy of Galen and Aristotle. The sick never languished long under his hands, being always killed or cured in three days."

Helmont took over, lock, stock and barrel, much of Paracelsus' natural philosophy. He believed that every material process of the body is presided over by a special *archaeus* or spirit, and that all physiological processes are purely chemical ones brought about by specific ferments. He was indeed the first man to realize the importance to the body of ferments and of gases and particularly of carbonic acid, which he called *gas sylvestre*. He also seems to have had some vague notion of the phenomenon of immunity. Psychological functions were assigned by him to different organs: memory to the brain, desire to the spleen, and volition to the heart. Jean van Helmont was, however, a down-to-earth scientist as well as a speculative philosopher and he regarded exact measurement as of the greatest importance to medical research. "He it was who first suggested the use of the balance which Lavoisier, at a subsequent period, consummated; he was aware of the fact of the expansion of water by heat, and of the diminution of the bulk of the atmospheric air by burning substances in it; he first used the term saturation, in relation to the process of solution, and corrected the erroneous notion, previously entertained, that the dissolved matter was destroyed or annihilated; he introduced sal-volatile as a medicinal agent."

Dr. Meryon ends his excellent biographical sketch of van Helmont with the sad reflection that he died, like Descartes, through falling

"a victim to his own doctrine of error, refusing to be bled for a severe inflammation of the lungs". He died in 1644 at the age of sixty-seven. We do not necessarily have to agree with Dr. Meryon's reflection.

FRANCISCUS SYLVIUS (1614–1672)

Franciscus de le Boë, better known by the name of Franciscus Sylvius, may be regarded as van Helmont's successor in the leadership of the Iatro-chemical school of physiology. He was professor at Leyden and he started his work by eliminating the alchemical trimmings that the Iatro-chemical school had inherited from van Helmont and placed physiology on what he believed to be a sounder chemical basis. He demonstrated that fermentation, accompanied by the formation of gas, was only one of the many chemical processes occurring in the human body. He investigated the various digestive juices of the body, such as the saliva, bile and pancreatic juice, and came to the conclusion that a study of the body's acids and alkalis not only threw a great deal of light on the nature of life, but also provided a useful guide to medical treatment. His ambition was to explain all other physiological phenomena in chemical terms, and firmly believed that this could be done.

But Sylvius has other and stronger claims to be remembered than as the propounder of an excellent but somewhat limited view of physiology. He made valuable contributions to our knowledge of the brain and, what was of far greater importance than this was the fact that he revived the ancient Hippocratic practice of teaching medicine to students at the patient's bedside. In that tiny infirmary at Leyden containing only twelve beds, there was inaugurated the modern practice of "walking the hospitals". Sylvius describes his method of instruction as follows: "I have led my pupils by the hand to medical practice, using a method unknown at Leyden or perhaps elsewhere, i.e. taking them daily to visit the sick at the public hospital. There I have put the symptoms of disease before their eyes; have let them hear the complaints of the patients, and have asked them their opinions as to the causes and rational treatment of each case, and the reasons for those opinions. Then I have given my own judgement on every point. Together with me they have seen the happy results of treatment when God has granted to our

cares a restoration of health; or they have assisted in examining the body when the patient has paid the inevitable tribute to death." No better description could be given of the methods of the teacher of clinical medicine than this.

The Iatro-chemical school of physiology survived the vicissitudes of the eighteenth and the nineteenth centuries and it may indeed be said that it survives even at the present day. Those who belong to it are convinced that life will eventually be explained in terms of chemistry alone, and some more imaginative members of this school go even further and believe that the day will eventually arrive when men will be able to create life within their chemical laboratories. Justus von Liebig (1803–1877), Professor of Chemistry at Giessen, was so sure that everything could be accounted for in terms of chemistry that he had the following words inscribed over the doors of his laboratory: "God has ordered all His Creation by Weight and Measure."

THE STUDY OF DIGESTION

Knowledge of the physiology of digestion was advanced by the Iatro-chemists, but it was increased also by the work of another amateur physiologist belonging to the Church, namely that very gifted Italian priest, the Abbé Spallanzani (1729–1799). The Abbé showed, first, that the churning movements of the stomach aided digestion but that they were not essential to it, and, second, that digestion did not involve, as some people had supposed, putrefaction. He also proved that digestion differed from the process of fermentation by which wine was made. He demonstrated that gastric juice was secreted by the walls of the stomach and the idea that the juice contained a free acid seems to have been in his mind, although he did not state this clearly. Finally he noticed that gastric juice curdled milk.

Two other investigators carried the Abbé's researches considerably further, the one an English physician, William Prout (1785–1850), the other an American Army surgeon, William Beaumont (1785–1853). Prout not only demonstrated the presence of acid in the gastric juice but showed that it was essential to the process of gastric digestion, although the actual liquefaction of the food was brought about by a different agent. Beaumont took up the research at this point where Prout had left it and, through a very

fortunate accident, he was able to throw a great deal more light on gastric digestion. As an army surgeon he had been called upon to look after a half-breed Canadian, Alexis St. Martin, suffering from a serious abdominal wound, and although the wounded man ultimately recovered, he was left afterwards with a persistent fistula of the stomach. The patient and the surgeon then became partners in a valuable piece of physiological research. Through the artificial opening Beaumont was able to obtain pure gastric juice, uncontaminated with food, and through it he was also able to observe the walls of his patient's stomach. He was in a position therefore to make observations very similar in nature to those which were to be made a hundred years later by Pavlov with his artificially contrived fistulae in dogs. Beaumont's chemical analysis of the gastric juice showed him that it contained free hydrochloric acid plus another chemical substance which, some years later in 1835, Theodore Schwann proved to be the ferment pepsin. Beaumont's direct observations of his patient's stomach clearly indicated that the digestive juices were only secreted by the stomach when it received food and that mechanical irritation of its lining alone gave rise to only a minimal amount of gastric secretion.

ELECTRICAL PHENOMENA

So far all the attempts made to explain vital processes had been of a mechanical or chemical nature, but in the last years of the eighteenth century and the opening years of the nineteenth century electricity was discovered, much to the interest of physiologists. Two of the physicists who had been responsible for electrical discoveries applied their methods to the investigation of physiological phenomena with exceedingly interesting results. Luigi Galvani (1738–1798) of Bologna showed that nervous action could be brought about by an electrical current, and nine years later Alessandro Volta (1745–1827) of Pavia, the inventor of the "Voltaic pile", demonstrated that muscles could be thrown into continuous contraction by repeated electrical stimulation. For a time this knowledge lay fallow and then nearly a century later E. Du Bois-Reymond (1818–1896), the great French physiologist, made use of it. He not only confirmed that an electric current evoked activity in a nerve but he proved that a nervous impulse was associated with the passage of a change in

electrical potential along the nerve. At a much later date medicine became greatly interested in these "currents of action" as they are called, and from the simple observations of Galvani and Volta have been derived the electro-cardiograms and the electro-encephalogram of the present day.

THE BROTHERS WILLIAM AND JOHN HUNTER

No account of Georgian medicine would be complete without mention being made of the two brothers, William and John Hunter. Like many another ambitious Scot, William Hunter (1718–1783), the elder brother, gave up his work in Scotland in order to go south and make a greater name for himself in the City of London. On arrival there he was fortunate enough to be invited by the well-known anatomist, Dr. James Douglas, to make his home with him and to act as tutor to his young son. After the death of his kindly patron William Hunter visited Leyden and then, on his return to London, he founded the Windmill Street School of Anatomy. (*See* Plate 19.) For many years this was the centre of anatomical instruction in London, but William Hunter's work there did not absorb all of his time so that he was able to practise medicine as well. He was a courtly and elegantly dressed man who in time became the leading obstetrician in London. Stephen Paget sums up William Hunter's character and his life in the following breathless sentence: "He never married; he had no country house; he looks in his portraits a fastidious, fine gentleman; but he worked till he dropped and he lectured when he was dying." Clever, efficient and hardworking though William Hunter was, he was eclipsed in all of his qualities, with the exception of elegance and fastidiousness, by his younger brother John.

JOHN HUNTER (1728–1793)

The youngest member of a family often burns to show his elder brothers and sisters that though smaller than they, he is a far greater person. John Hunter was the youngest of a family of eleven and this desire to excel everybody else was very firmly implanted in him. William, his senior by ten years, was making a career for himself in London, and he, John, would do the same—only on a much bigger scale. His mind was made up and he set out from home on horse-

back and two weeks later reached the great city. William gave his younger brother a human arm to dissect in the Anatomy School, which John accomplished in a masterly manner. John was also privileged to learn surgery under two very eminent surgeons, Cheselden of St. Thomas's Hospital, and Percival Pott of Bart's, and he could have had no better teachers. Threatened a few years later by tuberculosis, he was advised to live for a time in a warmer climate and this he managed to do by serving as a staff surgeon for four years in Belle Isle and Portugal. As soon as his health was restored and he was able to return to London he embarked on intensive work on comparative anatomy, this being the subject for which he was afterwards to become so famous. There was no trace of the academic scholar in John Hunter, and he found it difficult both to lecture and to report his own discoveries in reasonably good English. He was not really a student at all but a brilliant field naturalist, interested in all forms of life, from grasses to the Irish giant whose skeleton he coveted during the giant's life-time and secured at his death for the sum of four hundred pounds.

John Hunter proved to be a better surgeon than his brother William, and he introduced a new ligature operation for the serious condition of aneurism. But surgery was for him only a means to an end and as soon as his surgical practice was sufficiently remunerative to allow of his doing this, he moved from his Golden Square consulting rooms first into his brother's house in Jermyn Street and then to a much larger establishment in Leicester Square. Here he had room enough to store the 13,600 specimens which formed his museum. He also bought a country house with plenty of land round it, conveniently situated in the neighbourhood of Earl's Court, and there he kept a large number of birds, fishes and animals. It was while living in this small country estate of his that John Hunter was happiest. He spent the whole of the summer there, rising at daybreak—he allowed himself only four hours' sleep—to feed his animals. His desire for new animals and new specimens was insatiable. In a letter to Jenner, who was now living in his beloved Gloucestershire, Hunter writes: "I want a nest with cuckoo's eggs in it; also one with a young cuckoo; also an old cuckoo. I hear you saying that there is no end to your wants."

Jenner might well say that, for Hunter's letters to Gloucester-

shire are all in the same vein. "Cannot you get me a large porpoise?" "Have you any eaves where the bats go at night?" Not that Jenner's professional welfare is neglected in this correspondence, for Hunter does not fail to give the younger man helpful advice. For example, Jenner is interested in the phenomenon of hibernation and writes to Hunter to tell him that he is investigating the subject. "I thank you for your experiment on the hedge-hog," Hunter writes to him in reply to his letter on this subject, "but why do you ask me a question by way of solving it? I think your solution just; but why think, why not try an experiment?" This letter is frequently quoted, for in that last phrase "why think, why not try an experiment?" lies the whole of John Hunter's philosophy of life. His scientific curiosity knew no bounds. Though his income barely met the rising costs of his great Earl's Court establishment, he was extravagant enough to pay the expenses of a young surgeon to visit the Greenland whale fisheries, solely in order that he might obtain certain information about the behaviour of whales. At Earl's Court a staff of nine was employed and in Castle Street there were three resident and close on a dozen outside workers. Fashionable surgeon though he was by now and able to charge big fees, he was never out of debt. What made things much more difficult for him was that his health was none too good.

It was while overworking at the Earl's Court establishment that he suffered from his first attack of angina pectoris, a disease for which he himself was entirely responsible. Many years previously he had inoculated himself with discharges from a venereal patient in order to find out whether gonorrhoea and syphilis were separate illnesses or merely different symptoms of one and the same disease. Through bad luck he inadvertently selected for his inoculation experiment on himself a patient who was suffering from both gonorrhoea and syphilis, and as a result of the inoculation he contracted both diseases simultaneously. Not only was this responsible for his coming to the entirely wrong conclusion that there existed only a single variety of venereal disease, but it led to his developing a syphilitic thickening of the arteries which was ultimately to kill him. After having suffered from one or two attacks of angina, Hunter was well aware of the constant peril in which he walked. He knew that a sudden rise in his blood pressure provoked, say, by a burst of anger

against a colleague, would be fatal to him, and he knew also that he suffered fools but poorly. What John Hunter anticipated would eventually happen did actually happen at a meeting of the governors of the hospital at which he worked. He collapsed suddenly and died in the board-room of St. George's Hospital.

Dr. Singer describes John Hunter's place in the story of medicine admirably in the following few sentences. "His complex and interesting character demands better treatment than it has yet received. As an investigator his powers were superb but like Leonardo he was handicapped at every turn by literary incoherence. Nevertheless with him surgery begins to appear, at last, as a real Science and not as a mere applied Art. Hunter brought to bear on the subject a mind stored with ideas drawn from Comparative Anatomy and Pathology. Quick to detect analogy, shrewd in his scientific judgements, tireless and unsparing of himself in his pursuit of truth, a victim of disease inflicted in the service of science to which he was tragically a martyr in his death he shows as a heroic figure rendered no less heroic by some very human failings. Fully to appreciate so incoherent a writer it is unfortunately necessary to wade through many works written in his own clumsy and ill-arranged manner. . . . The museums of Natural History, as now constituted in all civilized countries, have been influenced by, if they have not been derived from, that which he literally gave his life's blood to found. He was right when he murmured softly to a friend in one of his later illnesses, 'You will not easily find another John Hunter'."

He was right in saying this for Hunter was far more, and knew himself to be far more, than a successful surgeon and a brilliant comparative anatomist. He was the inspiration of a whole generation of young doctors. No man had a profounder effect on his young contemporaries than he had, and it was no accident that during the next few decades it was the surgeons and not the physicians who dominated the medical world. For Hunter had entirely changed the face of surgery. He had found it little more than a trade carried on frequently by men of doubtful reputation, but he left it an honourable branch of the healing arts. All this had been achieved within the short space of a life-time by a man who as a lad had no liking for academic studies but badly wanted to know all about "birds and bees and grasses".

CHAPTER IX

The Age of Science and of Specialization

IN the nineteenth century the advance of science quickened its pace and science and scientists obtruded themselves more and more on the notice of ordinary men and women. During the previous two centuries scientific research had been the preoccupation of a few privileged men possessed of the ability, the leisure and the means for devoting themselves to the study of Natural Philosophy, as science was then called. What these men were doing, what they thought and what they discovered was of little or no interest to the man in the street. In the eighteenth century the scientists became less aloof, and rumours of their discoveries often reached the public. During the latter half of the nineteenth century scientists were drawn right into the open and were hailed by the more intelligent members of the crowd as leaders of thought, which in fact they were, since by that time the great Scientific Age of the world had begun. What was also of importance was widespread recognition of the fact that the scientists were dispensers of material gifts as well as of ideas. New scientific discoveries began to revolutionize industrial methods and were of immense importance to commerce and political economy. The scientists quickly responded to their new popularity with the people, took to publishing accounts of their discoveries in the press and were sometimes prevailed upon to give popular lectures.

The nineteenth century was also the beginning of the Industrial Age, an age that was made possible by the great technological advances of the scientists. The immense potentialities offered by scientific discoveries to industry were realized more quickly in Great Britain than in many other countries owing to the existence there of a prosperous and educated middle class. Thanks to this, middle-class Great Britain was given an excellent start in the industrial race being run by the various European nations.

A third feature of the nineteenth century was the rapid rise of specialism. Whenever knowledge increases beyond a certain point, specialization becomes inevitable, for no one is any longer able to master it all and a process of division must take place. This process has been particularly rapid in medicine. When the writer of this book arrived as a student at St. Bartholomew's Hospital in the year 1905, the medical specialists in that great institution could have been counted on the fingers of his two hands. Now it would be difficult to estimate how many specialists are to be found in one of our large general hospitals, but if we were to include subjects ancillary to medicine, such as chemistry, physiology and anatomy, then we would be likely to find between thirty and forty of them.

This breaking up of medical knowledge into a number of different pieces occasions considerable difficulty to the medical historian. Hitherto I have been able to present events in some sort of historical perspective, but with the division of the main trunk of medicine into a number of diverging branches, it is useless to attempt to do so any longer for a line of events has been replaced by a network of events which cannot be arranged in chronological order. The story that is being told breaks up into a multitude of stories, as confusing in their relation to each other as are the stories narrated by Scheherazade. Moreover, as the great physiologist Claude Bernard has said of modern science, "The names of the prime movers disappear in a general fusion and the more it advances, the more impersonal and detached it becomes." So also is it with advances in medicine. As the story of medicine nears its end it becomes more and more impersonal. This being so, it will be better for all concerned that the method of telling it should be changed. Instead of struggling to give an account of medical events in proper sequence, a series of medical problems will be stated and then the manner in which medical men and other experts have tried to solve them will be described. But before this new method of dealing with our subject is begun, something must first be said about the medical man himself for it is not only the doctor's methods which have changed with the passage of time, but also the doctor himself. A brief account must therefore be given of the transformation the medical man has undergone during the last few centuries.

THE EARLIER TYPES OF DOCTOR

In the Middle Ages and at the time of the Renaissance three kinds of doctors were to be found—the physician, the surgeon and the apothecary—and of these three the first was the undoubted leader of his profession. (*See* Plate 10.) In France these three categories of doctors were represented by a *grande bourgeoisie* of physicians, a *petite bourgeoisie* of clerical barber-surgeons, and a proletariat of outcast surgeons, the *barbitonsores*, and like their English prototypes all three of these classes of medical men heartily disliked each other and had as little to do with each other as possible. The seventeenth-century French physician has been described by Garrison as often being "a sterile pedant and a coxcomb, red-heeled, long-robed, big-wigged, square-bonneted, pompous and disdainful in manner, making a vain parade of his Latin". (*An Introduction to the History of Medicine*, F. H. Garrison.) Instead of studying his patient carefully the physician of that period was usually preoccupied with concealing his own ignorance with a clamour of words. He would wrangle for hours about some fantastic theory which had no relationship at all to the questions on which a practical decision was urgently needed. It was of this type of physician that the great dramatist Molière made such excellent sport in his comedies. Molière never had any use for the medical profession, partly because of the pomposity of the physicians and partly because no doctor had been able to cure him of the particular malady from which he was suffering—consumption. It is unlikely that the English physician of that time was in any way better than his colleague across the Channel. There were of course conscientious and able men amongst the physicians, men who were both devoted to their patients and modest as to their own knowledge, but such men were in a minority.

THE BARBER-SURGEON

The barber-surgeon of that period was an even less likeable character than his superior the physician. William Clowes, Queen Elizabeth's private physician, described them as being "No better than renegades or vagabonds, shameless in countenance, lewd in disposition, brutish in judgement and understanding." This was undoubtedly true of the men who were known as cataract-gouchers

and of lithotomists and also of the tooth surgeons who turned up at fairs and attracted their patients by the power of their voices. But after the Renaissance much-needed legislation was passed, both in France and in England, for the express purpose of improving the status of the barber-surgeons. The Paris Faculty took the barber-surgeons under its wing in 1505, whilst in England the Barber Company was united with the small but exclusive Guild of Surgeons to form the United Barber-Surgeon Company in 1540. Thomas Vicary, the eminent anatomist, became the first Master of this Company and Holbein the Younger has painted the picture of a disdainful Henry VIII handing over the Statute of the new Company to him without even bothering to look him in the face. In passing, it may be interesting to note that the English surgeon of today who discards the title of "doctor" and insists on being called "mister" does so in deference to this scene. He is reminding us of the time when every surgeon of any repute was a "master" surgeon of the Guild of Surgeons, but the modern surgeon would have caused less confusion if, like his predecessor, he had called himself "master" instead of "mister".

The parallel improvement in the status of the surgeon began in France with the success of the barber-surgeon Félix in relieving Louis XIV of a very painful condition. For this act he was ennobled and Félix's successors Mareschal and La Peyrome also continued to do excellent work. In spite of the opposition of the physicians to all improvements in the status of the surgeon there was founded at St. Côme—the ancient College of Barber-Surgeons—five new chairs of surgery, and this upward movement culminated in 1731 in the establishment of an Academy of Surgery.

THE APOTHECARY

The older apothecaries prepared medicines for the physicians and did not themselves prescribe them. At a still earlier date drugs ordered by the physicians were supplied by the grocers, but in 1617 the apothecaries managed to obtain a special charter for themselves and by this means got rid of the grocers. Their success brought upon them the displeasure of the physicians who saw in the apothecaries potential rivals in practice. They were right in foreseeing this difficulty for at a later date this rivalry between

physician and apothecary actually materialized. And in many ways it was fortunate that the apothecaries had gained more power, for when the great plague attacked London in 1663 the great majority of the physicians fled, whilst the apothecaries gained prestige by remaining at their posts. The chief failing of the apothecary was that he was often extortionate in his charges, an apothecary being known to make as much as a hundred and fifty pounds out of a single patient. Yet the physicians were really to blame for this. The official Pharmacopoeia of the College of Physicians contained an incredible assortment of so-called remedies. Nature had been ransacked for them and they included such unpleasant items as the eyes of crabs, the feathers of partridges, live spiders rolled in butter, ants' eggs, and the excrement of dogs. There were also remedies that were difficult to obtain and consequently very expensive, such as lunea or powdered human skull and still more costly powdered Egyptian mummy.

Nicholas Culpepper (1616–1654), deeply versed in herbalism and, like the followers of Rudolf Steiner, also interested in the influence of the heavenly bodies on the growth of plants, reacted very strongly against the prescribing of all this filth. He first translated the physician's Pharmacopoeia from Latin into English, and then revised it, which brought on his head much abuse.

Fortunately the standing of all three representatives of the medical profession, physician, surgeon and apothecary, was raised in course of time by the granting of royal charters to the Colleges of Physicians and of Surgeons and by the founding of the Society of Apothecaries.

During the nineteenth century the old triad of Physician, Surgeon and Apothecary gradually transformed itself into the new triad of Physician, Surgeon and General Practitioner or Family Doctor, and this arrangement worked admirably. The general practitioner became the linchpin of the whole medical apparatus, around which everything revolved, his great asset being that he was acquainted with the patient and was often familiar with his whole background. Equipped with all this knowledge he was in a good position to take a wide and balanced view of the patient's illness and to prescribe for him appropriate treatment. In other words he was the patient's friend as well as his doctor, a man in

whom he could put his trust and to whom he could impart confidences he would have been unwilling to have given to anyone else.

NURSING AS A PROFESSION FOR WOMEN

Another event occurred in the nineteenth century which was to be of immense benefit to medicine. Good nursing is of primary importance both to the patient and to the medical man responsible for his treatment. It may indeed be the factor which determines the issue of the case; with skilful nursing the patient will recover. Without that he will in all probability die. Yet it was not until the beginning of the second half of the nineteenth century that nursing came to be regarded as an art and an art about which a great deal had to be learnt. During the Middle Ages the nursing of the sick was the responsibility of certain religious sisterhoods and devoted to their duties though many of these nuns undoubtedly were, they were given little or no instruction in nursing. Otherwise there were no educated women amongst the nurses, a fact explained by the low repute of nursing as a profession. Those who were forced to adopt so menial a calling as nursing as a means of earning a living were slatternly, dowdy and often intemperate women who served Dickens as a working model for his portrait of Sairey Gamp. Garrison quotes a leader of *The Times* of April 15th, 1857, which gives us a very good idea of the hospital nurse of that day. "Lectured by Committees, preached at by chaplains, scowled at by treasurers and stewards, scolded by matrons, sworn at by surgeons, bullied by dressers, grumbled at and abused by patients, insulted if old and ill-favoured, talked flippantly to if middle-aged and good humoured, tempted and seduced if young and well-looking—they are what any woman might be expected to be under the same circumstances." This is a just and revealing appraisal of the state of nursing in the year 1857. When it is remembered that the remuneration of a nurse at that time was five pounds a year, that only one nurse was allotted to a ward containing seventeen beds, and that the working day for a nurse was from 6 a.m. to 7 p.m., it will not seem surprising that no woman of any ability ever thought of taking up such work.

Reform in nursing started in Germany and the first people to open a school for the teaching of nursing were the Protestant pastor

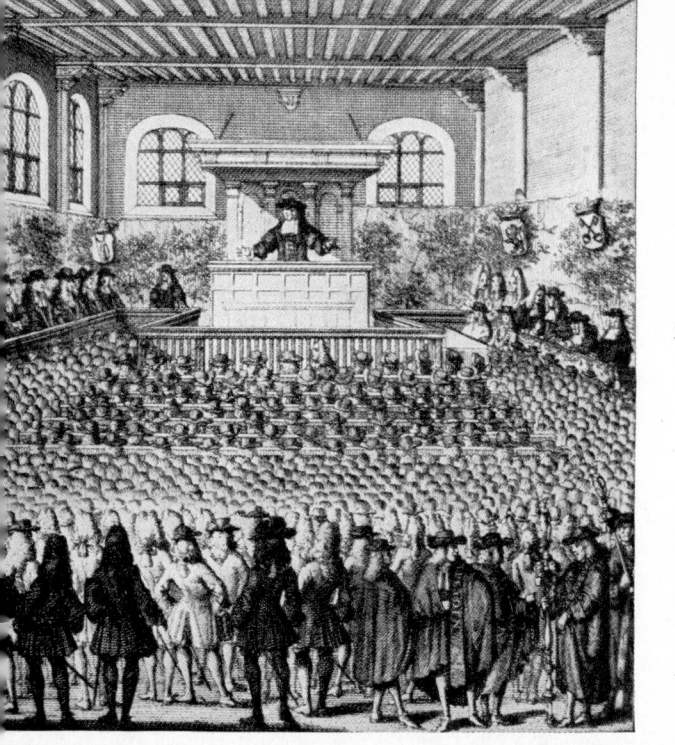

Hermann Boerhaare giving an academic lecture at Leyden

The Anatomy School in Great Windmill Street showing Dr. William Hunter dissecting

(From a lithograph after Rowlandson in the Wellcome Collection)

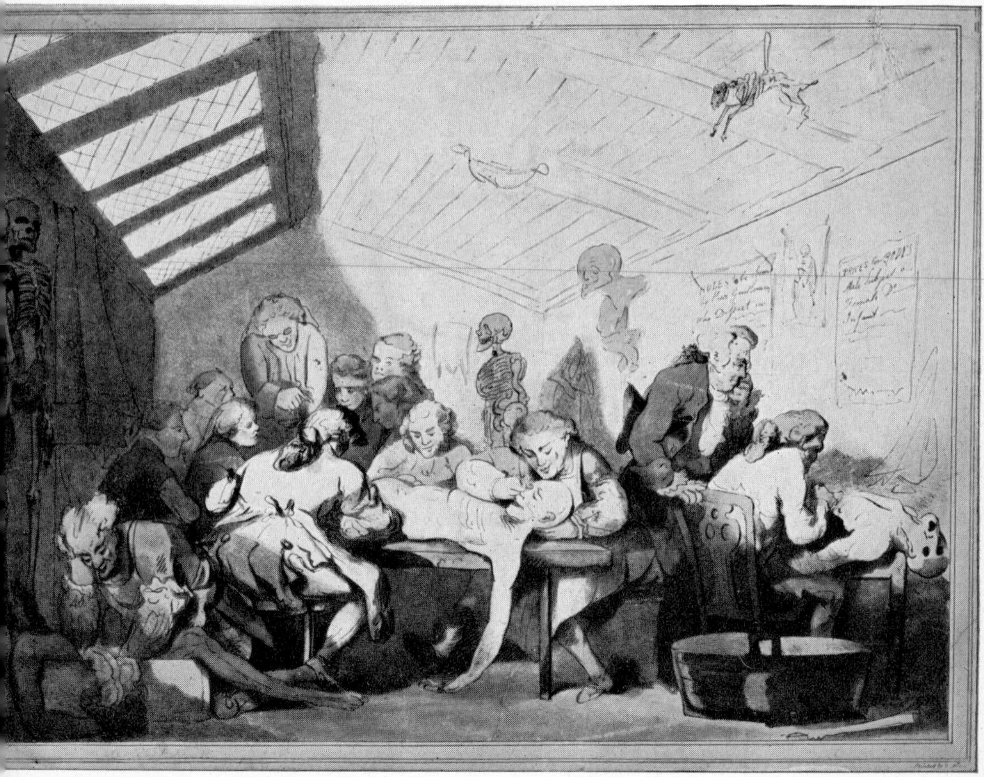

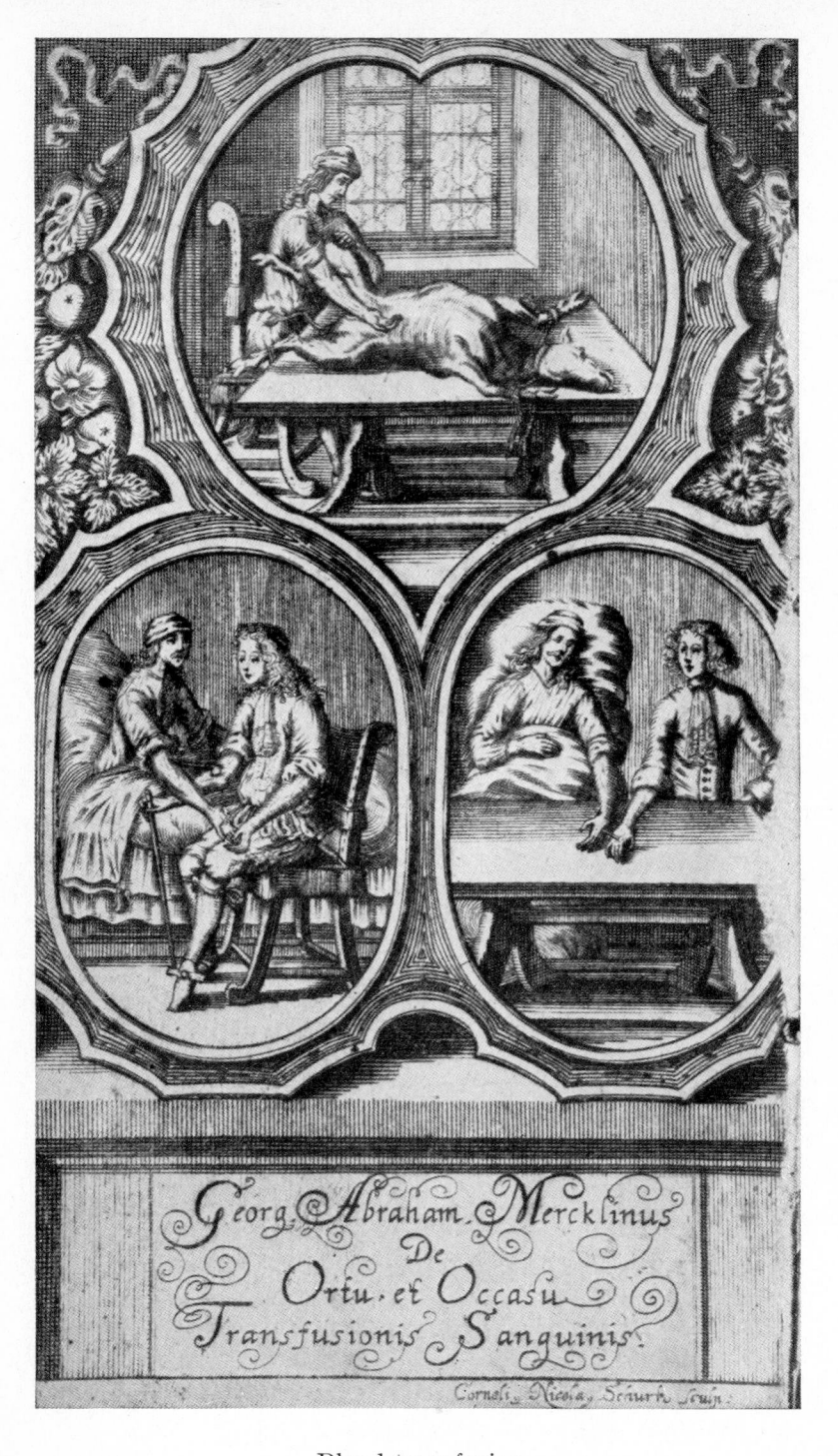

Blood transfusion

(From *Transfusionis Sanguinis* (1679), G. A. Mercklins. British Museum)

Theodor Fliedner (1800–1864) and his wife Friederike. In 1833 they turned the garden-house of their vicarage into a home for discharged women prisoners and three years later they opened the first school for deaconesses. The nursing school of the Fliedners served as a model for similar training places established later both within and outside Germany. The original establishment of the Fliedners was visited in 1840 by Elizabeth Fry and a few years afterwards by another English lady named Florence Nightingale (1820–1910). The latter was so impressed by the good work being done by the Fliedners at Kaiserworth that she underwent a course of training there, and on her return to England she spent three years visiting and investigating the nursing arrangements at the various English hospitals.

Florence Nightingale's opportunity came with the outbreak of the Crimean War in 1854, an event which was followed almost immediately by the complete collapse of the army medical services. No one could have been better fitted than Florence Nightingale to undertake the crusade on which she was shortly to embark. To start with, she was highly educated and a lady by birth, and no such person as this had ever given a thought to nursing in England. She possessed immense courage and determination and, what was of great value to her, she had friends in high positions in the administrative services. She knew also how to enlist public opinion in her favour, and she made great profit out of the feeling of shame which swept over England when it became known that whereas France had a number of religieuses to nurse their sick and wounded soldiers England had nobody. The Secretary of State for War invited Florence Nightingale to visit the Crimea for the purpose of organizing a nursing service there and she went without any hesitation. The first thing she did on arriving at the seat of war was to remove the control of the nursing staff out of the hands of the military authorities and to make women entirely responsible for it. The second thing she did was to pay no attention whatever to the archaic military regulations and to consider only local conditions and what it was possible for her to do with them. She was an admirable organizer and administrator and she also possessed the valuable gift of being able to select the right women to work under her.

At the end of the Crimean War she returned to England and,

with the money that had been raised in her honour, she endowed a
school for nursing at St. Thomas's Hospital. The example set by
St. Thomas's was followed by other hospitals with immense profit
to nursing in general. Amongst the later, indirect results of Florence
Nightingale's work in the Crimea was the establishment at Geneva
in the year 1864 of an International Red Cross Committee.

The Problem of Infection

Because this chapter is concerned chiefly with the medical
advances of the nineteenth century, the century in which the great
Pasteur was to make his revolutionary discoveries and in which the
germ-theory of disease was to be developed, infections will be a
suitable subject for discussion. Now although it was Pasteur who
supplied the evidence in favour of many illnesses being due to infection he was far from being the first person to advance a germ-
theory of disease. The oldest formulation of this theory is probably
to be found in a treatise *De Re Rustica*, by a certain Tarentius
Rusticus, who writes as follows: "If there are any marshy places,
little animals multiply which the eye cannot discern, but which
enter the body with the breath through the mouth and nose and
cause grave diseases." This idea was revived in the Middle Ages
by Fracastorius in his work *De Contagione* and again in 1656 by
Kirscher, when he reported that he had discovered "tiny worms"
in the blood and in pus from plague victims in Italy. Kirscher
was on the right track but it would of course have been quite
impossible for him to have actually seen the bacilli of plague through
the very primitive microscope he was using.

It was not until Leeuwenhoek actually discovered micro-
organisms in 1683, with the help of a far more efficient instrument,
that a firm basis was provided for the germ-theory of disease.
Hitherto the idea of infection by hostile forms of organism had been
entirely speculative but now men had been given a visual proof of
the existence everywhere of minute forms of life. And at the right
moment the genius appeared who not only established an entirely
new science of bacteriology but who provided humanity with some
means of defending itself against bacterial infection. Pasteur's
discoveries are of such immense importance that he and his work
must be dealt with at considerable length.

LOUIS PASTEUR (1822–1895)

Pasteur began life as a schoolmaster and it was his special interest in the structure of crystals which first encouraged him to embark on scientific research in addition to his teaching. He happened to have come across a book in the school library in which a German crystallographer had stated that the two salts of tartaric acid and paratartaric acid were of identical chemical composition and that they differed from each other only in the way in which they rotated the plane of polarized light. This greatly interested him and he decided to investigate the matter for himself. His examination showed that paratartaric acid was actually a mixture of two tartaric acids which possessed different optical activities, one of them rotating polarized light to the right, and the other rotating it to the left.

This discovery by a young unknown schoolmaster gained for him the support and the friendship of several eminent French chemists and as a result of this he was elected to the post of Professor of Chemistry at Strasbourg. From Strasbourg he went to Lille, and finally he reached Paris as Professor of Chemistry. Now one of the most important industries carried on at Lille happened to be the fermentation of beet sugar for the production of alcohol. Pasteur's advice was sought on this subject and he agreed to investigate the whole process of fermentation. After studying it and experimenting on it he read a paper on the germ-theory of fermentation before the Societé des Sciences of Lille and showed that all the transformations of organic matter brought about in nature were brought about by various forms of micro-organisms. Within two years of his arrival at Lille Pasteur, who at the start had been interested in science purely because it threw light on philosophy, was transformed into a devoted servant of the community, a man who was trying to solve by scientific means the practical problems brought to his notice by his fellow citizens. This was symbolic of the new role science was playing in the nineteenth century.

In 1860 the Academy of Sciences awarded Pasteur its experimental physiology prize for his studies on fermentation. Having solved this problem Pasteur now embarked on a much bigger one of a more philosophical nature, the question of spontaneous generation. It was believed by many biologists at that time that life could

be evolved out of inorganic matter, but by means of a beautifully contrived series of experiments Pasteur proved that this was definitely not the case. He showed clearly that life could arise only from life.

We now find him turning his attention again to matters that were of practical importance to local industry. In 1865 a disease spread widely amongst the silkworms and threatened to ruin the silk industry of the South of France. Although Pasteur had never seen a silkworm or a mulberry tree before, he undertook to investigate the epidemic. For four years he devoted himself to this problem and in the end he solved it. The success of his silkworm campaign brought him into contact with the subject of epidemics in general and he became convinced that epidemics amongst cattle and human beings could be overcome by the use of the appropriate scientific measures. Yet he was averse from entering the domain of the veterinary surgeons and the doctors, for not only had he had no medical or veterinary training, but he was fully aware that the experts on these subjects would resent his intrusion into their worlds. There was yet another and still more cogent reason why he should reduce rather than increase his commitments. In 1868, when only forty-eight years old, Pasteur had suffered a cerebral haemorrhage which had endangered his life and had left him with a permanent weakness of the left arm and leg. But the subject of infection was of such immense importance that he found it impossible to consider very seriously his personal convenience and the state of his health. He started to work on the subject of infective diseases.

The belief that illnesses were caused by micro-organisms had long been in his mind and ten years previously he had written the following in a paper dealing with the subject of fermentation and putrefaction: "Everything indicates that contagious diseases owe their existence to similar causes." So also when studying airborne micro-organisms in connection with his experiments on spontaneous generation he had written: "It would be interesting to carry out frequent analysis of dust at different seasons, and in different localities. The understanding of the phenomena of contagion, especially during the period of epidemic disease, would have much to gain from such studies." His more recent work in silkworm disease had still further strengthened this belief that micro-organisms were responsible for many diseases.

Nor was Pasteur alone in this belief, for others had also been struck by the similarity between the processes of fermentation and of illness. Several physicians and veterinary surgeons were carrying out experiments with the idea of proving that this was the case but their experiments were often so loosely contrived and so defective that Pasteur felt that they were "more likely to compromise the good cause than to serve it". In spite of all the arguments that could be brought against his doing so, he decided in the end to tackle the problem himself on a large scale and to choose for his experiments the illness of cattle known as anthrax.

THE INVESTIGATION OF ANTHRAX

The subject of anthrax is one of those nodal points in the history of medicine at which a number of different lines of research flow together, for anthrax was a disease in which a great many scientists had been interested long before Pasteur. Pasteur's attention was directed to it. In 1845 two French workers found in the blood and the spleens of cattle that had died of anthrax large numbers of microscopic, straight and motionless rods. But they had failed to make any further use of this all-important discovery. Their findings were confirmed ten years later by yet another microscopist, Pollender, who suggested that the rods represented some contagious element in the disease. Several other scientists were of the same opinion as Pollender but none of the experiments they had carried out in the hope of establishing their thesis had proved conclusive. The whole problem of anthrax was therefore in a state of muddle when Pasteur made up his mind to deal with it.

Pasteur did not know that he had been forestalled in his research on anthrax by a brilliant young German doctor named Koch. This country practitioner had made for himself a primitive laboratory in his own home in which he proposed to carry out research on anthrax. He had frequently seen cattle attacked by this fatal disease when making his rounds in his country practice, and he had long wanted to investigate it. Now, with a laboratory of his own, he felt himself to be in a position to carry out research on the subject. First he established the fact that the disease was transmissible from mouse to mouse, and then he had the original idea of placing minute particles taken from the spleens of infected animals within

small collections of sterile blood. The microscope he used for examining the particles was very primitive but when he watched what was happening to the tiny fragments of spleen he had placed in the blood serum he noted that the rods of anthrax were growing into long filaments and that round bodies were developing within them. (*See* Fig. 8.) These round bodies were obviously spores and he found that they were highly resistant to injury. This obviously explained why anthrax was so successful in spreading and in maintaining itself. Koch discovered that other bacilli besides anthrax, such as the hay-bacillus, also produced spores, and he learnt how to differentiate between true anthrax and the septicaemia of cattle with which anthrax was so often confused.

Pasteur heard of Koch's experiments and acknowledged their value, and he made additional experiments of his own to confirm the causative role played by the anthrax bacillus. For example, he filtered cultures of anthrax through membranes that were fine enough to hold back the bacilli and then showed that when rabbits were injected with the clear filtrate they did not become infected by it. Pasteur's experiments, together with those of Koch, constituted very strong evidence in support of the germ-theory of disease.

For Pasteur there now followed years of endless experiments by which many new forms of pathogenic germs were discovered and more and more illnesses were proved to be due to infection. The two decades which followed Pasteur's and Koch's intensive work on anthrax have sometimes been referred to as the Golden Age of bacteriology on account of the rapidity of the progress of this new department of science. But it is doubtful whether the name is a fitting one, for all that really happened at this time was that two men of genius, Pasteur and Koch, were blazing a new path by providing the world with a new technique, and that a whole army of workers—good, bad and indifferent—were following their lead. In other words, an entirely new department of science had been opened up in the form of a bacteriological laboratory and many were now hard at work within it.

PASTEUR'S WORK ON IMMUNIZATION

By providing the germ-theory of disease, with satisfactory scientific proofs, Pasteur had made a big contribution to medicine

and had he immediately retired from all further work his name would still be one of the most important in the roll of medical discoverers. But Pasteur was a man who had no wish to retire and who actually never did retire. It was true that he had suffered a stroke and had had to take some time off for this, but this was not allowed to make any difference to the amount of work he would afterwards undertake. The world contained so many sceptics, there was so much stubborn

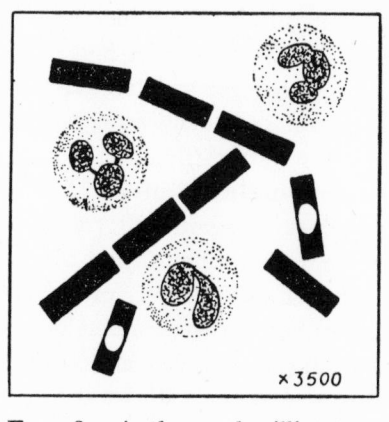

×3500

FIG. 8.—Anthrax bacilli, two containing spores. Also leucocytes magnified 3500 times

opposition still to be overcome, so much complacency waiting to be destroyed, that it was quite impossible for him to rest.

Having proved that a great many diseases were caused by micro-organisms, the next and much more formidable problem was to discover some means of protecting both men and animals from infection. Pasteur was well aware of the fact that there were many diseases from which people suffer only once because they thereby acquire an immunity to it. He had been deeply impressed by the excellent results obtained by Jenner's method of vaccination against smallpox and this made him wonder whether there was any reason why vaccination should be a preventive method restricted to only one disease, namely smallpox. "We must immunize against the infectious diseases of which we can cultivate the causative micro-organisms," he later announced to the world. But the method of doing this was

a question which would undoubtedly require a great deal of thought and a vast number of experiments before it could be answered.

As so often happens when a man is brooding over a problem, a fortunate accident helped Pasteur to find the answer. The word "helped" has been used here because unless a man with the keen and observant mind of Pasteur had seen the significance of the accident that happened in the laboratory, no great discovery would have been made. In the year 1879 Pasteur was carrying out experiments on chicken cholera and his work had been interrupted so that the cultures of the bacillus of cholera he had previously prepared in his laboratory became rather too old for inoculation purposes. Because he had failed to produce cholera after injecting this old culture into fowls he was forced to wait until he could obtain a fresh and virulent growth from a new outbreak of fowl cholera. But when he inoculated his former chickens again with this fresh culture he found to his great surprise that they remained entirely free from signs of cholera. Yet when other chickens, never previously inoculated, were injected with it, they promptly succumbed to the disease, thereby proving that the new culture was a virulent one. Pasteur immediately saw in this occurrence an analogy with what happened after cowpox inoculation, that is to say that the inoculated person does not acquire smallpox. A new and important principle had been established, that if an animal were inoculated with micro-organisms of diminished virulence, it developed in its blood some substance which protected it against a future and more virulent infection by the same organism. "It is characteristic of experimental science," wrote Pasteur, "that it opens ever widening horizons to our vision," and the vistas opened up now by these new experiments of Pasteur's on fowl cholera were truly immense. The great problem of immunity had come into view and, undaunted by the fleetingness of human life, Pasteur set out to explore it. He was confident now that vaccination could become a general technique applicable to all forms of infectious diseases and that it would no longer be necessary to depend, as formerly, on the chance discovery of some naturally occurring immunizing agent, such as cowpox. Within four years Pasteur had proved his case to the hilt and had shown how an immunity could be obtained to the following infections: chicken cholera, anthrax, swine erysipelas and rabies. The most dramatic of these numerous

achievements of Pasteur's were his discovery of the means of obtaining immunities against anthrax and rabies, and the stories of these discoveries must be told.

IMMUNIZATION AGAINST ANTHRAX

Pasteur had previously made an observation which was to help him now in his search for a means of immunizing animals against anthrax. He recalled that long ago a group of eight sheep had been maintained without any loss of life in a field in which animals dead from anthrax had previously been buried. He also recalled that when these said animals had afterwards been inoculated with virulent anthrax cultures, several of them had managed to resist the infection. This encouraged him to attempt to make a vaccine out of attenuated anthrax bacilli but he immediately came up against the difficulty that anthrax bacilli produced spores which were very resistant to modification. The formation of spores had somehow to be prevented and this Pasteur eventually managed to do by adding weak antiseptics to his anthrax cultures. At a later date he substituted for antiseptics the method of keeping the anthrax bacilli in shallow culture plates at a temperature of 42 to 43 centrigrade. After eight days had been passed in these conditions the anthrax bacilli became comparatively harmless to both rabbits and sheep. Pasteur felt that he was now ready for the great public test of the vaccine he had prepared and arrangements were made for this test by him and the local farmers.

Twenty-four sheep, one goat and six cows were assembled for the test at Pouilly le Fort and on April 28th, 1881, Pasteur arrived to carry out the first vaccination on them. A second vaccination was made on May 17th, and then on May 31st the animals were injected in the presence of many onlookers with virulent anthrax bacilli. The same virulent cultures were also injected into twenty-nine unvaccinated animals. It was then agreed that Pasteur and his assistants Chamberland, Roux and Thullier should depart and return again on June 2nd to witness the results of what they had done. The great day arrived and as Pasteur's party drew nearer to the pens it heard the sound of loud cheering. The results of the great experiment had surpassed all expectations. "All the vaccinated sheep were well. Twenty-one of the control sheep and the single goat were

dead of anthrax, two other control sheep died in front of the spectators, and the last unprotected sheep died at the end of the day. The six vaccinated cows were well and showed no symptoms, whereas the four control cows had extensive swellings at the site of the inoculation and also febrile reactions." It was an immense triumph for Pasteur and his vaccination methods.

As Dr. René Dubos, Pasteur's biographer, points out, it is strange that Pasteur should have selected rabies as the next subject for immunological study because in France only a few people died of this trouble every year. What also made rabies an unsuitable subject for study was that nobody knew anything about its cause and this rendered experiments on immunization against it specially difficult. But Pasteur retained certain vivid memories of his childhood when a mad wolf had charged through Jura, biting men and beasts as it went, and as a small boy he had watched the wounds of one of the wolf's victims being cauterized with red-hot irons at the blacksmith's shop. Rabies was therefore for Pasteur a supreme challenge which he could not do otherwise than accept. He promptly set to work. First came certain experiments in an attempt to discover the cause of the disease, and as rabies is due to an organism invisible under the microscope these preliminary experiments were quite unsuccessful. It was obvious, however, to Pasteur that the infecting organisms, whatever they might be, were present in the central nervous systems of the persons or animals attacked, for other animals could be infected by injecting into their brains fragments taken from the central nervous system of those that had died of rabies. But how could a weak vaccine of the invisible agent of the disease be prepared? Here was a difficulty which would have seemed insuperable to the vast majority of men, this difficulty of preparing a weak vaccine of an unknown bacteriological agent. There exists in the Pasteur Institute a famous portrait of Pasteur by Edelfeldt which shows the great bacteriologist gazing fixedly at a glass flask and obviously deep in thought. (*See* Plate 22.) The flask at which he is looking is a flask in which his assistant Roux had suspended the spinal cord of a rabbit previously dead from rabies, in order that he might discover how long the infective agent managed to survive the process of drying. It was at the moment of gazing at the flask containing the rabbit's shrivelling cord that the idea was born in

Pasteur's mind of protecting dogs from rabies by inoculating them with a series of emulsions of dried cord, beginning with a cord fourteen days old, following with one thirteen days old, then twelve, and so on until a fresh cord could be used. The idea was put to the test and the experiments succeeded. Pasteur found that he could immunize dogs against rabies in this way.

Then there came for Pasteur an emotional struggle as to whether he would ever be justified in putting this method of immunization to the test on a human being. Fortunately fate decided the issue for him. A young boy, Joseph Meister, who had been bitten by a mad dog was brought to him and he was assured by both the physician and the physiologist who had brought the boy that their patient would undoubtedly die unless Pasteur could manage to save him. Pasteur's doubts were settled and Joseph Meister was given thirteen successive inoculations of fresher and fresher infections of the spinal cord, ending with an entirely fresh emulsion. There are scientists who lose all feeling in the heat of research, scientists who are prepared if necessary to take considerable risks with human life, including their own lives, provided only that their research brings them nearer to the truth they are seeking. Pasteur was not one of these fanatics. Vallery-Radot gives us an account of him at the time of this first test of his vaccine on a human being. "Pasteur was going through a succession of hopes and fears and an ardent longing to snatch little Meister from death. He could no longer work. At nights feverish visions came to him of this child, whom he had seen in the gardens, suffocating in the mad struggles of hydrophobia like the dying child he had seen in 1890." His restlessness and his anxieties rose as stronger and stronger emulsions of cord were being used, but the child did not die. He recovered and three months later Pasteur was able to describe his case to the Academy of Sciences as a "tentative heureuse". Joseph Meister returned safely to Alsace and many years later, as a grown man, he became gate-keeper of the Pasteur Institute in Paris.

The second case to be treated in this way was a shepherd from the Jura who, whilst protecting some children from a mad dog, was bitten himself. He also survived and his heroic deed is commemorated in a statue which stands in front of the Pasteur Institute of Paris. In a few years' time some 2,490 people had

been immunized by Pasteur and his fame spread far and wide so that he became a world figure.

Pasteur's life illustrates the change that was taking place in the role of the scientist during the course of the nineteenth century. As has already been said, the scientist in former centuries had remained aloof in his laboratory and he was unknown to the world outside it. He was a solitary man engaged in work which frequently had no bearing on the lives of ordinary men and women, or so it seemed to them. Now, in the second half of the nineteenth century, all this was changed. The scientist ceased to be a natural philosopher interested only in discovering the laws of Nature and unconcerned, as Michael Faraday and Claude Bernard had been unconcerned, with the practical application of the discoveries they were making. Scientists were now turning into practical men of affairs who were anxious that their discoveries should be of use to their fellow men. They were not seeking only abstract scientific truth as their predecessors had done, but looking for answers to problems of immediate importance to mankind. It will be noted that Pasteur started his scientific career by formulating useful directives for the French manufacturers of vinegar, wine and beer, and that he ended it by issuing equally effective directives for the control of infectious diseases.

But although Pasteur always kept in mind practical issues, he never allowed the philosopher and religious man within him to die, in the way that many of his fellow scientists did. "The man of faith is . . . likewise a man of supernatural revelation," he informed his scientific audience in his address to the College of Arbois where he himself had formerly been a student. "If you tell me that this is incompatible with human reason I shall agree with you, but it is still more impossible to believe that reason has the power to deal with problems of origins and ends."

Pasteur was a great man in every sense of that word. He died in 1895 at the age of seventy-three, twenty-seven years after he had suffered his stroke. He was not a medical man but his discoveries were destined to be of greater importance to medicine than those of any member of the medical profession. He was indeed one of those nodal points in the story of medicine from which lines travel out in every direction, impinging on and informing other lines of research.

One of these, namely the line which connects up with the main subject of this chapter, the infection of wounds, must now be followed.

THE NEW SCIENCE OF BACTERIOLOGY

Pasteur's work led to the establishment of an entirely new speciality in medicine, that of bacteriology. After his death there was intense activity in this new field of which research took two main directions. The Germans, under the leadership of Koch, sought to discover and to catalogue with characteristic thoroughness the infective agents of other diseases, whilst the French continued Pasteur's own special line of research on the problem of immunity.

Koch had done excellent work on the bacillus of anthrax in 1876; he had investigated the organisms responsible for the infection of wounds in 1878, and now in 1882 he made the discovery for which he is best known, the discovery of the bacillus of tuberculosis. He also laid down for the growing army of bacteriologists the criteria which must be satisfied if an organism is to be held responsible for the causation of a disease. He believed that these requirements were three in number: (1) the organisms must be constantly found in the lesions of the disease; (2) they must be obtainable in pure culture and their growth must be maintained through repeated generations of subculture; (3) the disease must be reproduced in other animals when such animals were inoculated from these cultures.

There were many problems in bacteriology which Pasteur had left unsolved, particularly the question as to the means by which immunity was gained. Disease-producing germs can be regarded as being almost ubiquitous, yet it is only a few people who become their victims. By what means does the human body defend itself from infection and how can the body's defences be artificially strengthened? These were the very important questions which needed answering, and in due course some sort of an answer was obtained to both of them. Amongst Pasteur's pupils was a young Russian, Elie Metchnikoff (1845–1916), who worked as a zoologist first at Odessa and then in Sicily. Whilst studying sea-anemones he noted the presence in them of amoeba-like cells which were capable of engulfing small particles and even bacteria coming into contact with them. From these early observations of his he evolved, at a later

date, the theory of phagocytosis, that is to say, the idea of the destruction of bacteria by the white corpuscles of the blood. Having heard of Pasteur's great discoveries, Metchnikoff promptly abandoned his work as a zoologist, hastened to Paris and became one of Pasteur's most devoted pupils.

Pasteur's actual successor in Paris was Emile Roux (1853–1933), who drew attention to the resistance offered to invading organisms by the blood plasma. He helped to perfect the preparation of anti-diphtheritic serum, and his term as director of the Pasteur Institute in Paris was marked by many other important discoveries made both by himself and his colleagues, such as Widal's discovery of the sero-diagnostic test for typhoid fever. More will be said in Chapter XIII about these bacteriological advances made subsequent to Pasteur's death.

MEDICAL ADVANCES RESULTING FROM DISCOVERIES IN PHYSICS

Pasteur started his career as a chemist and ended it as the greatest benefactor of medicine in the whole of the nineteenth century. But medicine was also destined to profit at the beginning of the following century from discoveries made in the realm of physics. The first of these was the discovery of X-rays by Röntgen, and the second that of radio-activity by the Curies. These advances in medicine must now be dealt with.

WILHELM KONRAD VON RÖNTGEN (1845–1922)

He was the child of a German farmer and a Dutch mother and was reputed to be but an indifferent student at Utrecht University, where he was studying physics. After taking his degree there he obtained the post of assistant to Professor Kundt at Würzburg and it was whilst carrying out some experiments with a Crookes' tube at Würzburg that his discovery was made. Röntgen was fifty years old at the time and he now held the chair of physics there. He interested himself, in his spare time from teaching, in the rays emitted from the cathode of a Crookes' tube. On the day in question he was working in a dark laboratory and was observing the effect of passing electric charges through a high-vacuum tube. The tube with which he was working happened to be completely covered by black cardboard and yet whenever he switched on the current he

became aware of a greenish glow coming from a small object situated on a neighbouring part of the bench. He turned off the current, let daylight into the laboratory, and found that the glow had come from a small piece of paper that was coated on one side with barium platino-cyanide. It chanced that the piece of paper had been lying on the bench near to the Crookes' tube, and it was clear to him that some hitherto unknown rays had passed through the black cardboard surrounding the tube and had rendered the barium platino-cyanide paper luminous. Röntgen next tried the effect of interposing other opaque objects, such as a thousand-page book, between the tube and the fragment of barium platino-cyanide paper, and still it became luminous whenever he turned on the current.

The most exciting moment of all came when Röntgen placed his own hand between the tube and the paper and he saw that the bones of his fingers cast long dark shadows on the luminous background of the glowing paper. Further experiment showed him that although these mysterious rays were invisible to the unaided eye, they produced an effect on photographic plates. Excellent skiagrams or photographic studies in shadows could be obtained of the denser structures of the body by this new form of photography.

Röntgen did not indicate to doctors how his discovery could best be put to practical use and there was no need for him to do so. The potential value of the new X-rays—X because nothing was known about them—was immediately realized by the medical profession. A new kind of specialist promptly appeared and a radiological or X-ray department was established at all the larger hospitals. At first the radiologist working there confined his attention to the diagnosis of fractures, the detection of calculi, and the location of foreign bodies within the tissues, but with further improvements in technique, the sphere of action was rapidly extended. By swallowing such opaque substances as barium and bismuth and afterwards exposing X-ray films, the stomach and the bowels of a patient could be outlined. So also, by the injection of certain compounds of iodine which were excreted in the urine, a shadow could be obtained of the kidneys. By such supplementary measures as these, more and more of the body's organs were brought within the range of X-ray examination.

But unexpected difficulties began to arise, for it was soon found

that X-rays could be as dangerous as they were useful. Radiologists were suffering from attacks of dermatitis or chronic irritation of the skin and sometimes this dermatitis became worse and eventually turned cancerous. Within the next few years some of the earlier pioneers in X-ray work lost their fingers and hands or even their lives as the result of this injurious action of X-rays.

Yet even a defeat can be turned to good account. Later, it was found that the agent which sometimes caused cancer might also be used as a method of treating cancer. Although X-rays were injurious to all living tissues, they were particularly injurious to the abnormal cells of cancer; and thanks to this selective action of theirs, they could be used for the destruction of malignant growths not curable by other forms of treatment. Deep X-ray therapy, as it is called, is now a recognized and very useful method of treating cancer.

The second discovery in physics which was to have important repercussions on medicine was the discovery of radium by Pierre and Marie Curie. The story of this great work on the part of the Curies is so well known that it need not be told again. In 1896, one year after Röntgen had presented medicine with X-rays, Henri Becquerel observed and gave an account of the phenomenon of radio-activity. Two years later radium was discovered and by 1900 enough of it was obtained for examination so that its unusual properties became known, including its capacity to cause burns. Curie-therapy, as it was at first called, was introduced into medicine as a method of treating malignant tumours alternative to that of exposing them to X-rays and it has proved particularly effective in the treatment of cancer of the lip and tongue, and also of rodent ulcer.

The rapid progess made by the physicists since the discovery of radium has contributed new remedies to the arts of healing as well as advanced the deadly science of destruction. Radio-active elements can now be made artificially by means of a comparatively small atomic pile and this means that isotopes, or radio-active forms of many of the chemical elements, are now available for medical research. These isotopes are now being used both in diagnosis and in treatment. Physiologists call these radio-active elements "tracers" and they make use of them in order to follow the chemistry of the body. For example, the isotopes of iron Fe 59 and Fe 55 behave exactly the same as does Fe 56, the usual form of iron given in cases

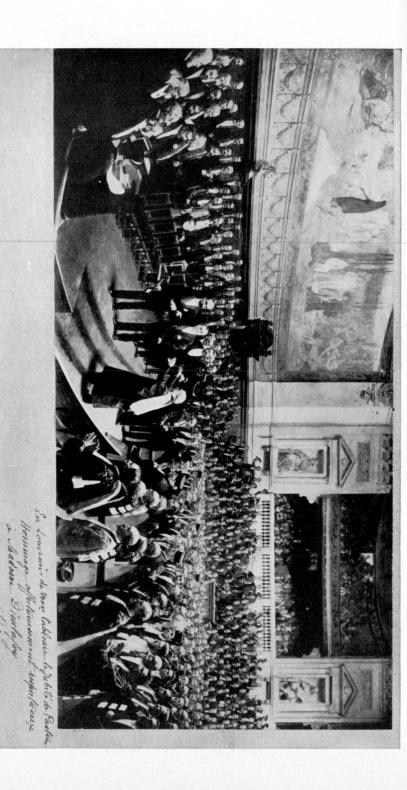

Lister greeting Pasteur

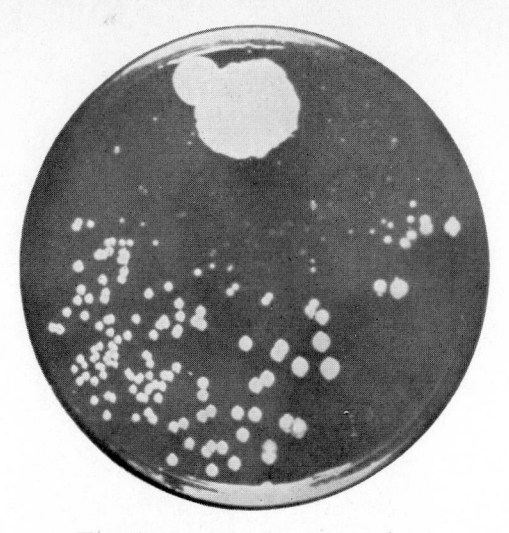

Fleming original culture plate

Louis Pasteur in his laboratory
(From the painting by Edelfeldt. Century of Progress, Chicago, 1933)

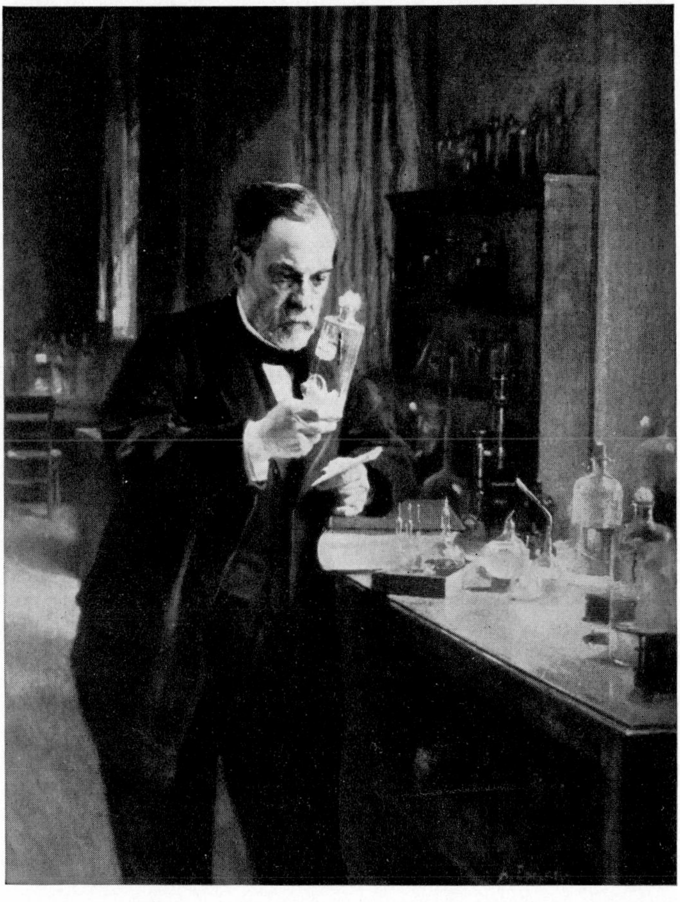

of anaemia. But the two isotopes Fe 59 and Fe 55 are radio-active and this means that the course they take in the body after being swallowed can be followed by means of a Geiger counter, an instrument used for the detection of radiations. All that need be done after the patient has swallowed his dose of radio-active iron is to bring the counter into proximity with various parts of his body and listen for a click.

Radio-active elements are also used for treatment. We know, for example, that some of the iodine we take in with our food is required by the thyroid, iodine being an important ingredient of thyroid secretion. If therefore we give a patient suffering from a malignant goitre radio-active iodine in place of ordinary iodine, some of that iodine is carried straight to the thyroid and the thyroid is thereby subjected to radio-activity. Much work is now being done on the treatment of malignant growths by means of the radio-active isotopes of many of the elements and it is likely that useful new forms of treatment will thereby be discovered.

CHAPTER X

The Story of Surgery

AS has already been said, surgery is an incredibly old branch of medicine, perhaps the oldest. The shout of the wounded hunter may well have been the first cry for help in the annals of medicine. The earliest picture of a surgical operation is probably that which can be seen in a tomb at Memphis, a picture which illustrates a priest-physician at work in about the year 2500 B.C. But the operations which the priest-physicians of Egypt did were superficial and comparatively simple surgical procedures such as operations for circumcision, castration and surface lesions of the limbs. They had to be superficial because the Egyptians, in spite of their skill as embalmers, were surprisingly unfamiliar with the deeper anatomy of the human body and for surgery knowledge of this kind is essential. What was true of the Egyptians was also true of all other people. Everywhere men instinctively revolted against the idea of dissecting the human body and in consequence of this the Babylonians, the ancient Jews and the Greeks were as ignorant of anatomy as were the Egyptians. At a later period Galen provided doctors with some information on this subject, but as he had only dissected the bodies of apes and pigs, his books were almost as misleading as they were helpful.

Surgery demands the following: (1) a precise knowledge of human anatomy; (2) a means of controlling the haemorrhage provoked by the operation; (3) some method of deadening pain, and (4) the control or, better still, the complete avoidance of post-operative infection. Modern surgery could not develop until these requirements were met. If, therefore, we are to understand the history of surgery we must start by investigating the foundations on which modern surgery rests, knowledge of the anatomy of the human body, the

avoidance of pain and the control of haemorrhage and post-operative infection. This chapter will be devoted to the story of anatomy and of the discovery of the means of dealing with haemorrhage.

THE HISTORY OF ANATOMY

In the Middle Ages the Church maintained a hostile attitude to the study of human anatomy and did everything within its power to discourage the carrying out of surgical operations. The Edict of Tours issued in 1163 declared categorically that the Church "abhorred the shedding of blood" (*"Ecclesia abhorret a sanguine"*). Two centuries later Pope Boniface VIII decreed that whoever cut up a human body or boiled parts of it in order to obtain human bones should fall under the ban of the Church. As a result of all these obstacles placed in the way of the study of anatomy and surgery, any operations which had to be done were carried out by barbers, sow-gelders, executioners, bath-house attendants and ignorant men of that kind. No respectable or educated person would have demeaned himself with such degrading work as surgery even if he had been willing to flout the views of the Church, which was unlikely, at a time when the Church was all powerful It is true that occasionally a barber-surgeon attained a certain amount of eminence but men such as Ambroise Paré were so rare that their influence on surgery was negligible.

In the latter half of the Middle Ages the Church seems to have slowly awakened to the fact that even physicians required some rudimentary knowledge of human anatomy, and the occasional dissection of a human body was permitted. The bodies used for that purpose—and they were very few—were those of executed criminals. Even then, a bargain was made between expediency and conscience. Before the executioner started to do his job, religious rites were performed over the selected criminal and special spiritual indulgences were allowed him in order to atone for the indignities about to be inflicted on his body. After the strangling act had been completed, the body was handed over to the university authorities and invitations were sent out to all prominent officials and gentry in the neighbourhood, inviting them to the dissection.

When those who wished to be present had taken their seats the Papal indulgence permitting the dissection was read aloud and the

seal of the university was affixed to the corpse. H. W. Haggard continues his description of the ceremony as follows: "Often as a preliminary to the dissection the subject's head was removed in accordance with the prejudice against exposing the brain, which according to the Christian conception was the seat of the soul. After these formalities an introductory oration was read and the physicians sang in chorus. Then came the dissection, which was a perfunctory affair. The physician in charge did not touch the body. Instead, it was opened by a servant, while the physician stood to one side and read aloud from Galen, pointing with a wand to the various structures as they were enumerated in the text. A celebration followed the dissection and there was a concert, banquet or theatrical performance. The whole affair occupied the greater part of two days and was concluded by ceremoniously burying the slightly mangled corpse." (H. W. Haggard, *Devils, Drugs and Doctors.* Heinemann, 1929.)

The dissections done by Vesalius at Padua were a turning point in the history of anatomy and a very marked difference is noticeable in the anatomical charts and diagrams issued before and after his time. Earlier anatomical engravings are almost always grossly inaccurate, whereas those produced after Vesalius had published his book are fairly reliable guides to the structure of the human body. In spite of the Church's concessions and of the stimulating influence of Vesalius, only slow progress was made in the subsequent teaching of anatomy owing to the perennial difficulty of obtaining bodies for dissection. So hard were they to come by that in the seventeenth century Rondelet, Professor of Anatomy at Montpelier University, was forced to make use of the body of his own dead child in order to demonstrate anatomy to his class. Yet little though the amount of human dissection was, that little provoked outbursts of public indignation against it. Even at so late a date as the end of the eighteenth century, a street mob attacked a building in which a certain Dr. Shippen, one of the founders of the University of Philadelphia, was demonstrating anatomy to a class of American medical students. On another occasion a gun was fired at this same unfortunate man as he was driving through Philadelphia. On this second occasion Dr. William Shippen only escaped murder by leaping out of his carriage and sprinting up a narrow alley.

In the nineteenth century the difficulty of obtaining bodies for

dissection still continued, even although the need for studying anatomy was by now more widely recognized. Now, good money can always be made by supplying what is badly needed and in 1827 two enterprising Edinburgh men, William Hare and William Burke, formed a partnership to find bodies for the anatomists. Their business started very gradually and at first without anything graver than a little dishonesty in dealing with the local authorities. One of the tenants of the house for vagrants run by Hare happened to die, owing to his landlord four pounds of rent. The parish authorities sent a coffin to the guest-house in which the old pauper's body was to be deposited, but Hare and his partner Burke filled this with tanner's bark instead and sold the body to Dr. Knox of the Edinburgh School of Anatomy. Nobody suffered as the result of this little deception and Hare and Burke enjoyed the pleasure of receiving for the body the nice sum of seven pounds ten shillings.

All parties had been delighted by this deal and in due course more bodies found their way by night to Edinburgh's famous Anatomy School. Everything might have continued satisfactorily for the ambitious Hare and Burke if they had confined their murders to obscure vagrants, whose disappearance would not be likely to attract any attention. But with bodies now worth ten pounds apiece, and an anatomist who was willing to take as many as could be delivered, the temptation proved too great for the partners. After the sudden disappearance from the streets of Mary Paterson, a well-known Edinburgh prostitute, and of "Daft Janie", an equally familiar figure to Edinburgh residents, enquiries were set on foot which led eventually to the arrest of Hare and Burke. Hare promptly turned King's Evidence, Burke was hanged, and the infuriated Edinburgh mob then turned its attention to the unfortunate anatomist, Dr. Knox, whose life was only saved by the prompt intervention of the police.

Dr. Robert Knox (1791–1862) was an inspiring teacher of anatomy and his classes became so famous that they numbered some five hundred people. His excellent demonstrations were attended not only by medical students and qualified doctors but also by noblemen, lawyers, artists and writers. The difficulties that Robert Knox now faced were considerable, for he must undoubtedly have wondered at times how Burke and Hare were

managing to lay their hands on so many high-class corpses. During the trial it was shown that as many as thirty-two people had been quietly suffocated by the two partners and that almost all of the bodies had found their way by night to the Edinburgh Anatomy School. Dr. Knox found himself in a very awkward position but he conducted himself in these difficult circumstances with the utmost coolness and bravery, and for a time it looked as though he had managed to weather the storm. He even resumed his anatomy classes for a few years and then quite suddenly, for some unknown reason, he retired, left Edinburgh in a hurry, and lived out the rest of his life in obscurity in London. Medical schools still lack a sufficient number of bodies for dissection.

The Control and the Treatment of Haemorrhage

The second basic requirement for satisfactory surgery was the discovery of some means of controlling bleeding and for remedying severe haemorrhage when it had occurred. The oldest and commonest method of stopping bleeding was by means of the cautery or by the application of hot pitch, but even so long ago as A.D. 1080 Roger of Palermo, Professor of Surgery at the famous Medical School of Salerno, made use of ligatures for this purpose. So also did the great Ambroise Paré advocate ligation and draw attention to the comfort of a man in whom haemorrhage had been arrested in this way, contrasted with the agony of a soldier whose wounds had been cauterized with pitch. Paré had even invented special artery forceps for application to bleeding points as a preliminary to tying these points off with ligatures. But in spite of the early introduction of these more merciful and efficient methods, many centuries had to pass before the brutal practice of cauterization was entirely abandoned. As so often happens in medicine, old inventions had to be rediscovered and reintroduced before they were generally accepted and it was only after Spencer Wells had redesigned Ambroise Paré's artery forceps and had brought them to the notice of the medical profession that they passed into general use.

Blood Transfusion

The remedying of collapse after a severe haemorrhage had occurred was a far more difficult problem to solve. Obviously the

best way of rectifying such an accident was to make good the patient's loss of blood, but how to do this puzzled medical men for many centuries. Prior to Harvey's discovery of the circulation of the blood, doctors had believed that something could be done to revive a patient by giving him human blood to drink, and this treatment was employed as late as the fifteenth century. An attempt was made to restore the strength of the aged Pontiff, Innocent VIII, by giving him fresh draughts of blood drawn from three vigorous boys, a treatment which ended disastrously with the death of the boys as well as of the Holy Father.

The first doctor to claim that he had actually carried out the difficult feat of transfusing blood into a vein was a Florentine physician, by name Francesco Folli, who published a book on the subject in 1680. Internal evidence disproves Folli's claim to be the originator of blood transfusion and all that his book does is to show that the subject of blood transfusion was being much discussed at that particular time. This is confirmed by other contemporary works of various kinds in which great interest in transfusion of blood is displayed by distinguished men of the calibre of Robert Boyle and Christopher Wren. Both of these men would appear to have carried out their own experiments on this subject.

There can be little doubt that the first man actually to carry out a successful transfusion, and then only on an animal, was an Oxford medical man named Richard Lower. His first efforts to transfuse blood from the jugular vein of one dog into that of another dog through a connecting tube ended in failure owing to clotting of blood in the tube. Lower then decided to unite an artery with a vein instead of a vein with a vein and he united the carotid artery of one dog with the jugular vein of another, making the connecting tube between them as short as possible. At first he employed a small length of quill for this purpose but afterwards he replaced this with a specially designed cannula. The following description of Lower's first successful transfusion is taken from his own book *Tractatus de Corde*.

"Having got ready the dogs, and made other preparations as required, I selected one dog of medium size, opened its jugular vein, and drew off blood, until it was quite clear from its howls and struggles that its strength was nearly gone and that convulsions were

not far off. Then to make up for the great loss of this dog by the blood of a second I introduced blood from the cervical artery of a fairly large mastiff, which had been fastened alongside the first dog, until this latter by its restiveness showed in its turn that it was over-filled and burdened by the amount of inflowing blood. I ligatured the artery from which the blood was passing and withdrew blood again from the receiving dog. This was repeated several times in succession.''

Lower explains that he was at pains to get his book printed as quickly as possible because "a certain Denys" was attempting to deprive him of priority in the matter of blood transfusion. The Denys to whom Lower refers so casually was no less a person than Dr. Jean Denys, Professor of Philosophy and mathematician at Montpellier, and physician to His Majesty Louis XIV. This distinguished French physician believed that depleted human beings could be restored to health by receiving blood from healthy animals and in 1667 he seems to have succeeded in transfusing about eight ounces of blood from a lamb into a boy with apparently excellent results. Encouraged by this success Denys repeated this treatment on another patient in the following year but this time with most unfortunate consequences. The patient died and his widow promptly brought a lawsuit against the professor. It is not surprising, therefore, that transfusion with animals' blood fell out of favour and that it was finally given up for good. We know now that the blood of an animal contains proteins which are totally incompatible with those of human blood. It is also known that the red corpuscles of an animal are rapidly destroyed in a man's blood serum, giving rise to serious anaphylactic phenomena. This means that transfusion with animal blood is not only useless but very dangerous. (*See* Plate 20.)

Mr. Samuel Pepys was a keen and intelligent observer of every-thing new, from witty plays and beautiful women to scientific in-ventions, and blood transfusion did not escape his notice. It will be of interest to look at these early experiments through his eyes. On November 14th, and in the year 1666, he made the following entry in his diary:

"Here (at the Pope's Head) Dr. Croone told me, that at the meeting of Gresham College tonight, . . . there was a pretty experi-ment of the blood of one dogg let out, till he died, into the body of

another on one side while all his own run out on the other side. The first died upon the place, and the other very well, and likely to do well. This did give occasion to many pretty wishes, as of the blood of a Quaker to be let into an Archbishop, and such like; but, as Dr. Croone says, may, if it takes, be of mighty use to man's health, for the amending of bad blood by borrowing from a better body."

A year later there is another entry in Pepys' diary:

"Among the rest they discourse of a man that is a little frantic, that hath been a kind of minister, Dr. Wilkins saying that he hath read for him in his church, that is a poor and a debauched man, that the College have hired for 20/– to have some of the blood of sheep let into his body; and it is to be done on Saturday next. They purpose to let in about twelve ounces; which they compute is what will be let in in a minute's time by a watch. They differ in the opinion they have of the effects of it, some think it may have a good effect upon him as a frantic man by cooling his blood, others that it will not have any effect at all. But the man is a healthy man, and by this means will be able to give an account what alteration, if any, he do find in himself, and so may be useful. . . ."

Eight days later Pepys dined with friends at a house of entertainment and made his final comment on transfusion:

"But here, above all, I was pleased to see the person who had his blood taken out. He speaks well, and did this day give the Society a relation thereof in Latin, saying that he finds himself much better since, and as a new man, but he is cracked a little in his head, though he speaks very reasonably and very well. He had but 20s. for his suffering it, and is to have the same again tried upon him: the first sound man that ever had it tried on him in England and but one that we hear of in France, which was a porter hired by the virtuosos."

Little or nothing happened now, so far as the transfusion of human blood was concerned, for a century and a half. The next date of any importance is 1818, the year in which a London medical man, Dr. Blundell, carried out, with the help of Henry Cline, a well-known surgeon, the first successful transfusion on a human being. The patient who was transfused was actually

moribund at the time that he received the new blood but he was temporarily revived by it. Dr. Blundell describes how the desperately ill patient received 12 to 14 ounces of blood from several donors during the course of half an hour, the blood being transferred rapidly from the donors to the recipient by means of syringes.

Blundell was sufficiently encouraged by what he had seen in this case to continue working patiently along the same lines, and in *The Lancet* for 1829 he was able to put on record the first human life to be saved by blood transfusion. The case was one of postpartem haemorrhage and the patient received eight ounces of blood taken by means of a syringe from the arm of Dr. Blundell's assistant. As a result of this treatment she completely recovered from the severe loss of blood she had recently suffered.

Throughout the whole history of this effort to transfuse blood the experimenters encountered the same difficulty, namely the liability of the blood to clot and to block the cannula, syringe or other instrument being used in the transfusion. Yet it may well be that the lives of some of these early patients were saved by this seemingly unfortunate accident, for nothing was known at that time about the existence of different types of human blood. This meant that the blood used for transfusion was often of an unsuitable nature. Not infrequently severe reactions were noted after transfusion but these were attributed to such minor accidents as the injection of air bubbles into the veins. It was not until 1901 that the existence of agglutinins in the blood was discovered simultaneously by two different researchers, Landsteiner in Vienna and Shattock in London. This gave a basis for the grouping of bloods and nine years later Jansky, working in Prague, described the existence of four types of human blood, which he called O, A, B and AB. As the group to which the donor and the recipient belonged could be determined in a few minutes by a comparatively simple test, the danger of mixing two incompatible types of blood was henceforth eliminated.

In spite of improvements in technique the difficulty of clotting still remained, and in the hope of avoiding this, attention was directed more and more to the use of anti-coagulents. In places as

far apart as Belgium, Buenos Aires and New York, researchers made trial of adding to the withdrawn blood weak solutions of potassium citrate and they published their results at the end of 1914 and during the early months of 1915. They had all come independently to the same conclusion, that an 0.2 per cent solution of sodium citrate was the best anti-coagulent available and that in this strength it could be considered non-toxic.

Nothing could have been more propitious than the discovery of an easier method of transfusion at that particular moment in history. Europe was now at war and thousands of wounded men were dying from haemorrhage on the battlefields of France, Belgium, Italy, Russia and Poland. A splendid opportunity was therefore offered doctors for testing out the value of blood transfusion and fortunately there were consultants now attached to the various medical services who would see that it was given a fair trial. But it was not until the early months of 1917 that the citrate method of transfusion was sufficiently developed for use on a large scale in the clearing stations of the British Army in France. A Canadian medical officer, Oswald Robertson, did a great deal to popularize this technique and there can be no doubt that thousands of lives were thereby saved. And not only lives, but limbs also, for a wounded man who has suffered a profuse haemorrhage offers far less resistance to invading organisms than does a man with a full complement of blood. Haemorrhage and sepsis are found to be very closely associated and by promptly making good loss of blood, wounds can often be protected from severe infection.

The great majority of the transfusions were carried out in the casualty clearing stations but there were many men who died from haemorrhage before they could reach these stations. Efforts were therefore made to remedy this. At that time those of us doing research on this subject believed that the valuable element in a transfusion was the blood corpuscles rather than the plasma, and Dr. Robertson devised a method of decanting off the blood corpuscles and preserving them in a solution of glucose. A large number of bottles of preserved blood corpuscles were therefore kept at a low temperature in the dug-outs of a casualty clearing station in the neighbourhood of Doullens for men in urgent need of transfusion. This casualty clearing station was also the headquarters of the Third

Army "Shock Centre" in which the writer of this book was carrying out his researches. In order to make a test of the value of transfusion in the forward area he attended all the trench raids in that section of the line, encumbered by a very large wooden box slung from his neck by a leather strap. In this box were two bottles of preserved corpuscles packed in ice, ready to be diluted with warmed saline and to be used as a transfusion. This effort to introduce blood transfusion into the front line trenches had an excellent effect on the morale of the raiders, but it has to be confessed that the difficult conditions met with in the trenches prevented it from ever becoming a very effective method of treatment.

Great advances have been made in the preserving and storing of blood since those crude efforts of the First World War, and before the outbreak of its successor, the Second World War, the Emergency Transfusion Service came into being. This service established "blood banks" all over the country and efficiency was still further increased by the discovery of a process whereby the plasma of the blood could be dried and stored in the form of a powder. This dried blood plasma which contained all that was usually required for resuscitation was readily portable, and it was suitable for use with all four blood groups. It provided therefore the ideal material for blood transfusion in difficult circumstances and was exactly what the writer had lacked in the trenches during the First World War.

Haemorrhage is no longer a grave anxiety to the surgeon and if he is of the opinion that the patient on whom he is operating has lost more blood than he can afford to lose, he orders a transfusion to be carried out on the operating table whilst the operation is being completed. Blood is kept in all the big hospitals ready for use or, if fresh blood is thought desirable rather than stored blood, a donor of the right group can be sent for and the blood drawn off. Two different researchers, Jansky and Moss, distinguished the blood groups by certain figures but unfortunately they numbered them differently so that the figures allotted by Jansky to the universal donor was that given by Moss to the universal recipient, and vice versa. This led to confusion and even to the accident of transfusing with the wrong blood. For this reason a new international code has been agreed upon and the four groups are now known by letters;

they are called AB (universal recipient), A, B, and O (universal donor).

In the following chapter the other two requirements of surgery, namely the prevention of pain and the avoidance of post-operative infection, will be dealt with.

CHAPTER XI

The Conquest of Pain

IT is the futility of pain which has distressed so many people, the persistent throb of a tooth throughout the long hours of the night for no apparent purpose. Yet pain has always a meaning at the start, even if it seems to lose this later. It is Nature's alarm, her method of calling our attention to the fact that something is amiss with us. It is also her means of ensuring that the damaged or diseased structure is rested and that conditions are made favourable for the action of her healing forces. It was said that pain was purposeful at the start for it has to be admitted that this signal of distress is sometimes unduly prolonged so that it continues sounding long after the injured man is fully aware that his leg is broken. Pain then becomes an obstacle to the patient's recovery by exhausting him and depriving him of much-needed sleep.

The first duty that the doctor is often called upon to fulfil is that of finding some means of relieving his patient of his pain and this he usually does by giving a sedative drug. From the earliest times man has sought for pain-relieving remedies and two of the first drugs of this kind to be used were mandragora and Indian hemp or hashish. The Egyptians believed that mandragora was the gift to medicine of no less a person than Ra, their Sun-God. The Roman herbalist and physician Dioscorides gives the following instructions for its use. "Boil down the roots in wine to a third part, and preserve the juice thus procured and give one cyathus of it to cause the insensibility of those who are to be cut or cauterised."

The mandrake plant has a long tap-root, often bifid, so that it roughly resembles a human figure. This probably gave rise to the superstition that it shrieked when uprooted and that its shriek brought about the death of those who heard it, or, if it did not

206

actually kill them, rendered them insane. For this reason the root
was merely loosened by the collector and then attached by a cord
to the collar of his dog. Through the dog's struggle to get away, the
root was freed from the earth. "Therefore," declares an old document,
"they did tye some dogge or other living beast unto the roots
thereof with a corde . . . and in the mean tyme stopped there own
ears for fear of the terrible shriek and cry of the mandrake. In
which cry it doth not only dye itselfe but the feare thereof killeth
the dogge. . . ." (*See* Plate 17.)

Mandrake was the most popular anaesthetic during the Middle
Ages and in the Elizabethan Age it was still being used as a narcotic,
as the following lines from Shakespeare show:

> "Give me to drink mandragora. . . .
> That I might sleep out this great gap of time
> My Antony is away."
>> (*Antony and Cleopatra*)

> "Or have we eaten on the insane root
> That takes the reason prisoner?"
>> (*Macbeth*)

The other drug, hashish, is of equally venerable age and when
Amos wrote (about 700 B.C.) on the subject of "the wine of the
condemned", he was probably referring to it. Herodotus relates that
hashish was not only eaten but that it was sometimes inhaled, and
if this statement is correct hashish inhalation must be looked upon
as being the first of all the inhalation anaesthetics.

Opium is also a very ancient narcotic drug and it was introduced
into medicine by the Chinese. Shakespeare refers to the combined
use of mandragora and of opium in *Othello*:

> ". . . not poppy, nor mandragora,
> Nor all the drowsy syrups of the world,
> Shall ever medicine thee to that sweet sleep
> Which thou ow'dst yesterday."

In *Romeo and Juliet* Shakespeare again speaks of the giving of a
narcotic draught and describes the effect it would have on Juliet

with such accuracy that he would almost seem to have experienced
the drowsiness following the use of the narcotic himself:

"This distilled liquor drink thou off:
When, presently, through all thy veins shall run
A cold and drowsy humour; for no pulse
Shall keep his native progress, but surcease."

Dioscorides refers to the taking of an alcoholic extract of
mandragora prior to an operation and this suggests that it was quite
usual for the Greek surgeons of ancient Rome to mitigate the pain
of an operation by giving their patients sedative drugs. Apuleius,
who wrote about A.D. 200, confirms this. "If anyone is to have a
member mutilated, burned or sawed let him drink half an ounce
with wine, and let him sleep till the member is cut away without
any pain or sensation." But for some reason this humane practice
of drugging a person before operating on him was abandoned during
the Middle Ages, the most likely explanation of this being that the risk
of giving an overdose was considered to be too great to justify it.
This was undoubtedly the conclusion reached in France for there is
a seventeenth-century document which gives an account of a barber-
surgeon, named Nicolas Bailly, who was arrested and tried for
witchcraft because he had administered a strong narcotic before
operating on one of his patients.

Although opiates were forbidden in France, cruder and much
less effective methods of stupefying patients seem to have been
considered justifiable there. The pleasantest of these alternatives
to the use of narcotic drugs was to make the patient drunk and the
unpleasantest was to throttle him. In the fifteenth and sixteenth
centuries it was realized that men and animals could be rendered
insensible by pressing on their carotid arteries so that their brains
were deprived of fresh blood. Paré occasionally made use of this
compression method as did also a certain Dr. Moore, a surgeon who
practised much later, in 1784. Surgeons also brought about the
local numbing of limbs prior to operating on them by the use of
tight tourniquets, and John Hunter suggested that the same effect
could be obtained and with less damage to the patient's limb by the
application of extreme cold. But the difficulties of putting into

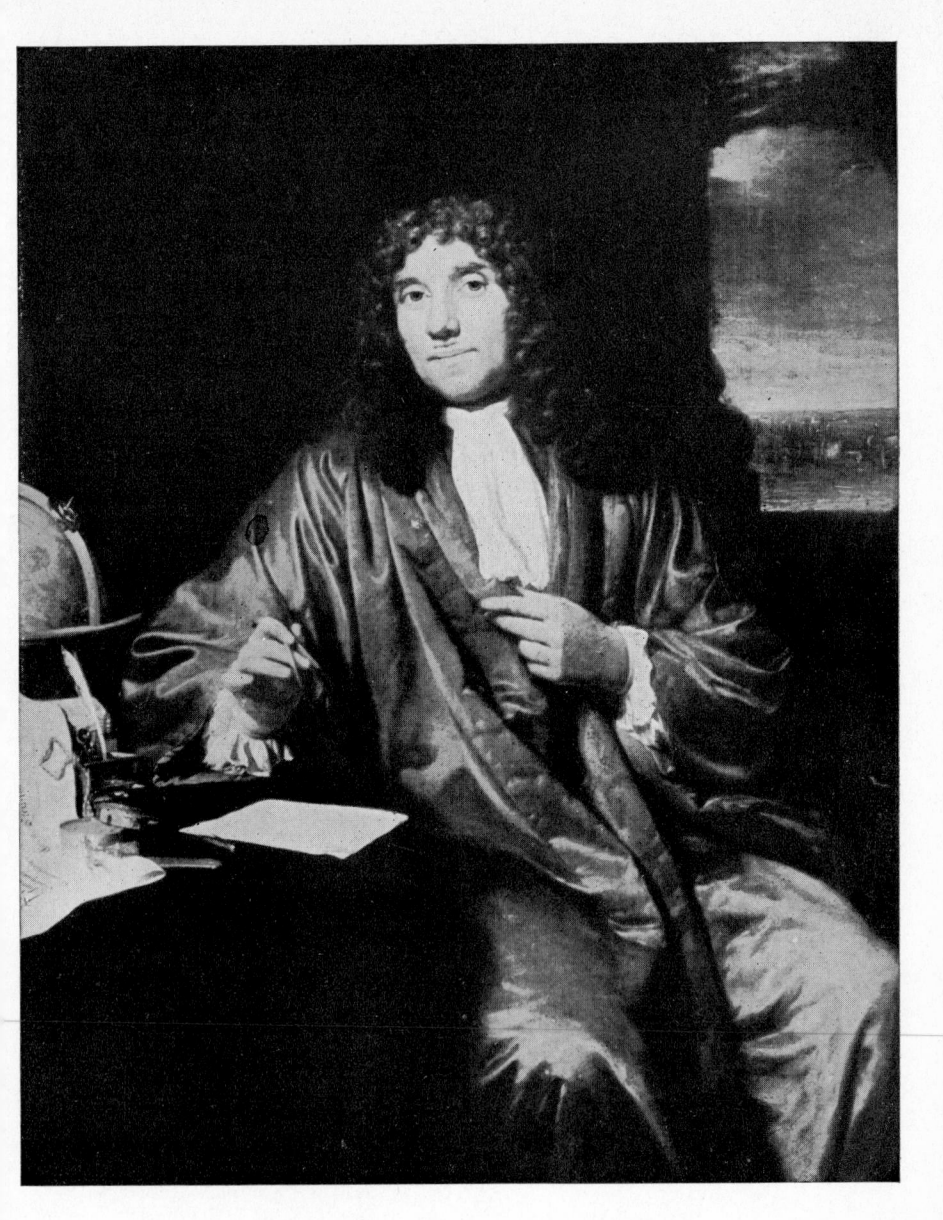

Anton van Leeuwenhoek, F.R.S.
(Portrait by J. Verkolje in the Rijks-Museum, Amsterdam)

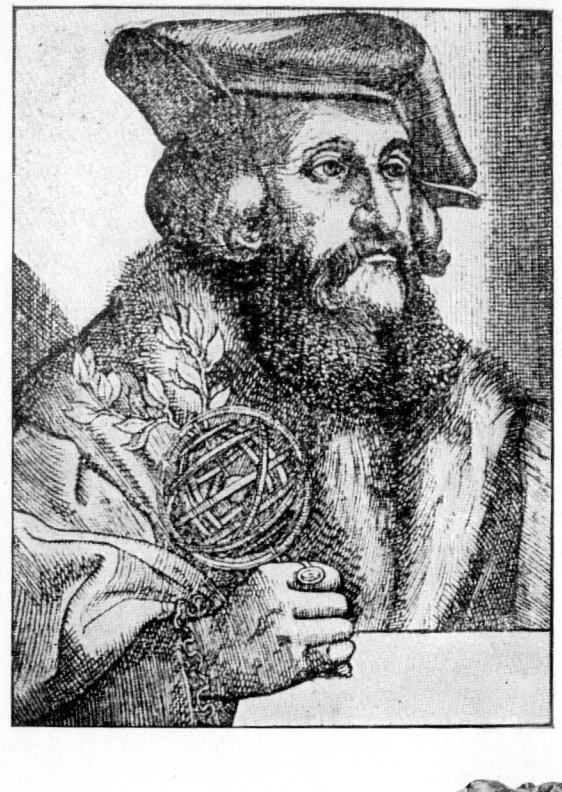

Hieronymus
Fracastorius
(From a contemporary woodcut)

Jenner vaccinating James
Phipps
(Bronze by Monteverde in the
Wellcome Museum)

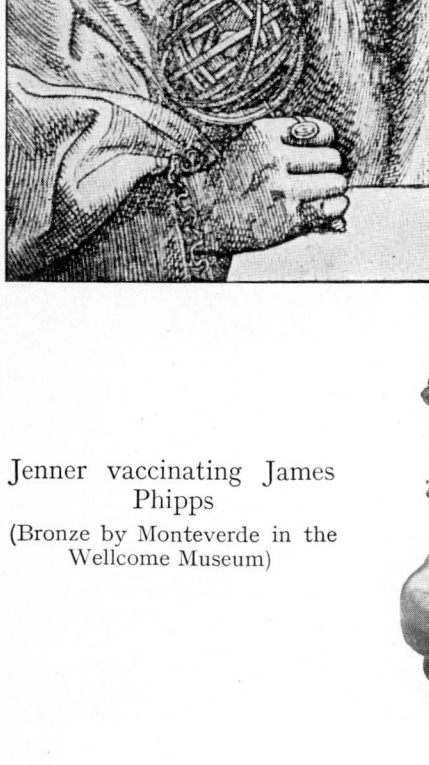

practice this anaesthesis by means of cold were found to be so great that it was soon abandoned.

The intense sufferings of a patient during an operation threw a great strain on the operating surgeon as well as on the patient himself and from contemporary biographies we learn how neither Abernethy nor Sir Charles Bell "could think of an operation without heart sickness". It was also said that John Hunter "turned pale as death" whenever he used the knife. The only way of reducing the strain was to complete the operation within a minimum of time, a requirement which was not always conducive to good surgery. The speed with which the surgeons of pre-anaesthetic days carried out their work is almost incredible. It is said that William Cheselden (1688–1752) was able to perform the operation of lithotomy (the removal of a stone from the bladder) in a minute, and that on one occasion he managed it in fifty-four seconds. Napoleon's great surgeon, Larrey (1766–1842), personally performed two hundred amputations of limbs by the circular flap method during the battle of Borodino alone.

How severe an ordeal an operation was to the patient in pre-anaesthesia days may be gathered from the very restrained account of such an operation given by a medical man who had evidently undergone it himself. This account is to be found in a letter written to Dr. Simpson, the discoverer of chloroform, in the year 1848.

"Before the days of anaesthetics a patient preparing for an operation was like a condemned criminal preparing for execution. He counted the days till the appointed day came. He counted the hours of that day till the appointed hour came. He listened for the echo in the street of the surgeon's carriage. He watched for his pull at the door bell, for his foot on the stair, for his step in the room, for the production of his dreaded instruments, for his few grave words and his last preparations before beginning; and then he surrendered his liberty and, revolting at the necessity, submitted to be held or bound, and helplessly gave himself up to the cruel knife."

That special branch of medicine now known as "anaesthetics" may be said to date from the day on which Sir Humphry Davy, the inventor of the miner's lamp, discovered the anaesthetic properties

of "laughing gas". The way in which this happened can be recounted in his own words. "In cutting one of the unlucky teeth, called the *dentes sapientiae*, I experienced an extensive inflammation of the gums, accompanied with great pain, which equally destroyed the power of repose and of consistent action. On the day when the inflammation was most troublesome I breathed three large doses of nitrous oxide. The pain always diminished after the first four or five inspirations, the thrilling came on as usual, and uneasiness was for a few moments swallowed up in pleasure. As the former stage of mind returned, the state of the organ returned with it and I at once imagined that the pain was more severe after the experiment than before." Sir Humphry Davy brought the matter to the notice of the medical profession and for a time "laughing gas" and its properties became a subject of great interest. But inhaling "laughing gas" was regarded as being a kind of parlour game rather than as a practical method of producing anaesthesia and in Great Britain no medical man made any further use of it. Had it not been for action taken in America the anaesthetic properties of nitrous oxide might well have been forgotten.

The first man to employ nitrous oxide for anaesthetic purposes was Dr. Riggs, a dentist living in the United States. Dr. Riggs attended a course of public lectures in which the intoxicating action of "laughing gas" was demonstrated by the lecturer. He was much impressed by what he had seen and afterwards discussed the anaesthetic properties of this new gas with an acquaintance and fellow dentist of his, a Dr. Wells. "Why cannot the gas be used for extracting teeth?" asked the latter, and straight away they decided to put the matter to the test. Next day a bag of the gas was obtained from the lecturer and, in Dr. Riggs' words: "Dr. Wells, after seating himself in the operating chair, took the bag and inhaled the gas and after he had been brought sufficiently under its influence he threw back his head and I extracted the tooth. . . . It required great force to extract it. Dr. Wells did not manifest any sensibility to pain. He remained under the influence of the gas for some time after, and immediately upon recovering from it, he swung his hands and exclaimed, 'A new era in tooth-pulling'." So runs Dr. Riggs' laconic account of the operation to be performed under a general anaesthetic.

Delighted with his own experience of it, Dr. Wells gave a number of demonstrations of nitrous oxide anaesthesia to his colleagues and in a comparatively short time the great value of the gas was established. But nitrous oxide gave too transitory an anaesthesia to be suitable for long operations and a search was immediately begun for some other gas or vapour which would have a more lasting effect. Ether was known to possess anaesthetic properties and Doctors Jackson and Morton of Boston, the former a chemist and the.latter a dentist, both claimed to be the discoverer of it. For many years a bitter controversy raged between these two men as to who had hit upon the anaesthetic properties of ether first, the truth probably being that they had made the discovery about the same time, but that Dr. Morton, encouraged by Dr. Jackson's experiments with nitrous oxide, had been the first to use it in dental practice. Actually neither of these two rivals could claim that he had actually discovered the anaesthetic properties of ether vapour for these had been described long previously by Sir Humphry Davy's great pupil, Michael Faraday. Faraday had rendered both animals and human volunteers unconscious with ether vapour but he had never gone any further and advocated its use as an anaesthetic because he believed that ether was too dangerous for such purposes. The history of the two anaesthetics, nitrous oxide and ether, was therefore precisely the same. In both cases the anaesthetic properties of the preparations had originally been discovered in England but no further use had been made of them. It was left to American enterprise to demonstrate their properties in medicine.

Dr. Morton must be credited with having been the first to realize the value of ether vapour as a general anaesthetic. The subject of his first experiment was his own pet spaniel, and having learnt to render his dog unconscious with ether he tried it out on his friends. Finally he anaesthetized himself. By the autumn of that year, 1846, he was so confident of his capacity to render anybody unconscious by this excellent method that he readily accepted an invitation to give ether to a patient in the Massachusetts General Hospital. It was a great event in his life and also in the history of anaesthesia, this first administration of a general anaesthetic in a large hospital. Morton was late in arriving at the hospital and those who were being kept waiting began to bandy sarcastic comments

on the subject of Dr. Morton and his ether anaesthesia. Then suddenly the absent anaesthetist made a dramatic entry into the operating theatre and without any delay he started to anaesthetize his patient. In the words of the hospital records, "after four or five minutes the patient appeared to be asleep, and the operation (the cutting out of a tumour) was performed. . . . To the surprise of Dr. Warren and the other gentlemen present, the patient did not shriek or cry". It was a great moment in the history of American medicine, this performance of an operation of a more formidable nature than the extraction of a tooth under a general anaesthetic, but it is unlikely that anyone present in the operating theatre that day realized the full importance of the occasion. (*See* Plate 18.)

The first surgical operation to be carried out in Great Britain under ether vapour was at University College Hospital, London, and Sir R. Reynolds, who was present at it, writes of it as follows: "Liston had consented to try the anaesthetic: I can see him now as he said to his students: 'Gentlemen, we are now going to try a Yankee dodge for making men insensible.' . . . At length Peter Square said, 'He is ready now, sir.' Liston's knife flashed in the air: I took out my watch to count the time, and the leg was on the floor in six and twenty seconds. Liston turned to his students and said, 'This Yankee dodge, gentlemen, beats mesmerism.'" The curtness of the comment and the restraint of the report are thoroughly British.

The next scene in this story of the general anaesthetics is in Edinburgh and in the house of Dr. Simpson, a well-known Edinburgh gynaecologist. As a student Simpson had watched Liston operate on a Highland woman without any anaesthetic and he had never forgotten what he had been forced to witness on that occasion. When therefore ether was introduced into England from America he immediately adopted it and used it in his obstetric practice. But he had not found ether entirely satisfactory in gynaecological work and he was now investigating other vapours that might possibly have anaesthetic properties. As his practice was a very large one the only time available for making trial of these vapours was usually at the end of a long day's work. The story of Simpson's discovery of the anaesthetic properties of chloroform has been told in a variety of ways, but the following account taken from a

description given by Dr. Simpson's colleague, Professor Miller, is likely to be reliable. "Late one evening—it was the 4th of November 1847—on returning home after a weary day's work, Dr. Simpson, with his two friends and assistants, Drs. Keith and Duncan, sat down to their somewhat hazardous work in Dr. Simpson's dining-room. Having inhaled several substances, but without much effect, it occurred to Dr. Simpson to try a ponderous material which he had formerly set aside on a lumber table, and which on account of its great weight, he had hitherto regarded as of no likelihood whatever. *That* happened to be a small bottle of chloroform. It was searched for and recovered from beneath a heap of waste paper. And with each tumbler newly charged the inhalers resumed their vocation. Immediately an unwonted hilarity seized the party; they became bright-eyed, very happy and very loquacious— expatiating on the delicious aroma of the new fluid. The conversation was of unusual intelligence, and quite charmed the listeners— some ladies of the family and a naval officer, brother-in-law of Dr. Simpson.

"But suddenly there was a talk of sounds being heard like those of a cotton mill, louder and louder; a moment more and then all was quiet—and then *crash*. The inhaling party slipped off their chairs and flopped on to the floor unconscious." (*See* Plate 17.)

Professor Miller's report of the happenings of that night is a very full one and ends with a description of the experiences of each of the participants in the inhalation game as he or she "went under" and "came to". The lady previously mentioned as being one of the party was a niece of Mrs. Simpson, and in her report she states that she fell asleep quietly with her arms folded across her breast and in the very act of exclaiming: "I'm an angel! Oh I'm an angel." Everybody was delighted with the properties of the new vapour and Dr. Simpson himself was so satisfied that within a fortnight he had administered it to at least fifty of his patients. The results had been uniformly excellent.

Yet chloroform could not be introduced into medical practice in Scotland without provoking an outcry against it. Many people protested that its use in child-labour was contrary to all biblical teaching, for had not God said to Eve: "In sorrow thou shalt bring forth children"? Chloroform was, therefore, denounced from many

a pulpit and in no uncertain terms. It was a "decoy of Satan," thundered one divine, "apparently offering itself to bless women; but in the end it will harden something and rob God of the deep and earnest cries which arise in time of trouble for help". Now, every Scot is something of a theologian and on hearing that his chloroform had been called a decoy of the Evil One, Simpson retorted that in the Holy Book could be found a full report of the first operation to be carried out under deep anaesthesia: "And the Lord God caused a deep sleep to fall upon Adam, and he slept; and He took one of his ribs and closed up the flesh instead thereof." This suggestion that God had created a precedent by making use of anaesthesia in His own work satisfied only a small section of the opposition and, as everybody knows, it was Queen Victoria who finally settled the ethics of the question by having chloroform administered to herself during the delivery of her seventh child, Prince Leopold. The announcement of this in the press was received with astonishment and grief, and even *The Lancet* was disturbed by it. The comment made by the Editor in May 1843 was as follows: "In no case could it be justifiable to administer chloroform in a perfectly ordinary labour." Yet the good Queen had allowed this and what the good Queen did was generally right. Again in 1857 the Queen accepted chloroform at her next confinement and thereafter chloroform became known in Great Britain as "anaesthesia *á la Reine*". The use of chloroform in childbirth was now considered fashionable and what was fashionable soon became moral.

LOCAL ANAESTHESIA

The idea of producing a local anaesthesia without any general loss of consciousness was never entirely set aside by surgeons. The older attempts to obtain it by compressing the pain nerves with a tourniquet and by the application of cold to the area about to be operated upon had not been very successful but it was believed that eventually a new and more satisfactory technique would be found. Later this belief was justified by the introduction of cocaine into medical practice. Cocaine is yet another example of a remedy coming from a primitive and ancient source. We owe it to the Incas of Peru who regarded the coca-plant with great veneration and made offerings of its leaves to their Sun God. The priests also

made a practice of chewing these leaves and, according to an old legend, they were capable of performing almost incredible feats of endurance whilst under its influence. And quite apart from legend, the modern Peruvians recognized that chewing the leaves of the "divine plant of the Incas" warded off hunger and fatigue. It was the custom in Peru to open up old Inca graves in the hope of recovering from them ancient and precious relics, and whilst doing this the excavators were very liable to develop sore throats due to the inhaling of the fine dust into which the uncovered bodies immediately crumbled on being exposed to the air. In order to guard against these sore throats those who were engaged in the digging usually chewed coca-leaves and it was mainly through this habit of theirs that the notice of European travellers was drawn to the medicinal properties of the coca-plant.

The first man to use cocaine for medical purposes was the Viennese surgeon Koller, who in 1884 discovered that it was of great value as a local anaesthetic in eye operations. But we owe almost all further developments in cocaine anaesthesia to the enterprise and the ingenuity of American surgeons. Solutions of cocaine were first injected into nerve endings by the American surgeon W. S. Halstead (1852), and three years later J. L. Corning introduced the technique known as spinal anaesthesia. This valuable method of employing cocaine consists of injecting it into the spinal canal so that it produces complete anaesthesia of the nerves lying below the level of the injection. The American surgeon, G. W. Crile, combined spinal anaesthesia with general anaesthesia, thereby reducing the shock of an operation. Chemists were not long in discovering the chemical structure of cocaine and for many years they have been synthesizing a number of new compounds of a similar nature to cocaine but much less toxic.

The story of anaesthesia is therefore very closely linked with medical progress in the New World. Not only were American surgeons much quicker to realize the great potentialities of nitrous oxide and ether as general anaesthetics, not only were they more enterprising in developing local anaesthesia than we were, but cocaine, the drug first used in local anaesthesia, came originally from the New World. We also owe to the Incas of Peru a preparation which is now being used on a big scale in conjunction with anaesthetics, the drug known

as *curare*. One of the requirements of the modern surgeon is that the muscles of the patient on whom he is operating should be fully relaxed, and the muscles of modern urbanized man are very seldom in this condition even when he is asleep. Curare possesses the special property of paralysing the nerve endings in the muscles and when the anaesthetist finds it impossible to obtain a good muscular relaxation by his anaesthetic alone he gives the patient an injection of this drug. It was used long ago by the old hunters of Peru who dipped their arrow heads in the poison because they found that by doing so they lost fewer of their arrows through the wounded prey escaping. The poison acted by being absorbed from the wound into the animal's blood stream and by quickly bringing about a paralysis of its muscles.

The administration of an anaesthetic has now become such a skilled proceeding that anaesthetics is recognized as a speciality in medicine. It is moreover a speciality which is of immense importance to the modern surgeon, who has made such spectacular advances during the last fifty years that he has been able to enter into areas of the body into which his predecessors would not have dared to intrude, into regions such as the brain, the chest cavity, the heart, the lungs and the great blood vessels. This remarkable surgical progress could never have been made had it not been for the parallel advances being made in the speciality of anaesthesia. (*See* Plates 28 and 29.)

CHAPTER XII

The Mastery of Wound Infection

THE final obstacle to satisfactory surgery to be removed was wound infection, and it was a far more formidable one than most people of today realize. We are so accustomed to hear of the uninterrupted healing of operation wounds and of our friends recovering without the occurrence of any complications that we are unable to realize how different everything was in pre-Listerian days. Not many years ago healing by the process known as "first intention", that is to say, without any inflammation, was the exception rather than the rule. What made post-operative infection particularly exasperating to the pre-Listerian surgeon was that general anaesthesia was permitting him to undertake operations which had previously been rendered quite impossible on account of the pain they entailed. But new developments in surgery were stifled because the further the surgeon extended his field, the greater was the risk he ran of post-operative infection. So serious was that risk that Sir James Simpson, the discoverer of chloroform, once said: "The man laid on an operating table in one of our surgical hospitals is exposed to more chances of death than was the English soldier on the field of Waterloo." And it was quite true that at that time an operation was almost invariably followed by fever and pain. Sir Hector Cameron, another surgeon of that period, wrote that patients in the surgical wards "only reached the terra firma of convalescence by swimming for their lives throughout weeks or months of severe and painful illness. Secondary haemorrhage, lock-jaw, erysipelas, blood-poisonings of various kinds and hospital gangrene were never absent from the hospital wards at any time; and repeated hospital gangrene and pyaemia—a most fatal form of blood-poisoning—became alarmingly epidemic."

Nothing could be done to prevent this deadly wound infection and this being so it seemed highly unlikely that the surgeon would ever be able to extend much further the field of his art. "What then is the surgeon to do?" asked Dr. Charles Bell, a distinguished nineteenth-century Edinburgh surgeon. "Is he to try experiments with ointments and plasters while the men are dying around him? Is he to seek for washes and dressings to cure such a disease as this? . . . NO! Let him bear this always in mind, that no dressings have ever been found to stop an ulcer, that no quantities of bark or wine, which a man can bear, have ever retarded this gangrene; let him bear in mind that this is a *hospital* disease, that without the circle of the infected walls the men are safe; let him therefore hurry them out of the house of death; let him change the wards; let him take possession of some empty house and so carry his patients into good air." (*Joseph Lister* by Hector Cameron. London, 1948.) If this was all the surgeon could do to curtail infection then indeed he was in a desperate situation.

JOSEPH LISTER

It was upon this scene of surgical despair that Joseph Lister entered when in 1860 he took up his post of Regius Professor of Systematic Surgery in the University of Glasgow. It happened that the problem of inflammation had long been uppermost in Lister's mind and that he had already done a little modest research on the subject of inflammatory reactions in the tissues. He accepted the prevalent idea expressed by Charles Bell that the terrible mortality rate in the surgical wards of the hospitals was due to the atmosphere of the wards being charged with something difficult to define, but that could be called "a poisonous miasma". It was only after a talk with Dr. Thomas Anderson, the Professor of Chemistry in Glasgow, that new ideas on this subject began to form in Lister's mind. Dr. Anderson referred in this talk to the interesting experiments being made in France by the chemist Pasteur and, acting on his advice, Lister obtained and carefully studied the reports of the Frenchman's work on micro-organisms. After reading the account of Pasteur's experiments Lister saw a much clearer meaning in the rather vague term "poisonous miasma". It was not so much the physical air that caused the spread of suppuration in the surgical

wards of a hospital as the content of microbic life with which that air was charged. Lister set himself the task of finding out how the microbe-ridden air and also how everything used in an operation, such as the surgeon's hands, his instruments and his ligatures, could be rid of these ubiquitous and poisonous forms of life.

Pasteur had already given some indication of how this could be brought about by demonstrating that organisms could be destroyed in three different ways—by heat, by filtration and by the use of antiseptics. Sterilization by filtration and by heat seemed to have very little application to the particular problem on which he, Lister, was now engaged so he devoted his time to the search for a suitable chemical antiseptic. Eventually he chose for his purposes crude carbolic acid and decided to experiment first with cases of compound fracture of the leg. He chose compound fractures to work with because they invariably suppurated badly and often ended in gangrene and the amputation of the limb. Lister believed that the reason why compound fractures became so badly infected was that the open wound acted as a gateway for the entry of germs into the deeper tissues of the leg. His problem, as he now saw it, was to devise some substitute for the barrier of skin that had been destroyed, something in the form of a dressing which would prevent the invasion of the wound by air-borne organisms. After cleansing the skin around the compound fracture very carefully, Lister placed over the wound a piece of lint soaked in crude carbolic acid, making the lint dressing sufficiently large to overlap it in every direction. In order to reduce the evaporation of the carbolic acid he covered the lint with a thin sheet of lead or tin, keeping the whole of these dressings in place with strips of adhesive plaster. These first ventures of his in antisepsis were very crude and the disadvantages associated with them soon became obvious. The impure carbolic acid caused intense irritation of the patient's skin, leading sometimes even to ulceration, and it was only after a purer carbolic acid had been obtained and other modifications had been made in his technique that this skin irritation was avoided.

Another thing which required investigation was how to sterilize the objects that came into contact with the wound during the course of an operation or even subsequently, such as the surgeon's hands, his instruments, the ligatures he inserted and the sponges he used

for mopping up blood. All of these points were carefully gone into and various methods of disinfection experimented with. The work was very arduous but the quick drop in the severity of post-operative infection in his ward more than compensated him for all this extra trouble.

Lister's first attempt to expound his antiseptic principles to his medical colleagues took the form of a series of articles which he published in *The Lancet*, articles in which were recorded his successes in the antiseptic treatment of compound fractures. Unfortunately Lister found great difficulty in putting anything down clearly on paper and his articles in *The Lancet* misled his readers as much as they instructed them. He managed to give them the impression that he was merely advocating the use of a carbolic acid in the treatment of compound fractures and as a result of this the far-reaching implications of his work were entirely missed by most of his readers. What made things worse was that *The Lancet*, which had at first supported him, now joined his critics, already both numerous and formidable. The great Sir James Simpson, the discoverer of chloroform, showed a singular lack of generosity towards his younger colleague and declared that there was nothing novel in any of Dr. Lister's ideas, even if they could be proved to be true, which was highly unlikely. In 1869 Lister added further to his troubles by daring to criticize conditions in the Royal Infirmary and by making too free a use of the word "pestilential" in his article. He went so far as to say that the conditions in the infirmary were so sickening and so heart-rending "as to make him (Lister) question the desirability of being attached to such an institution". He seems to have been surprised and alarmed at the amount of indignation evoked by his remarks on the subject of the Royal Infirmary and he attempted, a little belatedly, to pour oil on the troubled waters. "I rejoice to find," he replied in the correspondence columns of *The Lancet*, "that taking the results of the practice of all the four surgeons in the hospital, the death rate during the three years of the antiseptic period has been less, by fully one-fifth, than during the five previous years".

And Lister's statement about the fall in the mortality from infection was quite true. Slowly the effects of his new technique of operating were becoming apparent to those who had adopted it,

but the opposition to what was now known as "Listerism" was still formidable. Many of his opponents seemed to be under the impression that all that Lister had done was to have invented and recommended the use of a carbolic acid spray. It was essential that this limited view of his work should be corrected and at the International Medical Congress in London in 1881 he emphasized the fact that he had introduced improvements of great importance in other parts of his antiseptic operating technique. He added, "I am not prepared to say that our increased uniformity of beneficial results may not be due to this. . . . And it may be, for all I know to the contrary, that when the International Congress next meets I shall be able to speak of results of a still higher order, obtained without using the spray at all."

As the danger of post-operative infection receded Lister was able to advance into regions of the body into which surgeons had hitherto not dared to enter. He opened joints and wired broken bones with a daring that would have been followed by disastrous results had he acted similarly in former days. Some of his friends chided him for not reporting these new operations in the medical press but he did not do so because he knew full well that if other surgeons were to follow his example without using his new antiseptic technique scrupulously, their patients would undoubtedly die of sepsis. This was the busiest period of Lister's life, for he was carrying out bacteriological experiments in his small laboratory at home as well as operating on a great number of patients at the infirmary. He had also established contact now by letter with the great French genius on whose brilliant researches the whole of his operative technique rested. In one of Pasteur's replies he pointed out to Lister an error which he was making and advised him to change the form of experiment being used. "Next to the promulgation of truth," wrote Pasteur, "the best thing I can conceive that a man can do is the recantation of a published error."

Lister's thesis and his methods were by now being adopted by more and more surgeons, both abroad and in his own country—and particularly abroad. He was no longer alone, for several of the most eminent of the continental surgeons had reported favourably on his methods. In an address delivered in 1875 Von Nussbaum of Munich said: "Lister's treatment is already greeted by the whole civilized

world as an enormous advance. Everything new receives criticism, but such proofs can be obtained from it that one has no use for any words but those of gratitude and admiration. . . . Look now at my sick wards, recently ravaged by death. I can only say that I, and my assistants and my nurses, are overwhelmed with joy, and undertake all the extra trouble the treatment entails with the greatest zeal. The happiest mood possesses us, while before we went about hanging our heads. What wonders of conservative surgery has the future in store for us!''

From many other places there came similar reports and when Lister went abroad now, as he frequently did, in order to address a medical meeting or to visit a continental clinic, he was received there with acclamation. In 1877 the professorship of clinical surgery at King's College, London, fell vacant and an effort was made to get Lister appointed to it, but without success. Soon afterwards another post was specially created for him at the same hospital, a post which he accepted after much hesitation. And he was right to have hesitated, for his reception on reaching King's College was distinctly chilly, not only from his colleagues on the surgical staff but also from the sisters and nurses of his own ward. The latter had little relish for Lister's new-fangled methods and they were quietly and courteously obstructive to him. Before he had accepted his new post Lister had insisted on being allowed to bring with him from Edinburgh—and this was one of the reasons for his chilly reception at King's College Hospital—four young surgical helpers, Watson Cheyne, John Stewart, Dobie and Altham, and one of these young men has put on record the difficulties they met with in London. ''We four unhappy men wandered about, now in the wards of King's, now through the older and more famous hospitals, and wondered why men did not open their eyes. In these wards the air was heavy with the odour of suppuration, the shining eye and flushed cheek spoke eloquently of surgical fever. We would show them how things should be done. But how? We had no patients.''

And it was quite true that for a time Lister was starved of patients so that he had difficulty even in filling his modest allowance of beds. But a certain case on which he operated at King's made a considerable stir there. It was a case of a fractured knee-cap and Lister boldly cut down on the breakage and wired the two widely

separated fragments of bone together. "When this poor fellow dies,"
remarked a scandalized colleague, "someone ought to proceed
against that man for malpractice." But the poor fellow did not die
and as a consequence no action could be brought against Lister. On
the contrary the patient recovered the full use of his limb and by
doing this a number of new converts were made to the doctrine of
antisepsis. Yet another bevy of converts resulted from Lister's skilful
removal of a tumour from a wealthy young woman, whom the great
Sir Stephen Paget had refused to touch owing to the grave risk of
sepsis. More and more of the important men in London now looked
on Lister's methods with increasing favour—Jonathan Hutchinson,
Spencer Wells, Sir James Paget and Sir Tom Smith. Sir James
Paget now made handsome amends for anything he might previously
have said of a derogatory nature. In a public reference to Lister's
technique he stated: "Lister's success has been so great in contrast
with my failures that I cannot for a moment doubt its value."

Quite suddenly all serious opposition died down and honours fell
thickly upon him; first a knighthood, then a baronetcy and finally,
an honour that a medical man had never hitherto received, a peer-
age. It is probably that the second of these honours was postponed
a year or two owing to an unfortunate incident which had occurred
at that time. Prior to conferring on him the baronetcy Queen
Victoria had sent word to Lister asking him to make public his
opposition to vivisection, which at that time was the subject of a
Royal Commission. Knowing, as he did, that the surgical advances
for which he was being honoured could never have been achieved in
the absence of all the animal experiments previously made by
Pasteur and by many other scientists, Lister explained why it was
impossible for him to comply with the Queen's request. Tactful
though his answer had been, the granting of the baronetcy was
delayed a year.

The most dramatic moment in Lister's life occurred in December
1892, on that day when all the scientific world assembled in Paris in
order to celebrate Pasteur's seventieth birthday. The seating accommodation of the great lecture theatre of the Sorbonne was crowded
to overflowing and some two thousand five hundred people were
waiting there for Pasteur's appearance. Then at half-past ten precisely the great and now aged Frenchman was seen to enter the

theatre, leaning heavily on the arm of the President of the French Republic. The Presidents of the Senate and of the Chamber, the Ministers and the Ambassadors, then took their seats on the platform and behind them were ranged the official delegates of the five Academies, standing upright in their uniforms. Lister next came forward to present to Pasteur the official greetings of the Royal Society of England and in presenting them he spoke of the immense debt which surgery owed to Pasteur. The whole assembly then rose to its feet and Pasteur, unable to restrain his emotions any longer, threw his arms around the embarrassed representative of the Royal Society and kissed him on both cheeks. It was an intensely dramatic moment, this meeting of a great Scot and of a still greater Frenchman, and probably the most memorable moment in both of their lives. (*See* Plate 21.)

Lister was always aware of the disadvantages attached to the use of disinfectants and he sometimes made trial of operating without any "antiseptic contact" at all, relying only on the strictest cleanliness. No autoclave was available in the operating theatre in those days so a large kettle had to act as a substitute for it. The surgical sponges which had been stored in carbolic acid were rinsed out in boiled water and the patient's skin and the surgeon's hands were washed, first with a solution of one in twenty carbolic and then with boiled water. The instruments were kept scrupulously clean but not otherwise prepared for the operation. When an operation was conducted under these conditions without the use of any strong antiseptic the wound often healed by primary intention and/or with only a temporary reddening of the skin around the stitches.

But Lister had completed the great task he had undertaken and it was left to those who followed him to replace his school of antiseptic surgery with the school of aseptic surgery that has now supplanted it. Lister died on February 10th, 1912, shortly before his eighty-fifth birthday.

There have been many different estimates of his genius but perhaps the justest is that made by the French surgeon Lucas Championnière, an estimate which is quoted by H. C. Cameron in his *Life of Lister*. "Lister," wrote Championnière, "gave a scientific basis to surgery. He made it rest on established truths. He swept away the uncertainty in which the greatest surgeons up to that time had left

it. Inspired by the ideas of Pasteur, he conceived the idea that the infinitely little and its germs of all kinds, scattered everywhere in the outside world, strove against the natural efforts of the organism towards healing. His genius showed itself in this, that starting from a fundamental observation, verified scientifically, he succeeded in determining the general laws of repair."

IGNAZ SEMMELWEISS (1818–1865)

Whilst the story of Lister and of his successful application of Pasteur's discoveries to the problems of surgery is well known, the less happy story of the Hungarian, Ignaz Philippe Semmelweiss, who brought about a marked fall in puerperal fever in his ward by the introduction of aseptic and antiseptic measures, is much less familiar. In 1846 Semmelweiss, then only twenty-eight years of age, became an assistant in the obstetric wards of the Allgemeines Krankenhaus in Vienna. The first ward in this hospital had acquired such a bad reputation on account of its death rate from puerperal fever that women begged with tears in their eyes not to be placed in it. Semmelweiss was not long in noticing that this ward was different from the second ward (with a much lower mortality rate) in that students entered it straight from the dissecting rooms for instruction in obstetrics. But the work in the second ward was done only by the midwives who, of course, had nothing to do with the dissecting and post-mortem rooms. Moreover, the midwives were much more careful about cleanliness than were the students and they usually washed their hands before making a gynaecological examination. Semmelweiss describes how heavily the appalling mortality rate in the first maternity ward of the hospital, looked after by his gynaecological colleague, Dr. Klein, weighed on his own spirits.

"Almost every day," he wrote, "the sound of bells intimated that the priest was administering the last sacrament to the dying. I myself was terror-stricken when I heard the sound of bells at my door, and a deep sigh rose in my breast for the unfortunate mother who was a victim to a cause hitherto unknown. This worked on me as a fresh incentive that I should, to the best of my ability, endeavour to discover the mysterious agent, and a conviction grew day by day that the prevailing fatality in Clinique No. 1 could in no wise be accounted for by the hitherto adopted etiology of puerperal

fever." Semmelweiss tried various methods of reducing the mortality in his own wards but without any success. Then came an event which provided him with the clue he needed. Another colleague of his, Professor Kolletschka, fell a victim to blood-poisoning caused by a wound inflicted on himself whilst carrying out a dissection. Semmelweiss describes his discovery in the following words: "Kolletschka's fatal symptoms unveiled to my mind an identity with those I had so often noticed in the death-bed of puerperal cases."

Convinced now that puerperal fever was due to an infection carried from the dissecting rooms on the hands of the doctors and medical students, he issued strict orders that henceforth patients were not to be examined by anyone coming from the dissecting rooms. The results obtained from this one change surpassed all expectations. Within a few months there was a drop of his mortality rate from 12.24 per cent to 3.04 per cent and by the end of the second year it had fallen still lower to 1.27 per cent.

All that Semmelweiss managed to achieve by publishing the results obtained by the institution of these simple measures was to infuriate his colleagues. Not being of a stubborn nature, he promptly resigned and went off to practise gynaecology and obstetrics in the city of Pest. Here again he made no headway with his crusade in favour of cleanliness in obstetrics, and, by now utterly dispirited and exhausted, he became melancholic. Removed to an asylum in 1865 he died in that institution a month later of the very disease which he had been struggling to teach others to avoid by strict cleanliness, the disease of streptococcal blood-poisoning. Unlike that sturdy Scot, Joseph Lister, Semmelweiss was not properly equipped by Nature for the arduous and dangerous role of the reformer.

DR. OLIVER WENDELL HOLMES OF BOSTON (1809–1894)

This distinguished author and gynaecologist who preached the same gospel of cleanliness to the New World was fortunately of a much tougher build than Semmelweiss. He also was appalled by the mortality from puerperal fever in the lying-in wards of the American hospitals in which he worked and as early as 1843 he taught that childbirth-fever was an infectious disease carried from one patient to another on the hands of the *accoucheur* or the midwife. But all that this announcement produced was intense annoyance

on the part of a certain Dr. Meigs of Philadelphia who took grave exception to this idea that a physician's hands were likely to be unclean. He protested that a number of cases of fever had occurred in the practice of that eminent Edinburgh gynaecologist, Dr. Simpson, and it was ridiculous to suggest that Dr. Simpson's hands were unclean. To this Holmes replied that it was not in the least ridiculous to suppose this. After Dr. Simpson had handled two cases of puerperal fever, his next four patients had developed puerperal fever, thus clearly demonstrating "that a gentleman with clean hands can still carry the disease". Nothing was done as the result of Oliver Wendell Holmes' protest and his crusade in favour of clean hands made very little progress in America.

To many it will seem incredible that doctors should have been so stubborn in refusing even to consider the idea that puerperal fever was of a contagious nature when so much evidence already existed in favour of this. But old errors are difficult to destroy and there were medical men who remained sceptical of the new teaching long after Semmelweiss' death. At a meeting of the Paris Academy of Medicine in 1879 a distinguished gynaecologist was still capable of speaking with scorn of the idea that infection could be spread in this way. But fortunately no less a person than Louis Pasteur himself was present at that particular meeting and, interrupting the speaker, he mounted on to the platform, drew on the blackboard chains of streptococci, the organism responsible for puerperal fever, and reduced the speaker to silence. Pasteur possessed the open-mindedness and the ability to see and to admit error, which are qualities that are essential to any research. "Do not fear," he once said, "to defend new ideas, even the most revolutionary. Your own faith is what counts most. But have courage also to admit an error as soon as you have proved it to yourself that your idea is wrong. Science is the grave-yard of ideas. . . . But some ideas that seem dead and buried may at one time or another rise up to life again more vital than ever." No better description could be given of the attitude of mind required for scientific research than this one of Louis Pasteur's.

THE ASEPTIC SCHOOL OF SURGERY

Lister was forced to make extensive use of antiseptics, even after he had abandoned the use of his carbolic sprays, if for no other

reason than that he possessed no other satisfactory method of sterilizing the materials used at his operations and more particularly his
catgut ligatures. But from the very first the surgeons who followed
Lister strove to reduce their dependence on antiseptics, their aim
being to *exclude* micro-organisms altogether from the area being
operated upon instead of destroying them after they had got there.
In other words, they aimed at replacing antiseptic surgery by aseptic
surgery and in course of time this ideal was achieved. In 1886 Ernst
von Bergmann (1836–1907), the Berlin surgeon, introduced the
steam sterilization of dressings. In 1890 the American surgeon W.
S. Halstead, at that time working in New York, found that it was
impossible for him or for any other surgeon to be sure that their
hands were sterile and he recommended that surgeons should
henceforth operate in rubber gloves. Here was another step forward
and all over the world similar refinements were made in aseptic
technique; the use of sterile gowns, the wearing of caps and masks by
all those who were present at the operation, better and better
methods of sterilizing catgut and of rendering the patient's skin
aseptic—innumerable small improvements were contributed by
unnamed people, until the ideal aseptic surgery was at length
realized.

And now everything works so smoothly in the operating theatres
of our hospitals, and wounds unite with so little hindrance from
infection, that it is difficult for modern people to realize how brief is
the span of time which separates them from the days when gangrene
was an everyday visitor to hospital wards. Yet the older surgeon of
today is distanced from this period of septic surgery by only a single
generation.

When the writer of this book arrived, as a student, at St. Bartholomew's Hospital in the year 1905, the senior surgeon on the
honorary staff was a certain Mr. Bruce Clark, who frequently talked
to his dressers about the conditions which reigned at the hospital
when he was a dresser. The operations were then carried out in
a large, bare, boarded room, the surgeon wearing an old, blood-
stiffened frock-coat which it was considered contrary to etiquette to
have cleaned. In a cupboard of the theatre were kept balls of strong
twine, a pair of scissors, and several lumps of beeswax. On operating
days it was the duty of the dresser to cut two-foot lengths of twine

and to make ligatures out of them by the simple expedient of rubbing them with beeswax. The commonest operation was an amputation of a limb and after the bleeding vessels had been tied, the flaps were left open in order that the "laudable pus" might escape. The rounds in the ward were formidable affairs. "The procession was led by the surgeon with his house-surgeons . . . next two beadles bearing on a kind of stretcher a charcoal brazier with cauteries sticking in the red hot contents, and after these the sister, dressers and nurses. The patients lay with cradles over the limbs and when the bedclothes were raised the open stump was exposed with the beeswax strings hanging out. The surgeon pulled on these tentatively one by one, and if all went well they came away from the sloughed end of a clotted artery, but sometimes there was a gush of blood and instantly a house-surgeon snatched a cautery from the brazier and plunged it expertly into the wound." (Quoted from *Bruce Clark* by H. S. Crichton Starkey, in St. Bartholomew's Hospital Journal, December 1953.) The modern surgeon lives in an entirely different world from that known to his father and his grandfather and yet all that old world came to an end, so far as surgery is concerned, only a century ago.

CHAPTER XIII

Man *versus* the Micro-organism

IT would be a grave error to imagine that because micro-organisms are responsible for illnesses in man, he and all micro-organisms are implacable enemies. But for the world of micro-organisms no life could survive on this planet. All animals depend ultimately on plant life for food, some eating the plants directly and others, such as the carnivores, indirectly by preying on the plant-eaters. If by some unfortunate accident the scientists were to discover a method of destroying all micro-organisms on this planet and were misguided enough to put this method into use, man and all other living creatures on this earth would perish. Without the aid of the bacteria the nitrogen cycle in the soil would stop, the soil's reserves of nitrates would quickly be exhausted and plants would then cease to grow. For a brief time man might manage to remedy this disaster by falling back on the big deposits of nitrates still available in such countries as Chile, but when these supplies had been exhausted, starvation would not be very far off. In a few months humanity, freed of all bacterial infections but emaciated by starvation and ridden with scurvy, would perish on this earth.

There are many micro-organisms which live on symbiotic terms with us, such as the bacteria which inhabit the large bowel and consume the indigestible residues of our food as it passes along the intestine. There are also bacteria which lodge in our mouths, throats and nasal passages, snatching a precarious living from albuminous exudates and from cells cast off from the mucous linings. But as we know to our cost, all bacteria in these regions are not prepared to live on friendly terms with us. Just as there are gangsters and profiteers as well as honest tradesmen in the world, so are there predatory organisms as well as the amiable bacteria that live on symbiotic

terms with us—the bacteria of disease. There is a theory that these predatory forms of life were evolved out of the more friendly ones. According to this idea the struggle for existence became so fierce in the bacterial world within us that new methods of obtaining a livelihood had to be devised. Instead of remaining satisfied with fortuitous supplies of food in the way of exudates and exfoliated cells, some of the bolder organisms evolved methods of attacking the living cells in our tissues. This gangster form of life was made possible for them by the development within them of toxins or poisons by means of which our resistance to them could first be lowered and then overcome. The strong similarity which exists between certain harmless and certain predatory forms of organism, such as between the bacillus coli communis (the ordinary inhabitant of the bowel) and the typhoid bacillus, and between the diphtheroid bacillus and the true bacillus of diphtheria, support this theory. But there are also weighty arguments to be brought against it. It can, for example, be argued that a predatory form of life is not always an advantage to an organism, as is the case when the cholera bacillus slays its own host, thereby destroying simultaneously its livelihood and its home. Now, what is not to an organism's advantage cannot have been evolved by natural selection, and this is an argument that can be brought against this idea that predatory organisms have been evolved out of harmless ones.

Man is anthropocentric in his outlook and when we look at disease from our ordinary human standpoint we are unable to find any meaning in it. For us it seems to be nothing but an unfortunate and useless happening. But if we stand a little further away from the subject and try to look at disease more objectively, it begins to acquire a new significance. We see, and perhaps for the first time, that infection is not necessarily a meaningless accident but that it is the inevitable outcome of the conditions of life on this planet. The law is that one form of life must live on another form so that an unstable balance is maintained between the various components of Organic Life on the earth. From man's point of view such a thing as an influenza epidemic is an unmitigated disaster but from the viewpoint of the virus which brought about that epidemic it is a magnificent triumph. The balance has momentarily shifted in favour of the viruses but in a week or two the former equilibrium between man

and the virus of influenza will probably be re-established. Even in the absence of any serious epidemic the scales are for ever swinging first in one direction and then, a little later, in another. Some pathogenic organism happens to catch us at a slight disadvantage when our resistance to it is diminished, and as a result of its attack we become ill. Then our bodies mobilize their resources and after the struggle of illness our health is restored, only to fall a prey again to some new foe for whose onslaught we are not properly prepared.

It is the unfamiliar foe that is most likely to defeat us owing to the unpreparedness of our defence against it. This was tragically illustrated by the epidemics of measles which wrought such havoc amongst the American Indians in the middle of the nineteenth century. Because they had not previously encountered the viruses of measles or of smallpox and had acquired no resistance to these diseases, the Redskins died in their tens of thousands. The importance of this factor of resistance derived from past infections is also very well shown by the mildness of the manifestations of syphilis seen in Europe today compared with those which were described a century ago. The reason for this is that syphilis has existed in the western world for so long that the great majority of its inhabitants have inherited defences against it.

Infection with germs is a common cause of illness. Because we do not know the cause of every disease it is impossible to state statistically how often it is responsible for it. For example, in spite of the immense amount of research devoted to that subject, we are still ignorant of the cause of cancer and are unable to say whether unknown viruses are the cause of it or not. All that can be said of sickness in general is that infection with hostile organisms of one kind or another—bacteria, viruses, plasmodia, vibrios or parasites—account for a great deal of it.

THE RISE OF PATHOLOGY

Just as modern surgery with all its refinements was unable to start until a number of obstacles had first been cleared away, so medicine in its modern sense could not be properly understood until a satisfactory pathology had been provided for it. For a thousand years all ideas about diseases were based on the pathology of the four humours and if this theory were to be abandoned an alternative

pathology had to be found to put in its place. It was not until Rudolf Virchow (1802–1902), Professor of Pathology of Würzburg, brought out his *Cellular Pathology* in 1858 that medical men obtained what they needed. Virchow's pathology made the cell the centre of all study and he likened the body to a state in which every cell was a citizen. Disease could be pictured as a condition of civil war within the state. Virchow was the first man to describe the phenomenon of leucocytosis, that is to say, the increase in the number of white blood corpuscles which occurs at the onset of infections and which is one of the means by which we prepare ourselves to repel the attack. He showed how the leucocytes engulfed the invading bacteria and other foreign bodies and thus acted in the capacities of policemen and scavengers to the body. His researches on the activities of the white blood corpuscles were carried further by the Russian biologist Elie Metschnikoff (1845–1916). Metschnikoff showed how each type of corpuscle had its own appropriate work to do in repelling the body's invasion by hostile organisms. One type helped to neutralize the poisons liberated by the invading germs and another kind of white corpuscle, the phagocyte, engulfed and digested the organisms themselves after they had been rendered innocuous. (*See* Fig. 9.)

Virchow was one of those versatile men who possess an immense range of interests and who are capable of making valuable contributions to whatever line of research they care to take up. As a young man he had accompanied Dr. Schliemann on one of his visits to the excavations being carried out by his orders on the site of the ancient city of Troy and afterwards on his return home he wrote a masterly treatise on the subject of the Trojan War. At a later date he founded the important scientific journal known as *Archiv. fur pathologische Anatomie*, in which many of his own discoveries were subsequently to be published. He was a contemporary of the great Frenchman Pasteur, to whose discoveries his own work on cellular pathology often proved to be complementary, yet, such are the vagaries of fate, there is no record of Pasteur and Virchow ever having met.

THE STUDY OF INFECTION

Medicine required not only a workable pathology but knowledge of the way in which micro-organisms managed to establish their hold on the body. This information would be very valuable, for by

knowing better the enemy's strategy measures could sometimes be adopted to defeat it. What needed studying therefore was modes of infection, a subject which had interested medical men long before Pasteur had promulgated his germ-theory of disease and Virchow had put forward his cellular system of pathology. Before discussing the more recent discoveries in connection with this all-important

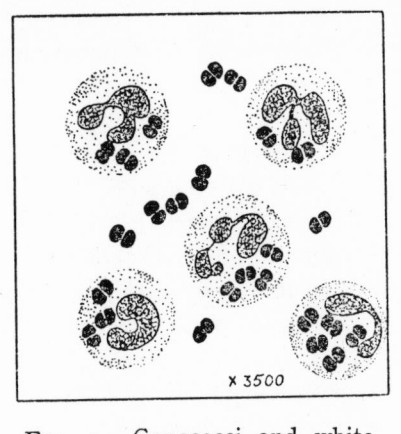

FIG. 9.—Gonococci and white
blood corpuscles

subject, it will be of interest to recapitulate some of the very earliest ideas concerning the spread of contagious diseases.

As has already been said, the oldest formulation of the theory that illness is disseminated by minute forms of life is to be found in the writings of the Latin author Tarentius Rusticus and in his work *De Re Rusticus*. I am indebted to Dr. R. C. Macfie for the following quotations from it. Tarentius Rusticus wrote: "If there are any marshy places, little animals multiply which the eye cannot discern, but which enter the body with the breath through the mouth and nose and cause grave diseases." Lucius Moderatus Columella puts forward a very similar theory at a somewhat later date, and in various forms it reappeared and was restated throughout the Middle Ages, being formulated with the greatest clarity by that perspicacious Veronese nobleman Hieronymus Fracastorius (1483–1553) in his work *De Contagione*. Fracastorius was a fellow student of Copernicus at Padua and although he never studied medicine he

was keenly interested in it. He was particularly interested in the manner by which a new disease, known as the Morbus Gallicus, was spreading.

In 1541 he published his great work *De Contagione*, in which he suggested that contagious diseases were disseminated by means of what he calls "seminaria" or tiny living particles "which multiply rapidly and propagate their like". He also describes the three methods by which an epidemic is able to spread; by infection through direct contact, by infection by means of "fomites", that is to say by infected clothes, utensils, etc., and by infection occurring at a distance through the air. When we remember that micro-organisms were utterly unknown at that time, that illnesses were regarded as being due to a disturbance of the balance of the four humours and that infectious diseases were attributed to such ill-defined causes as "miasmas", the insight of this poet and amateur student of medicine is truly startling. He dimly outlined the future science of epidemiology and foresaw the shape of things to come. (*See* Plate 24.)

As syphilis, the disease in which Fracastorius was so interested, illustrates very well the way in which knowledge was slowly acquired on the subject of the spread of disease a brief history of syphilis will be given. It is in any case a subject of considerable importance in the history of medicine, quite apart from the light it throws on contagion.

THE HISTORY OF SYPHILIS

It is generally believed that syphilis arrived in Europe in the year 1493 and that it was brought here by Columbus' men as a memento of their visit to the island of Española. We have first news of its reaching Europe from the writings of Ruy Diaz de Isla (1462–1542), a physician of some note who was living and practising at that time in Barcelona. Dr. Diaz de Isla actually witnessed the disembarkation of Columbus' sailors on their return from this, their first voyage to the New World. Several years later when Diaz de Isla was practising in Lisbon he wrote a treatise about the disease, calling it the "Disease of the Island of Española", that being the older name of Haiti, the island on which Columbus and his men had landed with such relief in their long, monotonous sail to the West. Diaz de Isla's story of the disease being brought from the New World is confirmed by two other Spaniards living at Barcelona at the time of Columbus' return,

Oviedo and Las Casas. Oviedo was a scholar and courtier, who had struck up a friendship with Columbus' son and who obtained his information about the disease from none other than the great navigator himself. The other Spaniard, Las Casas, made a voyage to Haiti himself as early as 1498 and when on the island he questioned the natives on the subject. The following is his report written after his return from this voyage: "I took the trouble, upon several occasions, to interrogate the Indians of the island as to whether the disease was of great antiquity and they answered 'Yes', that it dated from a period long before the advent of the Christians, the origin of it being beyond the memory of any man and nobody disbelieves this." Las Casas added the interesting information that when the disease broke out among the Spaniards it was in a much severer form than when it attacked the natives. This is of course true of all infective diseases, that they are far more virulent when they attack races that have never encountered them previously and because of this possess no resistance to them.

Extremely favourable conditions existed at this time for the dissemination of syphilis throughout Europe. In the year following Columbus' return, Charles VIII of France began his preparations for a great military campaign on which he was about to embark and mercenary soldiers flocked to his standard from all the neighbouring countries. Amongst these recruits were a number of Spaniards who had already been infected with syphilis and these men transported the disease first to France and then to Italy. At the time that Charles VIII was laying siege to Naples (1495), a plague of rashes and ulcerations broke out amongst his men and occasioned so much trouble that the siege had to be raised and the mercenary troops forming his army disbanded. The new disease was quickly spread throughout Europe by the returning soldiers, and as each nation in turn became infected it called the strange new illness by a different name. The French referred to it as the Neapolitan disease, the Spanish as the French disease and the British called it either the Morbus Gallicus or else the Greater Pox. The name syphilis by which it later became known was derived from a poem written in 1530 by Fracastorius, the Veronese nobleman already referred to. In elegant verse he describes the sufferings of a young shepherd named Syphilis who because he had incurred the wrath of the gods was smitten with

a loathsome disease. The theme of the poem was of no real importance. All that Fracastorius really required of it was that it should
give him an opportunity to describe the symptoms of the disease and
its treatment with mercury and guiacum or "holywood", two
remedies which reached Europe from the New World soon after the
disease had been imported.

It is only fair to add that there are a few authorities who discount
the writings of Oviedo and Las Casas and do not accept the theory
that syphilis was brought to Europe by Columbus and his sailors. But
the way in which outbreaks of syphilis occurred one by one in
the various countries of the Old World is highly suggestive of
a new disease being spread throughout Europe. Everywhere it was
regarded as a strange and terrifying complaint, and everywhere
resented as an intrusion from elsewhere. And because the date of its
appearance in Europe happened to coincide with great voyages of
discovery by which other parts of the world were being opened up,
syphilis was soon carried to the coasts of Africa and to the Far East.
The Portuguese were particularly responsible for its spread to the
Indies.

Syphilis was probably introduced into England by Englishmen
who had served as mercenaries in Charles' disbanded Italian army
and the first mention of it occurs in English literature in 1497. In the
same year the new disease reached Scotland and on September 22nd
of the following year James IV decreed that all persons suffering from
the disease were to leave Edinburgh immediately, and to go to an
island opposite Leith, there to be medically treated. The ordinance
also stated that any infected person who disobeyed this order and
was found residing in Edinburgh again would be branded on the
cheek with hot irons.

The fact that the mode of infection was not yet understood made
preventive measures against the new disease extremely difficult. It
was at first assumed that, like the plague and the sweating sickness,
it was spread through air contagion. No one had any idea, at that
time, that it was transmitted by sexual contact, but some were
of the opinion that infection might occur through the breath. One of
the accusations brought against Cardinal Wolsey when he fell from
power was that he had infected the King with syphilis by "whisper-
ing in his ear". There are several reasons for believing that Henry

VIII suffered from syphilis, but none for imagining that he contracted the disease in this way. Henry suffered from chronic ulceration of the legs, and portraits of Mary are suggestive of her having inherited syphilis from her father. Moreover, Henry's frequent matrimonial changes in his hope to obtain an heir may have been due to his fertility being reduced by the disease.

The French authorities seem to have been particularly alarmed by the rapid spread of the new disease. In 1497 an act was passed in Paris to the effect that all persons suffering from it were "forbidden under pain of death from conversing with the rest of the world". Parisians who had already contracted syphilis were isolated from their fellow citizens in the suburb of St. Germain. Visitors to Paris from other countries who were infected were ordered to leave the city within twenty-four hours, four sous being given to them to assist their return to the "Countries and Places where they were born, or where they had their abode when they caught the distemper, or where they please, under Pain of Death". Yet even in those days the French were extremely cautious on the subject of financial expenditure and the act goes on to say that "No person shall presume to take the said four Sous unless he be a Stranger or quit the city upon condition never to return to it." However carefully an act is framed and however heavy the penalties attached to infringing it there are always people who manage to evade it. This happened now in France. So many people preferred remaining anywhere in Paris to being expelled from it that the Faubourg St. Germain soon became unbearably overcrowded. Summary orders were therefore given that in future strangers found infected with the new disease in the Faubourg would be "thrown into the River, in Case they are ever hereafter found". By these drastic methods, the overcrowding of the Faubourg St. Germain was eventually remedied.

The Scots appear to have suspected earlier than any other nation that syphilis was transmitted by sexual contact. In the same year that Paris was framing ineffectual orders forbidding infected people from conversing with the rest of the world in order to prevent the contagion spreading, the town council of Aberdeen was enacting that: "For protection from the disease which has come out of France and strange parts, all light women must desist their vice and sin of venery and work for their support, on pain, else, of being branded with a hot

iron on their cheek and banished from the town." Brutal though this act was, it showed a much better understanding of the nature of the disease and of the measures required for its prevention than did the judicial decrees issued in France.

Dr. H. W. Haggard, to whose book *Devils, Drugs and Doctors* I owe the following information on the subject of the spread of syphilis in the New World, reports that the disease did not appear in the American Colonies until considerably later. The first outbreak of any importance occurred in Boston in the year 1646, that is to say, twenty-six years after the landing of the Pilgrim Fathers from the *Mayflower*. A certain John Winthrop records the appearance of the disease at Boston in his diary and points out that its coming was preceded by the birth of a calf which possessed three mouths, three noses and six eyes. A year after this monster was born the new disease came. John Winthrop announces its arrival as follows: "There fell out also a loathsome disease at Boston which raised a scandal upon the town and country though without just cause." If we discount the miraculous portent of the monstrous calf, John Winthrop's account and explanation of the coming of the disease is a very plausible one. He states that a Boston seaman went on a voyage and on his return home he infected his wife with syphilis. She bore him a child and at the same time developed a sore on her breast. This seems to have been the source from which "sixteen persons, men women and children were infected", but in what manner they became infected is not at all clear from his account.

When eventually the venereal mode of transmission was realized it provided excellent opportunities for blackmail so that many healthy people were maliciously accused of suffering from it. In Puritanical communities such as the early communities in America, the spreading of a rumour that a neighbour was suffering from a disease brought about by sexual laxity was an excellent way of paying off old scores and it was frequently used.

So many ridiculous theories had been advanced on the subject of syphilis that Jean Astruc, physician to Louis XIV, was constrained to review them and to point out to his contemporaries how ridiculous most of them were. After dismissing the more fantastic of these ideas off-hand, Astruc, who obviously possessed considerable clinical experience of the disease, refers to an infective theory which certain

people had advanced. He writes of this theory as follows: "There are some, however . . . who think that venereal poison is nothing else but a numerous School of little nimble, brisk, invisible living things of a prolific Nature, which when once admitted, increase, and multiply in Abundance; which lead frequent Colonies to different Parts of the Body; and inflame, erode and exulcerate the Parts they fix on; . . . in short, which without any Regard had to the particular Quality of any Humour, occasion all the Symptoms that occur in Venereal Disease." If Jean Astruc had been miraculously informed of the true nature of syphilis or been endowed with the faculty of precognition, he could not have given a better general description of syphilis than he did. Yet such is the fatuity of knowledge coming to us before the world is ready for it that Astruc, having given this excellent account of the nature of syphilis, dismisses the whole matter summarily as follows: "But as these are mere visionary Imaginations, unsupported by any Authority, they do not require any Argument to invalidate them."

This passage from the journal of a physician to Louis XIV is of great interest for it shows how an enquiring and intelligent mind can be brought within easy reach of a great idea and then sheer off, and for no other reason than that the idea is not as yet supported by any outside authority. Astruc was astute enough to realize that the notion that syphilis might be caused by innumerable, invisible, prolific and living things penetrating all parts of the body was equally applicable to other forms of illness besides syphilis. He continues his argument against an infective origin of syphilis as follows: "If it was once admitted that this Venereal Disease could be produced by invisible things swimming in the Blood, one might with equal Reason alledge the same Thing, not only of the Plague, as Athanasius Kirches the Jesuit has lately done, but also of the Small-pox, Hydrophobia, Itch, Tetters and other contagious Diseases and indeed all Distempers whatsoever; and thus the whole Theory of Medicine would fall to the Ground, as nothing could be said to prove the Venereal Disease depending upon little living things which might not be urged to prove that all other diseases were derived from the like little living things though of a different Species, than which nothing can be more absurd."

Two and a half centuries later the idea which to Jean Astruc

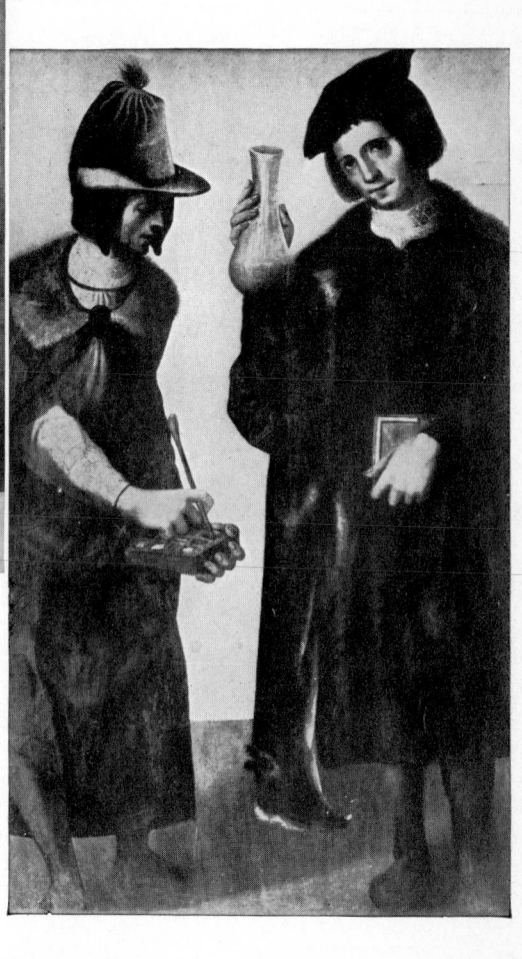

St. Apollonia, patron saint of
dentistry

St. Cosmos and St. Damian, the mediaeval
patron saints of medicine

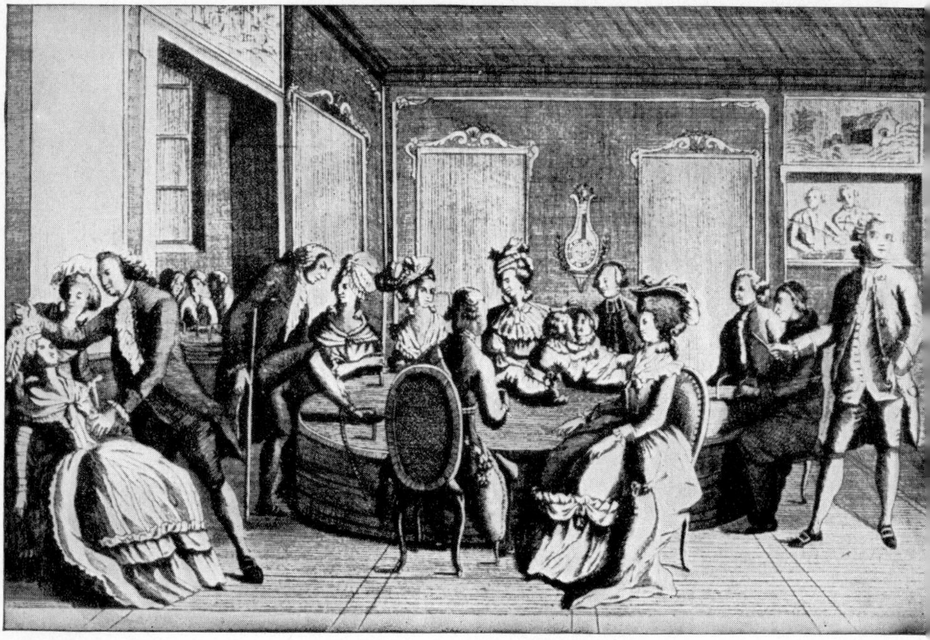

Mesmer and his patients

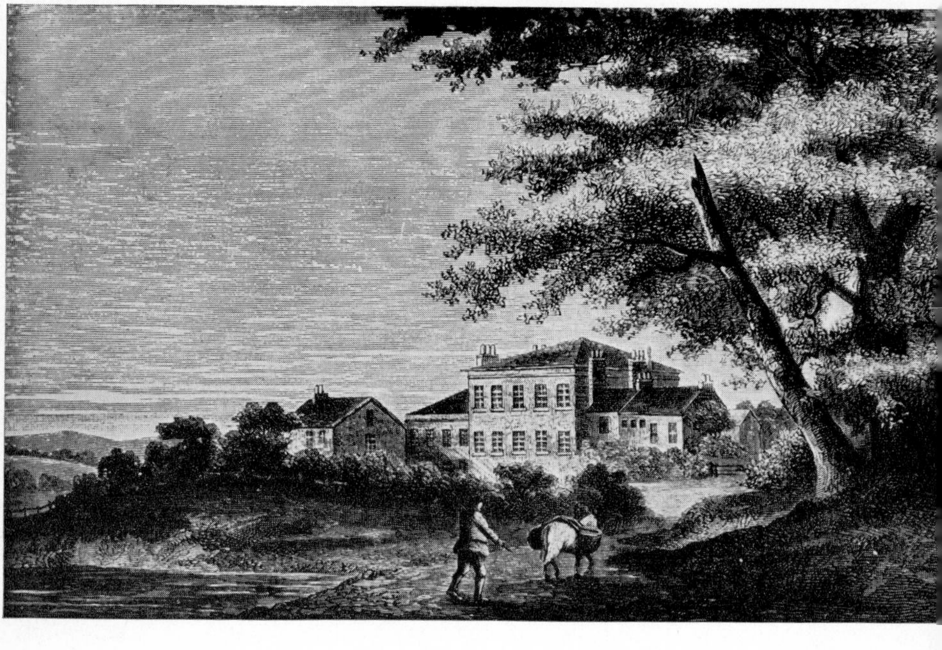

The Retreat at York

seemed too absurd to be credible, the idea that illnesses were derived
from "little living things", was proved to be true by the genius of
Louis Pasteur. But the advent of great discoveries cannot be hastened. They may be envisaged by solitary Thinkers but they will not
be accepted until the time is ripe for them. Even if Astruc had shown
less deference to authority and had had more confidence in this

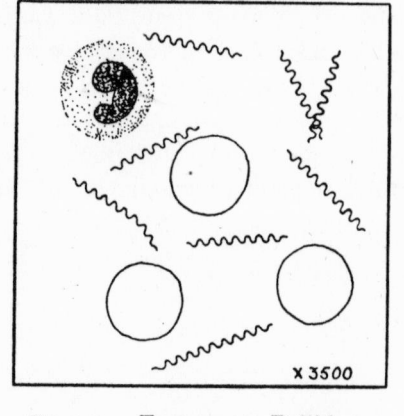

FIG. 10.—Treponema Pallidum

visionary view of infective processes, in all probability it would not
have quickened the pace of medical advance. The germ-theory of
disease which others besides Astruc had foreseen would have had to
remain a wild speculation until science had advanced sufficiently to
allow of its being put to an experimental test. And the experimental
test, so far as syphilis was concerned, lay very far ahead. Even after
Pasteur had proved the infective nature of disease and bacteriologists
had seen many of the infective agents of disease under their microscopes, the existence of "invisible things swimming in the blood"
could not have been demonstrated in the case of syphilis. The
difficulty of staining the infective organisms of syphilis and of growing them in culture delayed their discovery for fifty years after a
great many other pathogenic organisms had been seen. It was only
when Schaudinn and Hofmann of Berlin gave up using staining
methods and searched for the infective agent in syphilitic discharges
by what is known as the method of "dark ground illumination" that
the elusive spirochaeta pallida was seen. As the name suggests, the

spirochaeta pallida is a tiny, rather pallid, corkscrew-like organism seen outlined in palish light against a background of darkness.

The three great names which dominate the literature of syphilis are all German ones; F. R. Schaudinn (1871–1906) was the discoverer in 1905 of the causal organism of syphilis, now called either Spirochaeta or Treponema Pallidum. (*See* Fig. 10.) August von Wasserman (1866–1925), an assistant of Koch's, discovered in 1906 the blood reaction for syphilis called after him. Paul Ehrlich (1854–1915), also a pupil of Koch's, discovered in 1909 Salvarsan or 606, the first satisfactory remedy for syphilis. To these three famous German names can now be added a fourth name and this time a British one, that of Fleming. Penicillin is regarded now as the treatment *par excellence* for syphilis, a form of treatment which has to a great extent, but not entirely, supplanted the older treatment with salvarsan.

CHAPTER XIV

Man's Defences against Infection

IN the last chapter infective diseases and the means by which they spread were discussed. This chapter will also be devoted to infection but here the emphasis will be laid not on the attacking organisms, but on the defensive measures that man is adopting to protect himself against invasion. Because vaccination is a defensive measure of the very greatest value and because it was first used against smallpox, the chapter starts with a short history of that disease and the discovery of the principle of vaccination.

History of Smallpox

In all likelihood smallpox was first introduced into Europe by the Crusaders who brought it home from the Holy Land where the disease was common, and then later again by the Mohammedan conquerors of Southern Europe. It is true that smallpox never possessed the terrors of the plague but because it was endemic in Europe for many centuries it was responsible in the end for more deaths and suffering than the Black Death itself. During the seventeenth century one inhabitant of Great Britain out of every four eventually died of it and the frequency of pock-marks on English faces showed that almost everybody had at one time or another suffered from it. In his account of Queen Mary the Second's death from smallpox Macaulay wrote that it was "the most terrible of all the ministers of death. The havoc of the plague," he continues, "had been far more rapid but the plague had visited our shores only once or twice within living memory; and smallpox was always present, filling the churchyard with corpses, tormenting with constant fears all whom it had not yet stricken." In other words the plague was an occasional visitor to England whilst the smallpox was always here, sometimes a little less

in evidence and then flaring up again until it had attained the dimensions of an epidemic. It is computed that during the eighteenth century some sixty million people succumbed to it in Europe. More than 80 per cent of the inhabitants of any European country could count on being stricken with smallpox at one time or another, and a quarter of every nation was either killed, blinded, crippled or permanently disfigured by it. It is not surprising, therefore, that men sought eagerly for some method of avoiding this scourge, apart from the obvious measure of keeping away from those who had been stricken by it.

At a later date, after its conquest by Spain, the New World was to suffer equally severely from this disease. A negro slave in Cortez's conquering army is said to have introduced the disease into Mexico and there it spread south with such rapidity as to make the disease as effective a factor in the vanquishing of that country as the Conquistadores themselves. In many districts half of the native population died of it so that the invading Spaniards found the towns deserted and all resistance at an end. The same was to happen at a later date in North America when European settlers steadily pressed westward and dispossessed the North American Indian of his hunting grounds. Never having come across the disease before the Redskins were as susceptible to it as the Aztecs had been. Their defence was completely undermined by the triple alliance formed between alcoholism, tuberculosis and smallpox, and brave though they were in defending their territories it quickly collapsed.

The crimes, cruelties and crudities of men are recurrent themes in history and the idea of bacteriological warfare, about which so much has recently been written, is very far from being a modern one. Our forefathers were as quick to grasp the fact that disease is an invaluable ally in time of war as we are, and full use was made of smallpox by the early North American settlers in their offensive against the Redskins. Instructions were issued with a view to increasing the efficacy of smallpox as a means of exterminating the Redskins. The following Company orders are examples of this:

"You will do well to try to inoculate the Indians by means of blankets as well as to try every other method that can serve to extirpate this execrable race."

"Out of regard for them (i.e. two Indian chiefs) we gave them two

blankets and a handkerchief out of the smallpox hospital. I hope it will have the desired effect."

"I will try to inoculate . . . with some blankets that may fall into their hands, and take care not to get the disease myself." (*The Effect of Smallpox or the Destiny of the American Indian*, by W. E. and A. E. Stearn, 1945.)

It had long been realized that the great boon granted to those fortunate enough to recover from the smallpox was that they were extremely unlikely ever to be subjected to another attack of the disease. An obvious method of protection therefore would be to expose a person deliberately to a mild infection, at a time when he happened to be in a robust state of health, in the expectation that he would recover and henceforth be immune from further infection. It is difficult to decide where this preventive method was first put into practice, for some authorities maintain that it started in Africa and others that it began on the shores of the Caspian Sea. But so far as Great Britain is concerned it was in Turkey that the method was first seen and reported upon by Lady Mary Wortley Montagu, the wife of the British Ambassador there. She not only wrote to her friends about it but did her best to get it adopted by the medical profession.

Lady Mary was a beautiful, talented and much admired young woman. As a precocious child of eight she had been placed on the table by her proud father and toasted by his cronies at the Kit Kat Club, and as a high-spirited girl of nineteen she eloped from home with a Mr. Wortley Montagu who afterwards became Ambassador at the Sublime Porte. She loved both gaiety and excitement, and made it a habit to penetrate in disguise into parts of Constantinople where no ambassadress had any right to go. Afterwards she would write vivacious letters home about her escapades and about every subject under the sun. On April 1st, 1717, she indited a letter from Constantinople to her friend in England, Miss Sara Chiswell, and took as her theme the smallpox:

"Apropos of distempers I am going to tell you a thing that I am sure will make you wish yourself here. The smallpox, so fatal, and so general amongst us, is here entirely harmless by the invention of *ingrafting*, which is the name they give it. There is a set of old women

who make it their business to perform the operation every autumn in the month of September, when the great heat is abated. People send to one another to know if any of their family has a mind to have the smallpox; they make parties for this purpose and when they are met (commonly fifteen or sixteen together) the old women comes with a nut-shell full of the matter of the best small-pox and asks what veins you please to have opened. She immediately rips open that you offer her with a large needle (which gives you no more pain than a common scratch) and puts into the vein as much venom as can be upon the head of her needle, and after binds up the little wound with a hollow bit of shell; and in this way opens four or five veins. . . . The children or young patients play together all the rest of the day, and are in perfect health to the eighth. Then the fever begins to seize them, and they keep their beds two days, very seldom three. They have very rarely above twenty or thirty (pocks) in their faces, which never mark; and in eight days' time they are as well as before their illness. . . . I am patriot enough to take pain to bring this useful invention into fashion in England; and I should not fail to write to some of our doctors very particularly about it, if I knew any one of them that I thought had virtue enough to destroy such a considerable branch of their revenue for the good of mankind."

Lady Mary promptly ran into all the trouble that reformers meet when they attempt to interfere with matters which are considered not to be their business. The medical faculty foretold the most disastrous consequences were such barbarous treatment as had been suggested by Lady Mary ever to be put into practice in England. The clergy were equally shocked and spoke of the impiety of seeking to wrest out of the Deity's hands such rights as the bestowal of smallpox and pointed out how much worse everything would be if such matters were put into the sinful hands of men. The papers expressed strong disapproval and reprimanded a mother who appeared to be willing to risk the lives of her own children in such a callous manner. Nevertheless Lady Mary succeeded in persuading the Princess of Wales to have "ingrafting" practised in the royal nursery.

In spite of the apparent failure of Lady Mary Wortley Montagu's anti-smallpox campaign, the inoculation treatment she recommended did eventually establish itself in England and in great part through

the persistence of a man who possessed no medical qualifications at all, a certain Mr. Robert Sutton of Ingatestone, Essex. This enterprising man and his two sons opened a centre at Ingatestone to which people eventually came in large numbers for what was known as anti-smallpox inoculation. Sutton's success was due to the fact that he adopted a technique very similar to that which a modern doctor would employ were this now obsolete method of vaccination with smallpox itself to be reintroduced. He took his material for inoculation from a blister or vesicle before the serous fluid had been contaminated with secondary pyogenic organisms and become pus. As the result of this wise precaution he and his sons had only some five deaths amongst the seventeen thousand odd people they inoculated. Everything considered, this was a very creditable result.

In America a certain Mr. Cotton Mather assumed the part played in this country by Lady Mary Wortley Montagu. In America everything takes place on a big scale and the opposition provoked there was even fiercer than in England. A hand grenade was thrown through the window of the pioneer vaccinator's house but fortunately he was not at home. Dr. Zabdiel Boylston of Boston, another medical man who had been brave enough to give him professional support, got off with a mobbing in the street but fortunately some of the American clergy had the courage to defend the new idea. Encouraged by this enlightened support more and more people submitted themselves to the treatment and as a result the incidence of smallpox began to fall.

DR. EDWARD JENNER (1749–1823)

But an alternative method of obtaining protection against the smallpox was slowly coming into use in England, a method advocated by a certain Dr. Edward Jenner. (*See* Plate 24.) He was a Gloucestershire man and in that county there had long existed the belief that milkmaids who had suffered from a complaint known as cowpox would never contract the smallpox. Many years previously when Jenner was a medical apprentice at Sudbury, a young woman had come into his surgery for advice and the word smallpox was mentioned. "I cannot take that disease," she remarked, "for I have had the cowpox." Jenner never forgot this remark and many years later

and after he had gained far more medical experience he found that the Gloucestershire belief that milkgirls enjoyed immunity from smallpox was very widespread.

Now Jenner happened to be a personal friend of the great naturalist John Hunter, and it is more than likely that it was Hunter who jogged Jenner's memory and encouraged him to put the notion of an immunity conferred by cowpox to a practical test. Constitutionally Jenner was lazy and not really a very intelligent person and it took him twenty years to start his experiment on "vaccination". At last in 1796 he brought himself to vaccinate a boy's arm with cowpox matter and then, a month or two later, he inoculated the boy with matter taken from a smallpox pustule. The smallpox did not "take" and naturally Edward Jenner was delighted with the results. He repeated the experiment and, convinced now of the efficacy and great value of his vaccination method, he went off to London to educate the medical profession and to urge them to take up vaccination on a large scale.

Life in London became very uncomfortable for the country-bred Jenner. Although his method was being adopted far and wide many annoying things were happening; rivals were trying to claim priority, his supply of vaccine was frequently running out, cowpox was being confused clinically with smallpox, and threads that had been soaked with "lymph" from smallpox cases instead of cowpox were sometimes mistakenly issued at the headquarters of vaccination he had established in London. Several times poor Jenner fled from the noisy city back to his beloved Gloucester, there to quieten his nerves and at the same time to replenish his exhausted supply of lymph. But finally it seemed as though all his troubles were over, for the great value of vaccination had been widely acknowledged and Parliament had given him a tangible token of the nation's gratitude by voting him £10,000.

But alas, all Jenner's troubles were not yet over. It came to light that twenty years before Jenner had brought himself to carry out his first vaccination experiment, a yeoman farmer living in the next county had forestalled him. This enterprising farmer, Benjamin Jesty, had taken a stocking needle and with this simple instrument and without more ado he had boldly scratched cowpox material into the skins of his wife and children. He had even followed up this

family vaccination treatment by later scratchings with material taken from a case of smallpox, in order to make sure that his family was immune. Then Jesty had lost all interest in preventive medicine and had devoted himself to his farm. But on hearing that Dr. Jenner had been awarded £10,000, he enlisted the help of the village clergyman and of the local Member of Parliament. Letters claiming priority for Jesty were dispatched to the Jennerian Society in London, but all that came of this protest in favour of farmer Jesty was that he was invited to that great city. A portrait was painted of him in his yellow waistcoat and his wide-brimmed hat, and he was finally presented with a pair of gold-mounted needles to serve as a souvenir of his bold excursion into the realm of medicine. Jenner's reward was considerably more handsome than the farmer's. In addition to the £10,000 voted by Parliament, he received a knighthood and was presented to the Czar of Russia. But he was never a very happy man in London and it is said that it distressed him that he should not be able to explain to people how his method of vaccination worked. He spent his remaining years happily in Gloucestershire with his animals around him and died of apoplexy within a short time of his seventy-fourth birthday.

LATER WORK ON IMMUNITY

Many years were to pass before the question which had disturbed Jenner's mind during his latter years could be satisfactorily answered. Even Pasteur and his great contemporary Robert Koch were unable to throw much light on this question of immunity although their observations made it practically certain that the anti-bodies or protective substances on which immunity depended were developed in the blood. After the death of these two bacteriological geniuses their countrymen continued to work along two different lines of research. The Germans with characteristic thoroughness followed Koch's lead and set out to discover, classify and cultivate as many of the infective agents of disease as they could find, whilst Pasteur's fellow countrymen worked on the general problem of immunity.

The word "immunity" is derived from a Latin one signifying "exemption from military service", and it was soon found that immunity from diseases can be of various kinds. There is, for example, an innate form of immunity which preserves certain species

of animals from ever contracting certain diseases, and there is also an immunity which is acquired during the individual's life-time. This latter-acquired immunity can again be subdivided into two varieties, a natural, acquired immunity which follows automatically the contraction of a disease, and an immunity that is evoked by artificial means. Since this last-named artificially induced immunity is the only form of immunity which a physician can bring about, it alone need be discussed here.

Artificial immunity of this kind can again be subdivided into active and passive artificial immunities. It was the former immunity that Pasteur obtained when he injected increasing doses of infective organisms or of their toxic products into his animals or human patients. Pasteur's successors advanced his work a step further by discovering that after a high degree of immunity has been obtained for an animal in this way, the blood serum of this immunized animal is capable of protecting another animal, and it is this kind of immunity that is called passive immunity. The immunity obtained against diphtheria is an excellent example of a passive immunity.

DIPHTHERIA

The bacillus responsible for diphtheria was first discovered in 1883 by Edwin Klebs (1834–1913) of Zurich, a pupil of Virchow. In the following year Friedrich Loeffler (1852–1915), one of Koch's assistants, succeeded in cultivating this bacillus, and to commemorate the work on the part of these two men the organism responsible for diphtheria is now known as the Klebs-Loeffler bacillus. The next links in the chain of discoveries which was to culminate in our capacity to confer on children an artificial immunity to diphtheria was forged by another two people, Emil von Behring (1854–1917) and his brilliant Japanese colleague, Kitasato. They first showed that it was possible to produce a passive immunity against lock-jaw or tetanus, an immunity which was sufficiently strong to be able to withstand three hundred times the fatal dose of tetanus. A short time afterwards von Behring proved that the same could be done in the case of diphtheria. The immunity to the disease was conferred by injecting into a person the serum of an animal that had previously been immunized against diphtheria bacilli. Anti-diphtheritic serum of this sort was produced on a large scale in 1892 and its general use

soon led to a spectacular fall in the incidence and in the mortality of diphtheria.

It was in von Behring's and Kitasato's paper on the subject of tetanus that a word first appeared which has now become very familiar to everybody—the word anti-toxin. By this term is meant the anti-body or antidote produced by the blood to the toxins or the

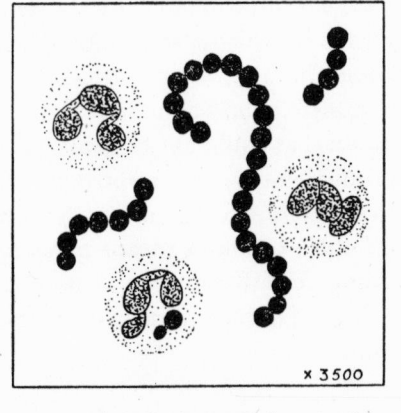

× 3500

FIG. 11.—Streptococci, the organism responsible for blood-poisoning

poisons liberated by pathogenic organisms and particularly by such organisms as tetanus, diphtheria and the plague. It is now possible by means of very fine filters to separate the toxins off from the organisms which have secreted them, and by injecting an animal with progressively increasing doses of toxins filtered off in this way a high degree of immunity to that particular toxin and consequently to that particular disease can be produced. The serum of an animal immunized in this way against tetanus toxin is now injected into every human patient with a wound which might conceivably be contaminated with tetanus germs. Anti-tetanus serum was used on an immense scale during the two world wars and brought about a great reduction in the incidence of tetanus.

Vaccines, as opposed to sera, were used as a means of obtaining immunity by Sir Almroth Wright, the great British pioneer of vaccine-therapy, and they were particularly successful as a preventive

measure against typhoid fever. In the South African War of 1899–1902 typhoid was responsible for more casualties than the Boers were, but in the subsequent two world wars typhoid was of very little account. This can be attributed almost entirely to the preventive inoculation introduced by Sir Almroth Wright. The vaccine he used was a mixture of the dead organisms of typhoid, para-typhoid A and para-typhoid B.

Excellent as were the results obtained by the immunologists, there still remained organisms to which a satisfactory immunity could not be obtained by vaccine-therapy. Streptococci and staphylococci, the organisms chiefly responsible for wound infections and blood-poisoning, were amongst those that could not be dealt with satisfactorily by either vaccine or serum-therapy, and unfortunately streptococci and staphylococci were very common organisms. (*See* Fig. 11.) This made the bacteriologists' failure to find a means of vanquishing them all the more disappointing. But fortunately a new line of attack was being developed, a line of attack which, ultimately, was to prove remarkably successful.

THE DISCOVERY OF THE SULPHONAMIDE DRUGS

In spite of the promising start made by Ehrlich in synthesizing a specific for syphilis, chemotherapy, or treatment of infections by synthetized drugs, did not make any real progress in the decades that followed his discovery of salvarsan. It would indeed be true to say that no real advance could be reported in chemotherapy until 1932, the year in which prontosil, the forerunner of the sulphonamide drugs, was produced. Whereas the discovery of salvarsan was due to the joint work of only two men, Ehrlich and his partner Noguchi, the sulphonamides were the result of contributions made by a great many people. The story of the discovery of these valuable drugs really begins with the work of a certain Viennese industrial chemist, called Gelmo, who synthetized a new compound that possessed the formidable name of para-amino-benzene-sulphonamide. Nobody thought of using this new product as a drug but it was found to be a very satisfactory red dye for wool. A preparation of a somewhat similar nature was synthetized in 1932 and given the name of prontosil. This time it occurred to several people that it might conceivably be of some therapeutic value and its action was tested. A year later Dr.

Gerhard Domagh published an enthusiastic paper in a medical journal in which he claimed that prontosil had the capacity to arrest the growth of certain organisms. He had found that mice that had been injected with many times the lethal doses of streptococci recovered if they received an injection of prontosil, whereas the control mice all died. The organisms on which prontosil appeared to have the most powerful action were staphylococci and streptococci, the two organisms which had responded so poorly to vaccine and serum-therapy. This was particularly welcome news to the medical profession.

Prontosil was soon available in sufficient quantity to allow of its being tried out on a larger scale and it stood up well to this test. The general opinion was that it was of great help in the treatment of certain infections and particularly in that of infections by the streptococcus. Many new workers now appeared on the scene and in 1935 a group of French researchers made the interesting discovery that prontosil broke down within the tissues into two different compounds, only one of which had any action on bacteria. This compound that was hostile to bacteria was then synthesized and it turned out to be no other than para-amino-benzene-sulphonamide, the compound which had originally been made by Gelmo and which hitherto had been employed only as a dye for wool.

Sulphanilamide, as Gelmo's original compound was now re-christened, was widely used and on the whole proved highly satisfactory. But as sulphanilamide was only effective against a limited number of organisms, manufacturing chemists were naturally anxious to find other compounds which would prove equally effective against other organisms. The research workers in May and Baker's laboratories at Dagenham set up as their particular target the discovery of a drug which would arrest the growth of the pneumococcus, the organism responsible for pneumonia. Numerous compounds were made and eventually they produced paramino-benzene-sulphonamide-pyridene (later known as M & B 693 or Sulphapyridine). Animal experiments showed that this new drug protected mice after they had been inoculated with many times the lethal dose of pneumococci. The research workers next tested the toxicity of the new drug on themselves and found that it was very low.

The first time it was tried out on a human patient suffering from

pneumonia was on March 18th, 1938, and, as is generally done when experimenting with a new drug, an apparently hopeless case was selected for this first test. A desperate case is chosen in these circumstances on the grounds that in the absence of some more effective remedy than medicine actually possesses the patient will certainly die so that nothing will be lost by trying the experiment on him. The patient selected for the purpose of this particular trial was a Norfolk agricultural labourer and within a short time of the start of the new treatment his condition was so much better that he was out of danger. Many other tests were subsequently made and with equally satisfactory results. For the first time in medical history a method of aborting a pneumococcal infection had been found.

The success obtained by the Dagenham team imparted a great impetus to research work of a similar kind elsewhere and a large number of new sulphanilamide drugs soon appeared on the market—sulphathiazol, sulphadiazine, sulphamethazine, sulphaguanadine and many others. Further investigation showed that none of these new preparations killed germs directly, as germs are killed, for example, by carbolic acid, but that they acted by interfering with the metabolism of the micro-organisms so that they were not properly nourished and ceased to grow. To put the matter crudely, the sulphanilamide drugs act by throwing a spanner into the organism's body chemistry or metabolism.

The outbreak of war provided an excellent opportunity for the testing of these new drugs on a very large scale and there can be no doubt that innumerable lives were saved by them. But as has so often happened before in medicine, the discovery of one effective remedy was quickly followed by the discovery of another still more powerful one. No sooner had surgeons been given the sulpha-drugs than they were presented with penicillin and as a result of these two gifts, deaths from wound infection were very greatly reduced. Something must be said about penicillin.

PENICILLIN

Sir Alexander Fleming's discovery of penicillin was of importance not only because it provided men with an exceedingly valuable remedy, at the precise moment at which humanity was about to engage in one of its periodic orgies of mutual destruction on an un-

usually big scale, but because it introduced a new device into medicine—that of conquering one micro-organism with the aid of another. The story of the actual discovery of *Penicillium notatum* is a hackneyed one but it still bears repetition. The fact that Fleming had for a long time been interested in the subject of bacteriophages, lyso-zymes and other inhibiting factors in the culture of organisms enabled him to profit by an accident which occurred in the summer of 1929. The weather had been both cool and damp and a mould, floating in the air in the neighbourhood of Paddington Station, drifted through an open window of St. Mary's Hospital. It happened to be the window of Dr. Alexander Fleming's laboratory and by good fortune it alighted on an exposed culture plate on which staphylococci were being grown. The contamination of cultures with unwanted moulds is a common mishap in a bacteriological laboratory and it usually ends in the contaminated plates being deposited in the sink for the "lab" boy to clean. Fortunately it was Dr. Fleming and not the "lab" boy who looked at this plate two or three days later and he noted that the colonies of staphy-lococci in the neighbourhood of the mould had begun to disappear. (*See* Plate 22.) Here was something worth further investigation. New experiments revealed two facts, first that the mould belonged to the genus *Penicillium* and second that whilst it was capable of in-hibiting the growth of a number of bacteria it had no action on others. More tests were carried out in order to make sure that it was not too toxic for use in medicine and it was after these tests had been satis-factorily passed that Professor Fleming was able to write about penicillin that "some day it would come into its own as a therapeutic agent".

But that day was still a long way off, for penicillin in its original crude form was found to be highly unstable. The next contribution to the research was made by Professor Raistrick of the London School of Hygiene and Tropical Medicine. He succeeded in finding a suitable nutrient liquid in which penicillin could be grown and also discovered that by acidifying the liquid and by extracting it with ether a small amount of penicillin was obtainable. But it was not until 1938 that any further progress was made. A brilliant team of scientists then began to work at Oxford headed by Professor Florey and Dr. Chain and this team eventually found a method of making a much more

concentrated solution of the drug. Then the pace quickened, for Britain was at war now and needed large supplies of the drug in order to combat sepsis amongst the wounded.

The scene now shifted to the United States where new research workers joined in the task of overcoming the immense difficulties which stood in the way of manufacturing penicillin on a really large scale. British and American chemists and manufacturers worked hard together throughout the year 1942 but all that they could manage to produce in the following year was just enough penicillin to allow of fifteen wounded men in the Eighth Army in Egypt being treated with it. Then the U.S. War Production Board took over the work of manufacturing penicillin and with the immense resources of America behind it the production of the new remedy rapidly rose.

Since the war, Great Britain has been able to produce more than enough penicillin for her own needs and has now become an exporter of it on a large scale. Great improvements have also been made in the purification of the drug, and the sodium salt of penicillin is now available in a crystalline form. Chemists have now unravelled its chemical formula which is as follows. (*See* Fig. 12.) The fine piece of team work which produced penicillin has been suitably rewarded. Fleming and Florey have received knighthoods and the Nobel Prize for Medicine in 1945 was divided equally between Fleming, Florey and Chain. The story of the production of penicillin on a large scale is a story of magnificent co-operation between a great many people. Doctors, scientists, engineers and manufacturing chemists, many of whom had previously been rivals, worked loyally together for a common aim, the good of the wounded soldier.

NEW PRINCIPLES IN MEDICINE

Sir Alexander Fleming has shown us that man has potential allies in that living film which covers the surface of this planet, the film we refer to as Organic Life. He has demonstrated that many of the moulds are at war with our own enemies, the pathogenic organisms, and this explains a phenomenon which had long been noted. Bacteriologists have commented on the fact that if cattle, dead from anthrax, are buried in a field, the anthrax bacilli will in course of time disappear from the soil in spite of the fact that they

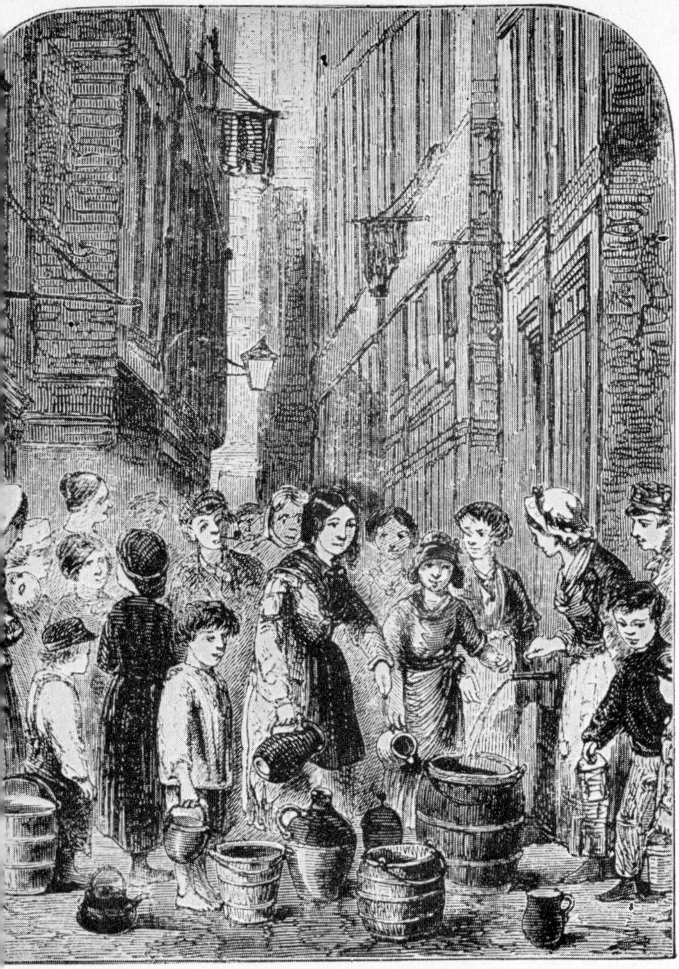

The water supply in Fryingpan Alley, Clerkenwell. Water available for twenty minutes each day

(From *Another Blow for Life*, by G. Godwin, 1864)

Elizabethan Quack with his patients

(From Wm. Clewes: *A Brief Treatise of the Disease called Morbus Gallicus*, 1585)

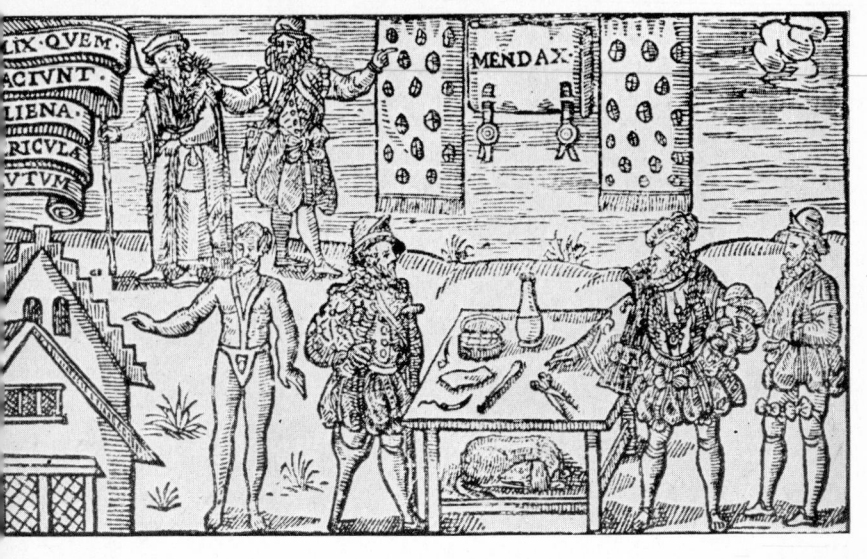

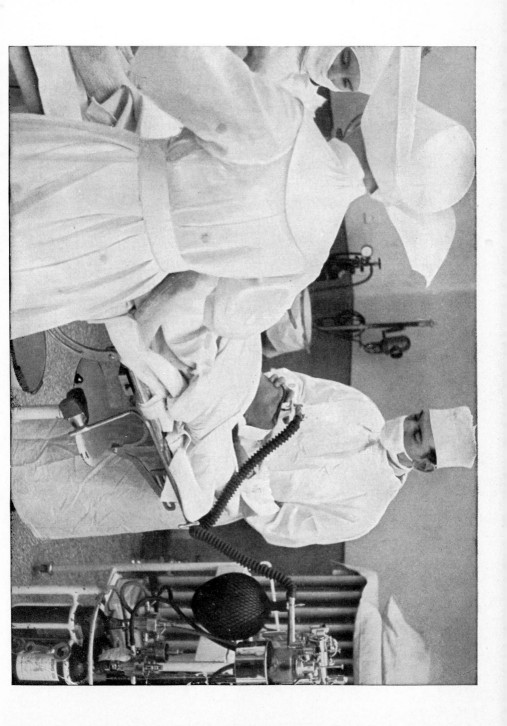

are spore-bearers. We can now be practically certain that their destruction is brought about by the action of moulds.

As has already been pointed out, penicillin is only active against certain forms of pathogenic organisms and it confers no protection against other varieties of them. Because of this limited action of

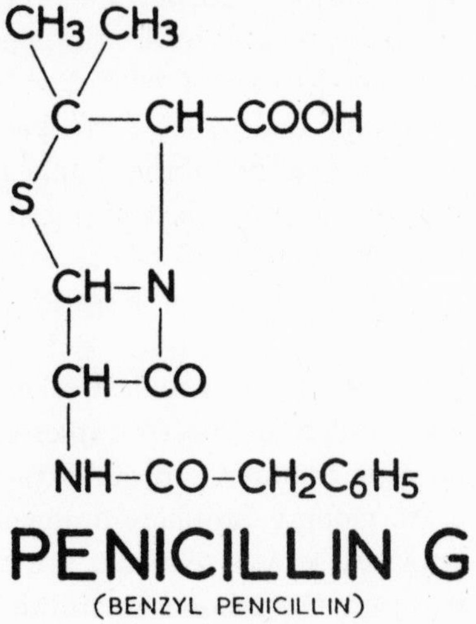

CH₃ CH₃

C—CH–COOH

S

CH–N

CH–CO

NH–CO–CH₂C₆H₅

PENICILLIN G
(BENZYL PENICILLIN)

FIG. 12.—Chemical formula of penicillin

penicillin an intensive search was soon started for other moulds that might be capable of destroying organisms on which penicillin had no action. As a result of this search several new allies have been found in Organic Life, streptomycin, chloromycetin, aureomycin, terra-mycin, and several others. The breadth of our front against the enemy is being gradually increased and there is every reason to believe that in course of time it will be increased still further.

So far so good, but it must not be imagined that our enemies in Organic Life have been idle all the time that we have been attacking them with the chemical poisons provided by the moulds. They have also made certain strategic moves which in turn have necessitated the adoption of certain counter-measures on our part. The first significant happening that bacteriologists noticed after the attack with the sulphonamides had begun was that strains of streptococci

and gonococci resistant to the action of this drug—there had always been some resistant forms—were turning up more and more frequently. A similar phenomenon has been noted since the introduction of penicillin; penicillin-resistant organisms seem to be on the increase. It is as though the enemy were getting the measure of our attack and were changing its tactics. But how can this new move on its part have been in action? Are pathogenic organisms managing to acquire an immunity to our poisons or are the special varieties which possess a natural resistance to them becoming more obvious to us because their non-resistant colleagues have been killed off? It is difficult to be sure about the nature of the changes that have occurred since the introduction of the sulphonamides and of penicillin. They suggest, however, that we must not be too optimistic of attaining the ideal that Louis Pasteur once dreamt of, a world free of all pathogenic organisms.

It is now quite obvious that the smallest of our foes—so tiny that they are only visible under an electron-microscope—the viruses, show no signs at all of succumbing to our attacks with drugs and moulds. And there are gloomy prophets amongst the doctors who shake their heads when these new remedies are mentioned and who proclaim that if we upset the balance maintained by Nature and destroy too many of the pathogenic bacteria, the viruses will increase so that great epidemics of virus infections will occur. Some of these prophets go so far as to say that the rise in virus diseases has already begun. (*See* Plate 30.)

Truth is usually to be found lying midway between two extremes, and although we need not be unduly disturbed by these gloomy prognostications we must bear in mind that Nature maintains a balance between the different components of Organic Life and that unexpected things generally happen when man blunders in to disturb it. There is a story of a village community that imported harmless snakes in order to get rid of a plague of rats and it is said that the originators of this clever plan had to face later the still greater problem of how to deal with the new epidemic of snakes. Man is clever but his cleverness often brings him to the brink of disaster as we of the atomic age are now beginning to realize. It is quite possible that our great success in the war against a particular breed of micro-organisms will eventually lead to unexpected consequences. Yet to

hold back because we cannot be sure of what will happen later would be absurd. The sulphonamide drugs and penicillin are of immense value to us and we must continue to use them, keeping a watchful eye on the incidence of other forms of infection, and particularly of the incidence of virus infections. And it may well happen that we shall eventually find some means of overcoming the smallest and cleverest of all our foes.

CHAPTER XV

Tropical Diseases

THE last two chapters have dealt with the warfare between the pathogenic organisms and mankind. The way in which the organisms attack and the means modern man has adopted for his defence were described. Earlier theories on the subject of contagious diseases were referred to, such as the idea of Fracastorius that they spread by direct contact through such articles as clothing and household utensils and, at a distance, by means of air-borne particles. But brilliant though the guesses of this pioneer epidemiologist of mediaeval Italy were, they revealed only two of the many methods by which infective diseases are disseminated. Biologists frequently point to the pollination of flowers and to other examples of symbiosis when they want to stress the interconnectedness of all forms of life on the earth, but still more striking examples of this could be found in works on pathology and epidemiology. The ingenuity with which some diseases are disseminated through the agency of intermediate hosts is such that the mind is left astonished by the inventiveness of Nature. How, one asks oneself, were all these intricate patterns of interwoven forms of life devised? By whom were these ingenious and elaborate methods of spreading infection thought out? The stages in the complicated process are so dovetailed into one another and each is so dependent on the other that it is difficult to believe that this intricate pattern of events was brought about by a concourse of accidents on divergent lines of the evolutionary process. Yet this is what the New Darwinists would have us believe was the case.

As excellent examples of these more elaborate methods of infection by means of vectors or intermediate hosts are to be found amongst tropical diseases, it will be appropriate to give the history

of some of the earlier discoveries in the tropical branch of medicine. We shall begin with the story of the commonest of all the tropical diseases, malaria.

MALARIA

The discovery that malaria was spread by mosquitoes is usually regarded as being a modern one but actually this is not the case. The idea that malaria and other diseases were transmitted by insects goes back to many centuries before Christ and the earliest mention of it is to be found in the works of the Brahmin physician Susruta who lived about 500 B.C. He gives an excellent clinical description of malaria and then goes on to attribute it to the bite of the mosquito. Columella (A.D. 100) wrote on the same subject in more general terms but it is obvious that he was obviously extremely suspicious of the mosquito as a spreader of diseases. In *De Re Rustica* he writes on the subject of hygiene and speaks of the need to choose a healthy locality for a dwelling. "Nor indeed must there be a marsh near the building," he writes, "nor a public highway adjoining, for the former always throws up noxious and poisonous steams during the heats and breeds animals with mischievous stings which fly upon us in exceeding thick swarms; and also sends forth, from the mud and fermented dirt, envenomed pests of water-snakes and serpents, deprived of the moisture they enjoyed in winter; whereby hidden diseases are often contracted, the causes of which even the physicians themselves cannot thoroughly understand." But as so often happens, these ancient ideas that malaria was closely associated with marshes and with the insects and other creatures breeding in them were forgotten, so that the responsibility of the mosquito for the spread of the fever had to be rediscovered a great many centuries later.

Malaria has often been called the scourge of the tropics and at one time it would have been correct to have called it the scourge of the world. It was one of the causes of the collapse of the Roman Empire for the ague was rampant not only in Rome itself but throughout the whole of the far-flung Empire, as far north as Great Britain and as far south as the North African coast. From the very beginning the Romans suspected the marshes as being the cause of it, as is shown by the French term for malaria, "paludisme", derived from a word meaning "marsh fever". We do not know whether

malaria existed in America in the time of the Romans but it was a common disease there by the sixteenth century. It was well known to Hippocrates also, and he was inclined to attribute it to the drinking of stagnant water. That Italy was a particularly bad place for malaria in the seventeenth century is shown by the fact that no less than eight cardinals and thirty secretaries died of this complaint in 1623 whilst attending a conference in Rome.

An unusual feature of the story of malaria is that its treatment has always been in advance of our knowledge of its cause, whereas in medicine the reverse is usually the case. As a rule our capacity to diagnose a disease is well ahead of our capacity to treat it. Yet for many centuries the Indians of Peru treated the fever successfully with a powder prepared from cinchona bark, and it is likely that the Indians' knowledge of the curative action of quinine reached them from their forebears the Incas. There exists a pleasing legend concerning a certain Countess of Chinchon, the wife of a Spanish Viceroy of Peru, whose life is supposed to have been saved in 1640 by the timely use of this remedy, but as A. W. Haggis has shown that this romantic story rests on very insecure foundations it need not be repeated. All that can be said with any certainty about this date 1640 is that it was about this time that the great English physician Sydenham first heard of the curative properties of cinchona bark and, managing to obtain some of it, he used it with conspicuous success during a serious epidemic of the ague in England.

THE DISCOVERY OF THE CAUSE OF MALARIA

The story of the discovery of the infective agent of malaria begins with a paper written in 1880 by Laveran, a French Army surgeon serving in Algeria, in which he stated that he had found protozoa or amoeba-like organisms in the blood of patients suffering from this fever. He published four treatises on the subject and received a Nobel prize for his work in 1907. Yet no real profit was derived from Laveran's discovery beyond the fact that the discovery of the characteristic protozoa in a patient's blood provided a means of more accurate diagnosis. All that had really been learnt about malaria from Laveran's discovery was that tiny parasites were present in the red blood corpuscles of patients suffering from it and that in successive blood smears these parasites grew and changed their

shape. With each new brood of parasites in the blood a fresh bout of ague fever began. But how did the protozoa get into the blood? That was the great question.

The next man to advance our knowledge of malaria was Ronald Ross (1857–1932), a young officer in the Indian Medical Service. Whilst he was on leave from India, Ross was fortunate enough to meet Sir Patrick Manson, the great expert on tropical diseases. Sir Patrick Manson showed him the malaria parasite in a patient's blood and expressed his opinion that it probably represented only a single phase in a much more elaborate life cycle. He spoke to Ross also of the non-human phases of the life cycle of the filaria parasite which caused the tropical disease of elephantiasis. He told him that this non-human stage of the filaria's life was passed within the body of a mosquito and he advised Ross to be on the look-out for a similar happening in the case of the parasite of malaria. It might well be that the malaria parasite, like filaria, also spent part of its life in a mosquito. Ross returned to India fired with enthusiasm for research on malaria, and in 1897 he spent many months on end examining various kinds of mosquito under his microscope but without succeeding in finding any malarial parasites in them. At last he tried a new species of dapple-winged mosquito which he had bred from eggs, and four or five days after these had bitten a patient suffering from malarial fever he found in their stomach walls little dark dots. He could make out that these dark specks were alive and were growing and multiplying; they could not be anything else than the parasite for which he had so long been searching. It was August 20th, 1897, the day that is now celebrated in the Ross Institute of Tropical Hygiene in London as "Mosquito Day", and that night Ross wrote in his diary:

"I find thy cunning seeds
O million murdering death."

Yes, he had found the seeds but there still remained the problem of how they got from the walls of the mosquito's stomach into the blood stream of human beings.

Before Ross could complete his studies he was posted to another part of India where there was very little malaria—at any rate, very

little malaria of the human kind. But encouraged by Manson, who now wrote to him regularly, he continued his research. This time he experimented with sparrows, for birds, like many other animals, have their own special form of malaria. Ross infected his speckled mosquitoes by feeding them on infected sparrows and afterwards he found the characteristic "spores" in their stomachs. Then on July 4th, 1898, he noticed a new thing, that the salivary glands situated round the base of the mosquito's proboscis were swarming with long thin "spores". (*See* Fig. 13.) It was obvious that these were about to leave the mosquito by the same route as that by which they—or it would be more correct to say the parent forms of these spores—had arrived. In other words it was by its bite that the malarial mosquito both received and passed on the infection. This Ross was able to prove by letting his mosquitoes bite healthy young sparrows and finding their blood swarming with malarial parasites some two weeks later. At a later date this experiment was repeated on human volunteers with similar results.

The outcome of this all-important discovery was a declaration of war on the anopheles mosquito. (*See* Fig. 14.) This anti-mosquito crusade was comparatively easy in the case of cities and large towns where all that was required was to cover in the cisterns, fill in pools, drain swampy grounds and clear ditches, but outside the towns it was a much more difficult problem to destroy the breeding grounds of the enemy. Yet this had to be done if malaria was to be eliminated. So the swamps in which the mosquitoes spent their larval stage were drained, grasses and other vegetation growing in ditches were cut down, and ponds, ruts and hollows in which water collected were filled in as much as possible. Large pools which could not be drained were treated with sufficient paraffin oil each week to form a thin film of oil on their surface, a film which prevented the mosquito larvae, living there, from obtaining sufficient oxygen for their development. The preparation known as D.D.T. is now added to the oil or kerosene used for this purpose and the walls and ceilings of houses in malarial districts are also sprayed with this mixture.

Much has been done by these and other measures to reduce the incidence of malaria, and many parts of the tropics in which it was formerly impossible for any white man to live have now been rendered comparatively free from it. Hong Kong, Shanghai, Singapore

LIFE CYCLE OF *P. VIVAX*

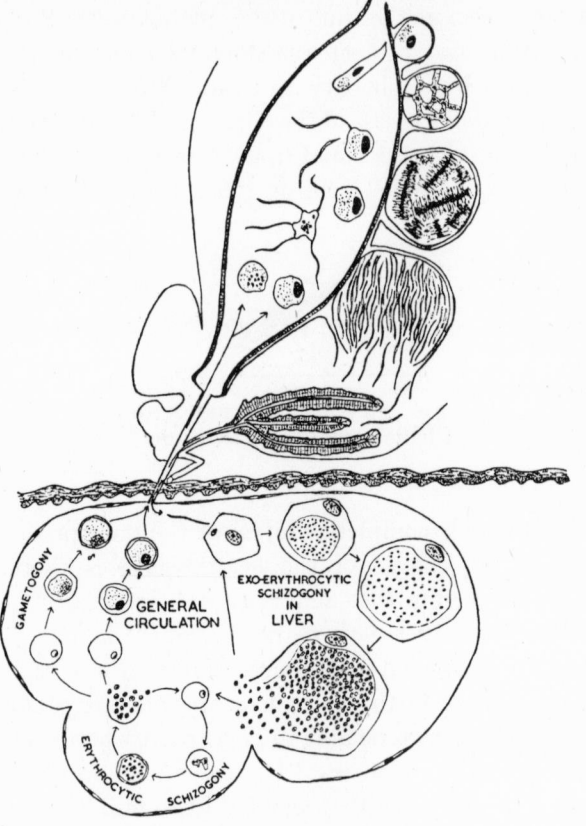

FIG. 13.—*The Plasmodium of Benign Tertiary Malaria*

The three separate cycles of evolution of the Plasmodium are shown in the diagram. Above the horizontal line of the skin is the development within the mosquito and below it, that within the human being. To the left is the development of the parasite in the blood and to the right, within the liver from which spores periodically enter the blood stream, thus reinfecting it.

and parts of the West Coast of Africa bear testimony to this fact, but the most striking proof of the success of the anti-malarial campaign was given at the time of the cutting of the Panama Canal. This great engineering project was started by Ferdinand de Lesseps in the year 1880 but it had to be abandoned eight years later on account of the unhealthiness of the climate. The combined death rate among the workers on the canal from malaria and yellow fever had by that time reached the level of 176 per thousand. In 1904 the

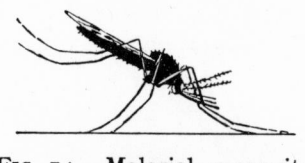

Fig. 14.—Malarial mosquito
female in resting attitude

Americans took over complete control of the enterprise and placed Colonel Gorgas in charge of the health services there. Sanitary brigades were formed in the canal zone and the measures which had proved so satisfactory a few years previously in ridding Cuba of malaria were now applied in Panama. Within a few years the mortality rate had fallen in the most dramatic manner. Colonel Gorgas was a big enough man to be able to give credit where credit was due and he wrote to Ross as follows: "It seems to me not extreme to say that it was your discovery that enabled us to build the canal on the isthmus of Panama." It was a generous gesture and it is true that but for the discoveries of Ross the Panama Canal could not have been built. But it must not be forgotten that a great many others had contributed to the solution of the malarial problem besides Ross, notably Laveran and Sir Patrick Manson. It is always thus in medicine that the great discoverer is the man who has had the privilege of adding the coping stone to a building on which a great many other people had previously laboured.

YELLOW FEVER

There are many similarities between the two tropical diseases malaria and yellow fever. Both were formerly widely spread in the

tropics, both have taken an immense toll of human life, both are diseases of great antiquity and both are spread by means of mosquitoes. Something must therefore be said about the history of yellow fever and about the brilliant research work which eventually revealed its several secrets.

In all probability yellow fever started in Africa and thence spread to the Americas and to Southern Europe at the time of, and in great part through, the agency of the slave trade. We are able to trace its journey as it reaches each new continent, much as we were able to follow the spread of syphilis to different countries in Chapter XIII. The following is a description of the "new distemper" as it was called by a Dr. Hughes who wrote an account of the arrival of the yellow fever in the West Indies in the year 1715:

"After a shivering fit, a violent fever comes, with excessive pains in the head, back and limbs, loss of strength and spirits, with great dejection of mind, insatiable thirst and restlessness and sometimes too with vomiting. . . . After some days are past the pain abates, as well as the fever . . . so that he appears to be better; but on a narrow view, a yellowness appears in his eyes and skin and he is visibly worse. About this time he sometimes spits blood, and that by mouthfuls; as this continues he grows cold and his pulse abates till at last it is quite gone; and the patient becomes almost as cold as stone and continues in that state with a composed sedate mind. In this condition he may perhaps live twelve hours without any sensible pulse or heat and then expires. Such were the symptoms and progress at this year the Year 1715."

Nothing need be added to Dr. Hughes' excellent description of the yellow jack, that terrible fever dreaded by sailors and by all whose business took them into the tropics. And not only into the tropics, for epidemics of it might break out almost anywhere in the world, in the temperate as well as in the tropical zones. In Boston and Philadelphia 5000 people died of the yellow fever in the course of a few months and then, quite suddenly, the epidemic faded away as mysteriously as it had begun. Another earlier epidemic of it was so fierce that it brought to nought the proud schemes of Napoleon Bonaparte, who in the year 1800 dispatched to Haiti an army of

30,000 men with orders that it should fortify the island and use it as a base for his colonization plans in Louisiana and Mexico. But the yellow fever intervened, causing 23,000 casualties in Napoleon's army, and, aided by this providential intervention on their behalf, a few resolute patriots were able to make Haiti what it still is, an independent Black Republic.

The ravages inflicted on the mariner at sea by the yellow jack were so devastating as to become legendary. The story of the *Flying Dutchman* was founded on the history of a ship that was condemned to haunt the seas around the Cape of Good Hope because, after a murder had been committed aboard, yellow fever broke out amongst the crew and no country would allow the stricken ship to enter its harbours. Ships often had to remain laid up in foreign ports or else be abandoned in tropical rivers until they were no longer seaworthy because the crews that had brought them thus far had all been buried. Nor was this so very long ago either. The writer of this book has talked with seafaring men who pointed out to him a stretch of river at Santos in Brazil where lines of foreign ships were formerly anchored because no new crews could be found for them. And it was by shipping that the dreaded fever was frequently carried to other lands. A ship which set sail from Sierra Leone in the year of Victoria's Coronation, 1838, brought the fever to the Gambia where it had been unknown before, and half of the population speedily became its victims.

The medical profession was completely baffled by the disease and by the way in which it behaved. One of the curious things about an epidemic of yellow fever was that it did not begin soon after the first case of it had appeared but some two weeks later. What was the explanation of this very long latent period before the epidemic started? It is reported that two Jamaican medical men, Drs. William and Bennet, debated so hotly on this subject that they were forced to fight a duel to settle their differences, a duel which ended in the death of both disputants.

Puzzles in preventive medicine resemble detective problems and this fact that an epidemic of yellow fever never began as cholera and Plague began, promptly, but at least two weeks after the appearance of the first case, was obviously an important clue to the nature of the disease. Where had the disease been lurking during these

fourteen days, collecting its strength as it were, until it was strong enough to attack its next victim? Dr. Josiah Clark Nott of Alabama was the first man to supply the correct answer to the riddle. He noted, what many other people had observed before, that mosquitoes abounded in the proximity of the dwellings in which yellow fever had broken out, and in 1748, a century and a half before Manson talked to Ross about his malarial mosquito theory, Dr. Nott wrote a paper in which he suggested that the mosquito was a carrier of both yellow fever and of malaria. This theory not only accounted for the delay in the start of an epidemic, but also for a fact which had often been noted—that a ship could carry the yellow jack from one port to another without there being any sufferers from the fever aboard. It carried it of course in the form of infected mosquitoes. But the idea of the mosquito being a yellow fever carrier seemed absurd to people who were considered of importance in the medical profession, and Dr. Nott's peculiar theory attracted no attention and was soon forgotten.

It was revived in 1881 by Dr. Carlos Finlay of Havana who went even further than Nott and specified the guilty mosquito, the *Aedes Aegypti*. This, he said, carried the infective organism of yellow fever from one man to another and not merely some toxin that it had picked up in the marshes. Finlay carried out a few simple experiments in support of his theory but the world was still not ready for the discovery of the pathology of yellow fever and nobody paid any attention to the fantasies of an obscure Cuban practitioner. It was not until Ross had published his malarial researches in India and medical men had become accustomed to the idea that a mosquito was responsible for the spread of malaria that Finlay's ideas about yellow fever were remembered and given consideration.

Because yellow fever was at that time exacting a very heavy toll of the American mercantile marine, an American Yellow Fever Commission was dispatched to Cuba with Walter Reed (1851–1902) and James Carroll (1854–1927) in charge of it. Obviously the best way of testing Carlos Finlay's mosquito theory was to allow volunteers to be bitten by the said yellow fever-bearing mosquitoes. A preliminary attempt to bring about infection by means of clothing and blankets previously used by former yellow fever patients having proved negative the two human guinea pigs, Carroll and Jesse Lazear

(1866–1900), allowed themselves to be bitten by a mosquito of the suspected variety, *Aedes Aegypti*. Both men developed yellow fever afterwards and Lazear died from it. It was afterwards proved that if a mosquito was to be an efficient agent of infection it must first have fed on a yellow fever patient during the first three days of his fever. It then remained a carrier of yellow fever for the whole of its life.

At the time of this fine and gallant piece of research the idea of ultra-microscopic viruses did not exist so that the actual infective agent remained undiscovered by the Commission. But even without this knowledge it was obvious that much could be done to reduce the incidence of the disease. By attacking the guilty mosquito on a very large scale, as the anopheles mosquito had been attacked in India, the incidence of yellow fever could be markedly diminished. This indirect attack on the carrier of the disease met with such conspicuous success that, as we have seen, de Lesseps was able to proceed with the digging of the Panama Canal without losing many of his labourers from yellow fever.

No tropical disease has claimed so many victims amongst research workers as yellow fever has claimed, for Lazear was to prove to be only the first martyr in the long course of the research. During its final stages Noguchi, the brilliant bacteriologist, fell a prey to the virus he had himself discovered. His death was quickly followed by the death of two of his colleagues, Drs. Adrian Stokes and W. A. Young.

Even after the virus and the mode of infection had been discovered problems requiring an urgent answer arose from time to time. For example, disturbing reports arrived from both South America and West Africa to the effect that epidemics of yellow fever were occurring in the jungle in spite of the fact that no case of yellow fever had previously been reported there and that no typical mosquito could be found in that region. What was the explanation of these mysterious epidemics? The problem was sufficiently important to warrant very careful investigation. By this time, not only had the virus been found but it had been proved that mice were also susceptible to it. Then Dr. Theiler demonstrated the fact that mice could be protected if they were given blood serum from a patient convalescent from yellow fever at the same time that they were being

inoculated with the virus. This "mouse-protection test", as it was called, was now used in the jungle regions in which these inexplicable epidemics had been reported and the test showed that large numbers of the local inhabitants must have suffered previously from yellow fever without knowing it because their serum had a protective action on mice. But where had these inhabitants managed to pick up their infections? People had noticed that epidemics of yellow fever were often preceded by the death of many monkeys in that neighbourhood, so the researchers started to examine carefully specimens of monkeys' blood. This, like the blood of the local natives, was found to be protective to mice showing that the great majority of monkeys had suffered and recovered from yellow fever.

So the whole chain of problems connected with the fever has now been solved. Primarily, yellow fever is a disease of monkeys and of other arboreal animals so that it smoulders there always amongst these agile inhabitants of the jungle and also within the bodies of their attendant mosquitoes. But every now and then infected monkeys make raids on the gardens of the villagers and they are accompanied on these expeditions by their attendant mosquitoes. The latter, being winged, easily enter the human dwellings and bite their inhabitants, thereby infecting them with the virus. Then, having perpetrated their villainies, the monkeys' attendant mosquitoes retire and the mosquitoes which prey on man take over the job. Should any newcomers who are susceptible to yellow fever arrive in that district there will be plenty of yellow fever virus about to start a first-class epidemic there.

The final step in this fine piece of research on yellow fever was the preparation of a vaccine which could give protection against infection. This vaccine is made from a virus attenuated by passage first through mice, and then through tissue cultures. It has proved very successful.

In Chapter V an account was given of the mediaeval plague known as the Black Death, but nothing was said about its cause. Something must now be said about this and about the subsequent history of this pestilence in Europe. From time to time the plague revisited these islands, there being a particularly bad epidemic in London in 1665, but these later visitations were far less serious than those that had occurred in the Middle Ages. In the earlier epidemics

the death roll had been so appalling that people wondered whether anybody would survive or whether humanity was doomed to annihilation. A fourteenth-century priest living in Ireland wrote about one of these earlier epidemics as follows: "The pestilence deprived of human inhabitants villages and cities, castles and towns, so that there was scarcely found a man to dwell therein; the pestilence was so contagious that whosoever touched the sick or the dead was immediately infected and died . . . many died of boils and abscesses and pustules on their legs and under their arm-pits; others, frantic with pain in the head, and others spitting blood. . . . I, waiting for death till it come . . . so I have reduced these things to writing; and lest the writing should perish with the writer and the work together with the workman, I leave parchment for the continuing of the work, if haply any man survive and any of the race of Adam escape this pestilence and continue the work which I have commenced."

This epistle written on parchment ends here abruptly, but in another handwriting is added "here it seems the author died". Yet the race of Adam survived this and many later visitations of the plague and eventually—but only in the closing decades of the nineteenth century—men discovered its true cause and the cure for it. We now know that plague is primarily a disease of rats and other small rodents and that it is from this source that man becomes infected. Older writers had suspected a close connection between the plague and rats but, as has so often happened in the story of medicine, this ancient knowledge was forgotten. The Egyptians even depicted Ptah, the god of pestilence, sitting with rats in his hand, and ancient Hindu teachers had been still more explicit in that they warned villagers to desert their houses whenever they saw a number of dead rats lying about. So also does there exist this saying in ancient Chinese literature: "A few days after the death of the rats, men pass away like falling walls." And what more graphic description could be given of the behaviour of men smitten in these earlier epidemics? They fell to the ground like bricks tumbling out of an undermined wall.

It was only in 1894, after Pasteur had given the necessary impetus to research, that serious efforts were made to discover the infective organisms of bubonic plague. Two bacteriologists investigated cases

of plague in Hong Kong, a Frenchman, by name Yersin, who had been a pupil of the great Pasteur, and Kitasato, a particularly brilliant Japanese bacteriologist. Quite independently and within a few days of each other these two workers found an organism in the buboes and in the blood of patients who had died of the plague. They succeeded also in growing this organism in culture plates and in producing plague in rats by inoculating them from these cultures. Rats were chosen partly because rats are used extensively in laboratory inoculation experiments, and partly because scientists by now were beginning to recognize that there was a close connection between rats and bubonic plague.

The next thing to be found out was how the infection was passed from the rat to the human being. The possibility that it might be through the contamination of human food by rat droppings was considered, but there were no observations to support this view. A Frenchman, by name Simon, was of the opinion that a much more likely mode of infection was by means of the fleas which infest rats, and shortly afterwards he confirmed his theory by discovering plague germs within these fleas. So now the whole story had been unravelled. Plague is a disease of rats and small rodents, in the same way that malaria is primarily a disease of monkeys, and when a serious epidemic of plague starts amongst the rodents, many of them die from it. Then the hungry and thirsty fleas are compelled to seek other hosts on which to live, including man. Wherever rats are to be found, whether it be in houses, ships, barns, warehouses or food-stores, there the plague is able to start, first amongst the rats and then later amongst men.

To eliminate plague the carriers of the plague germ or the *Pasteurella pestis*, as it is now called, have to be slain. The plague doctors of the Middle Ages who dressed themselves from head to foot in garments resembling boiler suits (*see* Fig. 4) and who wore gloves, goggles and cloth helmets were working along the right lines, for by covering themselves up completely they were less likely to be bitten by the fleas infesting the plague houses. But because these mediaeval doctors omitted to get rid of the garbage heaps and decaying rubbish which littered the streets and the lower storey of the houses and provided sustenance for rats, they failed to break the most easily breakable link in the chain of events

leading to man's infection. Modern man's intensive drive against the rat has materially reduced the incidence of plague. But he has in addition acquired certain valuable remedies against the plague. Streptomycin usually has a miraculous action when it is given early enough to a patient suffering from bubonic plague and sulphadiazine prevents its development in people who have come into contact with patients suffering from it. A protective vaccine has also been prepared against the plague, but the disease is becoming so rare now that it rarely has to be used.

ELEPHANTIASIS

This story of the unravelling of the sequence of events in the spread of tropical diseases should really have started with an account of elephantiasis for it was whilst investigating that disease that Sir Patrick Manson's attention was first drawn to the idea of its being spread by mosquitoes, and this in turn provided the clue to the mosquito's role in other tropical infections. In 1876 Manson evolved the theory that the swellings characteristic of elephantiasis were caused by the tiny worm-like filaria, previously found in the blood, making their way into the lymphatics and blocking these channels by their presence there. After examining hundreds of elephantiasis patients he found that there was a periodicity in the appearance of the filaria in their blood stream. They became particularly numerous towards sunset, attained a maximum at midnight, and then gradually diminished, so that by noon of the next day they had entirely disappeared. This suggested to Manson that the tiny filaria in the blood were the offspring of adult worms living in the lymphatics, and that the offspring sought the blood in order to mature there. He next began to speculate how the disease managed to spread from one patient to another and formulated the idea that it was through the intermediary of some "free-ranging, blood-sucking insect". This suggested that some sort of mosquito might be responsible for the spread of the disease. There was this in favour of the idea, the fact that the mosquito fed at night, just at the time when an elephantiasis patient's superficial blood vessels were most crowded with filaria. With the co-operation of a Chinese patient who was suffering from elephantiasis Manson put his theory to the test. The patient agreed to allow himself to be bitten by mosquitoes

and afterwards these mosquitoes were caught and examined. To Manson's delight their stomachs were found to be crowded with filaria, many of which were found to be in the act of burrowing through the stomach walls and of making their way to the muscles of the mosquito's chest. And as they progressed in the direction of the chest muscles Manson noticed that the filaria increased in size, getting ready to be injected into the blood of a human host by the mosquito. This excellent piece of detective work by Sir Patrick Manson was of the greatest practical value and it opened up new vistas in tropical parasitology, the idea that a very important part was played in the spread of tropical diseases by blood-sucking insects. After this idea had been accepted, it was much easier to see the part played by mosquitoes in the spread of other diseases.

Typhus is spread by fleas, ticks or lice, and the organism responsible for it is an extremely minute one, smaller than bacteria but a little larger than the viruses. The great advantage of knowing the various links in the chain of events leading to infection is that efforts can then be made to break the sequence in its weakest part. In the case of malaria the chief attack is directed against the larval stage of the mosquito's development, and in typhus the spread is brought to an end by intensive delousing operations. In former days this was a difficult and tedious matter, entailing the bathing of a great many people and steam disinfection of their clothes. But fortunately lice have been found to be very susceptible to D.D.T. and all that is now required is that a powder containing 5 to 10 per cent of D.D.T. in talc should be blown up the sleeves and the trouser legs and down the neck of all lousy people. In this way, very large numbers of typhus contacts can be deloused in a very short time and an epidemic quickly stopped.

The study of tropical illnesses shows how complicated the process of parasitism known as disease may become. In many cases it implicates three individuals: in yellow fever, monkeys, mosquitoes and man, and in plague the smaller rodents, their fleas and man. Now, man is a comparative newcomer on this earth, and long before he arrived here diseases had probably established a firm hold on some of the mammals nearest to him. Formidable alliances had also been forged between insects and viruses, alliances which were eventually

to be the means of carrying the virus infections to the newcomer, man.

These complex patterns of parasitism and illness probably started as much simpler processes in which one organism was contriving to live at the expense of another one; for example, the bacillus of plague was managing to live within the tissues of the small rodents. In course of time this same bacillus managed to infect also the vermin feeding on its hosts, and this conferred on it the great advantage of being able to spread much more rapidly than before, but still only amongst the rodents. Then man came along and with the help of the fleas the bacillus of plague succeeded in extending its sphere of action by founding colonies within him. Diseases, like everything else in the universe, have their cycles; they appear, they grow in strength, they reach their zenith, they decline and they disappear. One of the means by which a disease can postpone the inevitable decline is to find a new host and it is quite possible that by providing the plague bacillus with new facilities when it was on the downward trend, man presented bubonic plague with a new lease of life. But in course of time man's innate cleverness has come into play and by means of his preventive methods, his sulphonamides and his anti-biotics, he is now cancelling that lease.

Yet successful though man has been in getting the better of many of the pathogenic germs, life on the earth will always be for him a precarious venture. Even if he manages to avoid self annihilation in his next bout of reciprocal destruction, he must still exist surrounded by powerful enemies. As has already been noted, the viruses possess particularly efficient defences and also display great cleverness in initiating fresh methods of infection. It is likely also that new viruses will arise from time to time by the emergence of mutations, and as viruses are "the most labile and mutable of all living organisms" the appearance of new forms may be comparatively common events. There is always the risk therefore that some form of virus will arise in the future that takes man at a grave disadvantage. It would be a fitting end to the story of proud man that, having conquered the very big and made himself master of the earth, he should fall a prey to the very small. The Greeks were convinced that *"nemesis"* invariably followed *"hubris"*.

CHAPTER XVI

Deficiency Diseases

AS has been seen, the theory of the four cardinal humours of the body survived for many centuries and in the light of this theory illness could only be looked upon as being a disturbance in the balance of these four humours. The whole object of the medical man's treatment lay therefore in bringing about a restoration of the balance. Ancient Chinese medicine agreed with European medicine in this view of disease but postulated the existence of five instead of four cardinal humours. Medicine remained so content with this doctrine that it was only discarded in the seventeenth century after Harvey's discovery of the circulation of the blood.

The Iatro-chemical school of physiology founded by Jean Baptiste van Helmont (1577–1644) was in the direct line of descent from this school of the four humours. It looked upon life as being a series of chemical reactions, and because van Helmont was a great admirer of Paracelsus he postulated the existence of an archaeus or life-force which dominated and directed all these reactions. He also introduced the word "gas" into medicine and included under this term a number of ferments presiding over the various functions of the body, such as nutrition, digestion and movement. In view of later discoveries the hormonic view of physiology put forward by van Helmont was an extraordinarily clever guess.

The anticipation of future hormonic discoveries made by Theophile de Borden (1722-1776), a physician living at the court of Louis XV, was still more brilliant. De Borden, who later helped to found the vitalistic school of physiology at Montpellier, held that the various organs of the body were both federated with each other and dependent upon each other, but that they were all presided over by the stomach, the heart and the brain which formed a "tripod

of life". What was particularly perspicacious on his part was that he taught that each organ of the body fabricated a specific secretion which was absorbed back into the blood. Finally, he held that the integration of the body depended on the maintenance of a balance between these specific secretions formed by the organs. Borden's ideas were purely speculative and unsupported by any experiments or precise observations yet they approximated very closely to the modern idea of the hormonic balance maintained in the body.

Nearly two centuries had to pass before two physiologists working in a twentieth-century laboratory confirmed this idea that a chemical balance is maintained in the body by a number of hormones. In the year 1902 Bayliss and Starling found that a flow of pancreatic juice took place in a dog after food had been given it, even when the nerves running to and from the dog's pancreas had been completely severed. This clearly meant that the stimulus travelled to the pancreas by some path other than the central nervous system. Later it was found that what stimulated the pancreas to become active as soon as food was introduced into the stomach was a secretion manufactured by the duodenum, in other words a special chemical messenger which travelled to the pancreas by way of the blood stream. Bayliss and Starling gave to this chemical messenger the name of "secretin" and afterwards showed that it was only one of many hormones formed in the body. De Borden had been completely right in declaring that each organ of the body was "the workshop of a specific substance that passes into the blood". The organs which possess this ability to secrete hormones in a specially high degree are the endocrine glands, structures of the greatest interest, about which more must now be said.

THE DUCTLESS GLANDS AND THEIR INTERNAL SECRETIONS

Malpighi was one of the first scientists to examine the endocrine glands and to note that they possessed no ducts along which secretions could flow, and the first of these glands to be studied carefully by medical men were the suprarenals, two small glands situated just above the kidneys. In 1849 Thomas Addison (1793–1860), a physician to Guy's Hospital, read a paper in which he correlated certain symptoms, muscular weakness, progressive debility and bronzing of the skin, with pathological lesions of these small structures. Then

medical interest shifted to the thyroid, the study of which was the result of an accident rather than of design. Goitre, or enlargement of the thyroid gland, has long been a very common complaint in Switzerland, and after the introduction of antiseptic surgery Swiss surgeons were encouraged to attempt the removal of these unsightly swellings. Amongst those who succeeded in carrying out this operation was a Swiss surgeon, Theodor Kocher (1841–1917), but he found that he had produced in his patients very distressing symptoms by his removal of their thyroids. They became slow in their muscular and intellectual responses, their features coarsened and their hair became dry and fell out. If they were young patients, all further growth was arrested; in other words, Kocher found that by the complete removal of the thyroid he had produced a cretin. Similar symptoms of thyroid deficiency could be experimentally reproduced in animals by extirpating all thyroid tissue. Then, Moritz Schiff of Berne (1823–1890) elicited the still more valuable fact in 1884 that the distressing results of this total removal of the thyroid could be alleviated if the deprived animals were fed regularly on extracts of thyroid gland. The same treatment was applied to human sufferers from extirpation of the thyroid and they also were cured.

THE SEX GLANDS

That the removal of the sex glands of animals brings about marked changes in their bodies and temperaments has long been known. By means of castration the fierce bull has been converted into the placid ox, the stallion into the easily handled gelding, the cockerel into the capon, and the virile man into the stout, hairless and sexless eunuch. Castration experiments carried out on animals of different ages have clearly shown us that the chief function of the hormones of the testes and the ovaries is to stimulate the development of the secondary characteristics of sex. Although the secretions of the testes and ovaries are specific, the one making for maleness and the other for femaleness, it is an interesting fact that both male and female hormones are to be found in every individual. This may perhaps account for the existence of certain inter-sexual individuals in whom the distinctive characteristics of the two sexes seem to be mixed. In other words, it may explain the genesis of the markedly feminine type of man and of the markedly masculine type of woman.

THE PITUITARY

The pituitary is the most important of all the ductless glands, not only because it forms several secretions but also because it exercises control over the other ductless glands. It is situated at the base of the brain, lying tucked away in a deep depression in the skull, the pituitary fossa. The total removal of the pituitary in a young animal has a profound influence on its growth; all formation of new bone tissue is arrested, no more teeth are erupted and the mental and sexual development of the animal comes to an end. So far, attempts to obtain an active extract from the pituitary have been only partially successful. This is partly due to the small storage capacity of the pituitary. Whereas the thyroid maintains in its structure a great deal of its own secretion, the tiny pituitary is able to store within itself very little of its characteristic hormones.

THE PANCREAS

Although the pancreas is not, strictly speaking, one of the ductless glands, it manufactures a very important internal secretion which is essential to the carbohydrate metabolism of the body. If the pancreas of an animal is removed, diabetes follows its loss, a fact which clearly shows the close relationship between that gland and the body's carbohydrate chemistry. After the discovery of the various hormones great hopes were raised that the intractable disease of diabetes would be cured by giving diabetics the internal secretion of the pancreas. Fortunately the source of the secretion was known, microscopic examination of the pancreas having revealed the presence in it of collections of small cells, known to physiologists as the islets of Langerhans. It was accepted that these cells were responsible for the internal secretion and numerous extracts were made of the sweetbreads of different animals and injected into diabetics, but without benefiting them in the least. Hopes for the cure of diabetes by hormone therapy faded rapidly.

The man who ultimately saved the situation was a young Canadian, Frederick Banting. Although he was in general practice he managed to find sufficient time to make a special study of diabetes in his own small surgery. He was deeply impressed by the tremendous digestive power possessed by the juices of the pancreas and he began to wonder whether these potent secretions might not

sometimes act on tissues as well as on food. Was it possible that after the death of an animal its pancreatic digestive juices destroyed its own islets of Langerhans and that this explained why no satisfactory extracts of the internal secretion of the pancreas had ever been obtained? These thoughts came to him lying in bed one night and he decided to put his idea to the test. He would tie the ducts of the pancreas along which its digestive juices flowed and thus bring about a degeneration of the pancreatic tissues producing these digestive secretions. At two o'clock in the morning he scribbled on a pad of paper by his bedside: "Ligate pancreatic duct of dogs, wait six or eight weeks for degeneration. Remove the residue and extract." Then he went to sleep.

He carried out the experiment precisely as he had decided that night to do it and obtained the help of a colleague, Charles Best. A month after the ligature had been applied to the duct, the pancreas of the dog was removed and extracted with saline. He noticed that the size of the pancreas had been greatly reduced by the ligature and that its digestive juices were no longer active. But in contrast with this the shrunken pancreas provided him with an extract of internal secretion that turned out to be extremely potent. When it was injected into a dog that was suffering from diabetes, brought about by the previous extirpation of its pancreas, the diabetes was cured.

This was the original experiment which led in the course of time to the manufacture of insulin on a very large scale and which has brought about an entire change in outlook for patients suffering from diabetes. Before Banting gave his extract to any patient, he and his colleague Best injected each other for the purpose of testing its toxicity. Then, when satisfied on this score, they gave the extract to three human diabetics with results which were as satisfactory as those previously obtained with diabetic dogs. Few researches have proved so rewarding as this research undertaken by Banting and Best. Although insulin does not bring about a permanent cure of diabetes, it has allowed many thousands of people who would otherwise have died to live profitable and useful lives.

So far illnesses caused by a deficiency of one or more of the body's internal secretions have alone been considered, but illnesses

may also be the result of a deficiency in the diet. For the maintenance of health a certain quality as well as a certain quantity of food is necessary and deficiencies in the first of these two requirements have been responsible in the past for a great deal of ill-health. It is difficult to say when it first dawned on man that illnesses might be the result of an ill-chosen diet, but it is likely that this was one of the first discoveries made in medicine. Medical men, from Hippocrates onwards, have always paid great attention to the food taken by their patients and medical treatment has usually included precise instructions on the subject of diet. The best way in which to begin the story of diseases due to dietary deficiencies will probably be to discuss, first, the most striking of all deficiency diseases, scurvy.

SCURVY

Scurvy has been known since the earliest of times and it is quite possible that Job was a victim of it when he complained: "My bones are pierced in me in the night season and my sinews take no rest. . . . My skin is black upon me and my bones are burned with heat." It is at any rate certain that the Crusaders suffered badly from the scurvy. De Joinville tells us that the "Barber-Surgeons were forced to cut away the dead flesh from the gums to enable the people to masticate their food". And the Navy suffered even more than did the Crusaders from that very unpleasant disease. Few people realize how serious a problem scurvy was to the mariner and even to the mariner as recently as two hundred years ago. It is recorded that Lord Anson took six ships on a world cruise in 1740 and that he barely managed to struggle back to port again with a fleet under skeleton crews. He had lost some twelve hundred of his men through this disease alone during the voyage. Shorter voyages were considerably less dangerous to life but they were always attended by a great deal of sickness. Scurvy took such a heavy toll of sailors in peace and in war that it was looked upon by everybody as the chief danger of a sea-going life, an inglorious danger that was dreaded alike by officers and men.

Jacques Cartier, who sailed from St. Malo in May 1535 with one hundred and ten men for the purpose of exploring the coast of Newfoundland and the River St. Lawrence, gives a graphic account

of the ravages made by scurvy amongst his crew. "The said unknown sickness began to spread itself amongst us after the strangest sort that was eyther heard of or siene, insomuch as some did lose all their strength, and could not stand on their feete, then did their legges swel, their sinnowes shrink as black as any cole. Others also had all their skins spotted with spots of blood of a purple colour; then did it ascend up to their ankels, knees, thighs, shoulders, arms and neck; their mouths became stinking, their gummes rotten that all the flesh did fall out." (Hakluyt's *Collection of Voyages*, Vol. II, p. 280.)

The disorder spread so rapidly amongst Cartier's men that in six weeks only ten of them remained unaffected. "Then," writes Cartier, "it pleased God to cast his pitifull eye upon us and send us the knowledge of remedie of our healthes and recoverie." Cartier was fortunate enough to learn from a native "that the juice and sappe of the leaves of a certain tree" cured this complaint from which the native himself had previously suffered. The curative effect of the native's remedy upon the stricken crew was soon very apparent. "If all the physicians of Montpellier and Louvaine had been there," continues Cartier, "with all the drugs of Alexandria they would not have done so much good in one year as that it did in six days; for it did prevail, that as many as used of it by the grace of God recovered their health."

This report of Cartier's contains one of the earliest references to the use of a vegetable extract in the treatment of scurvy. But once again valuable knowledge and valuable medical remedies were forgotten and had to be rediscovered at a later date. Many examples of this loss and rediscovery of knowledge have been given in this story of medicine and it might almost be said that few remedies are introduced into medicine which have not been used before in some cruder form.

The credit for first making it known that scurvy was a deficiency disease and a disease that could be prevented or cured by giving the patient fresh fruit to eat is usually given to James Lind (1716–1794), a naval surgeon. Yet there is a much earlier account of lemon and orange being used by sailors to cure themselves of scurvy, dating as far back as 1564. In the third epistle of Ronsieus it is clearly stated that on a return voyage from Spain certain Dutch sailors suffered

severely from scurvy and that they cured themselves by eating some of the oranges and lemons that made up the main bulk of their own cargo. So also was Lind anticipated by more than a century by a certain John Woodall (1569–1643). Woodall had had much personal experience of life at sea whilst in the service of the East India Company and he was thoroughly familiar therefore with the symptoms of scurvy, bleeding from the gums, falling out of the teeth, skin rashes, and swellings in various parts of the body. He gives an excellent account of the various signs and symptoms of scurvy in his book and then goes on to recommend the use of "the juice of vegetables and fruit, and when none of these can be had, oil of vitriol". But even if Woodall was working along the right lines long before Lind was born, it was Lind who gave the first scientific account of scurvy and of its treatment with lemon juice. Lind must also be credited with having brought the matter to the notice of the authorities and with having given very precise instructions as to what must be done to prevent the disease. In his book is described a scientific experiment made by him when he was in H.M.S. *Salisbury* in the year 1747. Twelve of Lind's patients were typical cases of scurvy and to two of them he gave a liberal supply of oranges and lemons, whilst the others received no oranges and lemons but only non-dietetic remedies for scurvy. The effect on the fortunate two who were being supplied with the oranges and lemons was magical. "The consequence was, that the most sudden and visible good effects were perceived from the use of the oranges and lemons; one of those who had taken them, being at the end of six days fit for duty. The spots were not at the same time quite off his body, nor his gums sound, but without any other medicine than a gargarism of *elixir vitriol*, he became quite healthy before we came into Plymouth, which was the 16th of June. The other was the best recovered of any in his condition, and being now deemed pretty well, was appointed nurse to the rest of the sick."

But the ponderous machinery of the Services turns exceeding slow, and although Lind's book on scurvy was published in 1753 it was not until 1795, a year after James Lind had died, that Gilbert Blane, Commissioner of the Board of the Care of Sick and Wounded Seamen, succeeded in persuading the Admiralty to make

the use of lemon juice compulsory in the Navy. Thanks to this timely ordinance, Captain Cook was able to make his world voyages without being troubled at all by scurvy.

James Lind made other valuable contributions to the health of the Navy, and Trotter, writing at the end of the eighteenth century, rightly said of him that he "stands alone in the Navy as the father of nautical medicine". His interests were very wide. He studied jail fever and recommended that it should be treated by delousing. He advised that the sick whilst in port should be kept in specially equipped hospital ships and he even invented an apparatus for distilling fresh water from sea water.

THE DISCOVERY OF THE VITAMINS

The final step in the elucidation of the problem of scurvy was not taken till a century later when Sir Frederick Gowland Hopkins discovered the vitamins. He fed young rats on a *pure* diet of protein fats and carbohydrates, giving them sufficient of each type of food to maintain their growth; yet his rats not only failed to put on weight but became ill. When he added a small quantity of fresh milk to their food they all recovered and started to grow again. This confirmed, what had long been suspected, that health requires a diet not only adequate in protein fats and carbohydrates but also containing minute quantities of something else to which the name vitamins was now given.

Further investigations have shown that many diseases besides scurvy are due to vitamin deficiency. Amongst these are rickets, pellagra (characterized by degenerative changes in the skin and the mucous membranes), beri-beri and certain forms of infertility. All of these troubles can be cured by adding to the deficient diet "natural' foods in the way of milk, fruit and vegetables. The chemists have examined the chemical constitution of the various vitamins and they have succeeded in synthetizing some of them. The nomenclature and classification of the vitamins are based first on whether they are soluble in fats or in water, and after they have been subdivided in this way the letters of the alphabet are used to distinguish the different vitamins. The fat-soluble vitamins are A, D, E and K, and the water soluble B and C. Absence of vitamin C in the diet causes the symptoms of scurvy, and absence of vitamin B is

responsible for that strange disease from which many prisoners in Japanese war camps suffered so badly, beri-beri.

Just as Lind eliminated scurvy from the Navy by prescribing lemons, so did Admiral Takaki eradicate beri-beri from the Japanese Navy in 1882–1886 by insisting that the personnel should be given a more liberal and a better-balanced diet. This led in time to the discovery that the remedy for beri-beri lay in the rice husks and to the realization that the illness was entirely due to eating polished rice from which all the vitamin content had been artificially removed. And it is in this kind of way that medical discoveries are usually made. First, a medical man notes that some action or lack of action causes an illness, or that this illness is relieved by a certain form of treatment. He puts this knowledge into practice, working in the dark and without knowing the real explanation of what he is doing. Then at a much later date scientists throw light on what up till then has been an entirely blind proceeding. This was the sequence of events in the case both of scurvy and of beri-beri.

CHAPTER XVII

Public Health

THE doctor is the lineal descendant of the tribal medicine man and an important part of a medicine man's work has always been to protect his community from evil influences. He must take measures to counteract hostile spells directed against his tribe by the sorcerers of hostile tribes—in other words his magic must be preventive as well as curative. The same ought to be true of the medical man but unfortunately the doctor has always tended to neglect this important part of his work and there have been times in the history of medicine when preventive medicine has all but disappeared. For example, hygiene and public health sank to a particularly low level during the Middle Ages and remained in abeyance for a long time afterwards. The Romans paid great attention to the drainage, sanitation and water supply of their cities, and Rome possessed its cloacae or subterranean drains as early as the sixth century before Christ, in the age of the Tarquins. The Cloaca Maxima or main drain in use in Rome today actually dates back to that time. It also possessed a magnificent water supply and regulations enforced the cleanliness of its streets. So also did the earlier Minoan and Egyptian civilizations pay great attention to public health measures.

After the fall of the Roman Empire preventive medicine to all intents disappeared and it remained thus in abeyance during the whole of the Dark Ages. Nor was it only in the Middle Ages that hygiene and public health were neglected. Many English towns remained without sanitation or a satisfactory water supply as late as the seventeenth or even the eighteenth century. In the Stuart period the conditions under which the poorer inhabitants of London lived were truly deplorable. The houses were ranged along a system

of dark alleys rather than of streets, and because the overhanging storeys almost met overhead, little or no sunlight penetrated into these gloomy bye-ways. Foul streams trickled out of the houses to find their way eventually into the River Fleet, whilst heaps of garbage and of rotting refuse made it difficult to walk. Flies "pestered the houses in such multitudes that they lined the walls, and where a thread or string hung down it was promptly thick with flies, like a rope of onions. Ants covered the highways, swarming so thickly that a handful at a time might have been taken up, and the croaking of frogs was loudly heard even before the ditches sheltering them could be seen". (Quoted by S. Luff in *The Health of the People*.)

No improvement took place in these appalling conditions until the middle of the eighteenth century, when London, Birmingham and Manchester all obtained their Improving Acts (1762–1776). As a consequence of these, streams were covered in, the streets were paved and lighted, and sewers were laid down. Yet in most towns a continuous water supply to the inhabitants was still unavailable. Even in the great city of London householders had water for only an hour or two, three times a week, and as the water mains and the sewers ran close together and were sometimes broken, the water supply might easily be contaminated. That it often contained dangerous germs is shown by the fact that London suffered from a bad epidemic of cholera as late as the year 1831, an epidemic which was eventually traced to a communal pump situated in the neighbourhood of Broad Street. (*See* Plate 27.) What was badly required to counteract this neglect of all sanitary measures was a man possessed of a strong sense of mission capable of bullying the authorities into doing something to remedy the sorry state of affairs.

Such a man eventually appeared and in the unlikely guise of a philosopher. Philosophers are usually so detached from the practical affairs of life that they prefer to remain spectators of them rather than to get mixed up with them. Jeremy Bentham (1748–1832), the leader of the new libertarian school of philosophy, was a notable exception to this. He did not regard the philosophical slogan of the movement, "the greatest happiness of the greatest number", as only an abstract principle to be argued about but as something to be fought for, tooth and nail. Health was an essential requirement for the happiness of the many and, this being the case, Bentham set

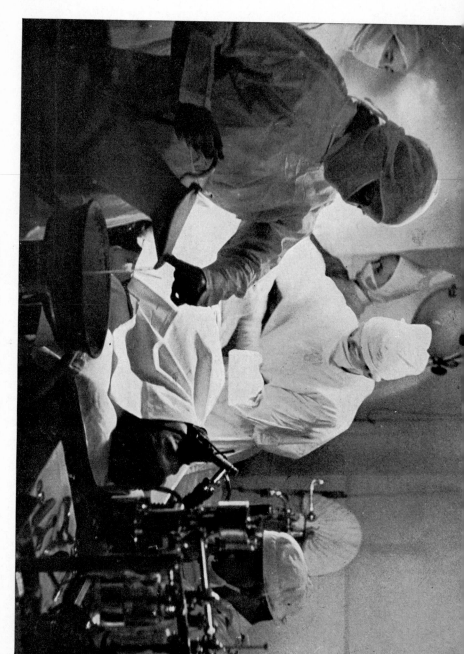

The modern surgeon at work
(*Picture Post Library*)

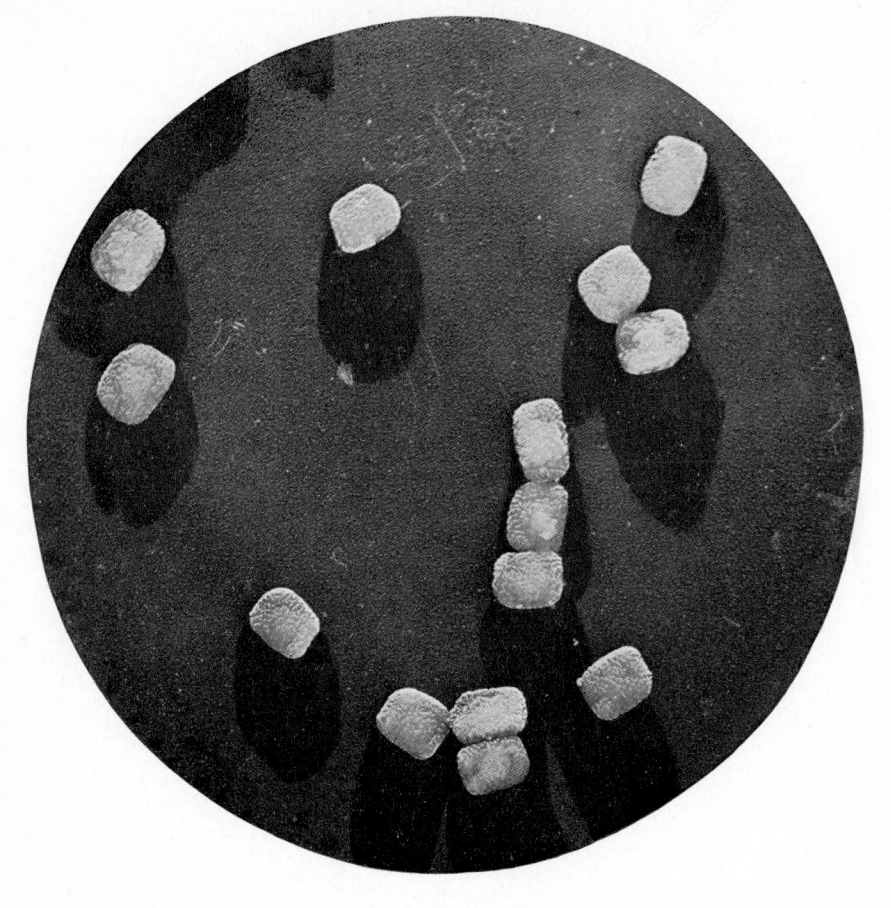

Vaccinia virus. Gold-shadowed and seen under the electron microscope

(Kindly supplied by I. M. Dawson and A. S.
McFarlane, National Inst. for Medical Research)

forth fearlessly to demolish everything which stood in the way of its attainment.

Like the great Moslem doctor Avicenna he started life as an infant prodigy. At the age of three he began the study of Latin; at five he learnt the violin and started also to speak French; and at thirteen he matriculated at Queen's College, Oxford. After a brilliant Oxford career he entered Lincoln's Inn and was called to the Bar. Not being dependent for his livelihood on his earnings as a barrister he was able to devote himself entirely to what was dearer to him than any private career—reform. It was not reform in any single sphere of human life for which he strove but reform in everything: in government, in legislation, in international relationships, in politics and finally in everything pertaining to health. Many of the suggestions he made in his *Introduction to Principles of Morals and Legislations* have now been adopted but they were unacceptable to the majority of his countrymen during his life-time. Bentham was prepared to consider any scheme for the greater happiness of the many and he was the natural centre to which all would-be reformers eventually gravitated.

John Stuart Mill and Edwin Chadwick (1800–1890) were amongst Bentham's disciples and the latter was to be the means by which some of Bentham's schemes were to be implemented. Chadwick was precisely the type of man needed to push sanitary reforms through Parliament against the active resistance and, what was far more difficult to overcome, the leaden lethargy of a Government that was not in the least interested in preventive medicine. The passing of a Poor Law Act in 1834 provided Chadwick with his first opportunity of applying pressure, an opportunity which he was not slow to take. A number of Commissioners were appointed by the Act whose duty it was to investigate the administration of the Poor Laws, and fortunately Edwin Chadwick was nominated secretary of the Commission. The Commission took its work seriously and appointed in turn a medical sub-committee which was to report to it the state of health of the citizens of London. The state of affairs revealed by the sub-committee was truly appalling. It reported, for example, that in a single London parish of 77,000 people, 14,000 of them suffered annually from some sort of fever and that 25 per cent of those who went down with fever died of it.

Chadwick promptly forwarded this report to the Home Secretary, together with a strong covering letter, and, as a result of his strong action, a Select Committee was nominated to enquire into the circumstances affecting the health of the inhabitants of the larger towns of England with a view to instituting improved sanitary arrangements for their benefit. This new Select Committee soon got to work and made three recommendations; the passing of a Building and a Sewerage Act, the setting up of local health boards, and the appointment of a number of sanitary inspectors.

These were excellent recommendations but in the meantime the Government of the day had lost the little interest it had originally possessed in the business of Public Health and took no action at all. Chadwick refused to accept this delay in implementing the Commission's recommendations, and taking advantage of a rising tide of public discontent, he again brought the matter forcibly to the Government's notice. A few years' respite was gained for the Government by the usual delaying measure of appointing a fact-finding committee, but finally it was forced to capitulate. In 1848 a Public Health Act was passed and this legislation measure can be regarded as being the first of many subsequent preventive measures to be adopted in this country.

The first round in the hard battle in defence of what Chadwick liked to call the "Sanitary Idea" had been won and he was now joined by a powerful ally, Thomas Southwood Smith (1788–1861), a graduate of Edinburgh University and a Physician to the London Fever Hospital. Southwood Smith strongly supported Sir Edwin Chadwick, as he had now become, in all he did by means of his writings and also in his capacity as a member of the newly appointed Board of Health. At a later date these two men were joined by two other health reformers, Dr. John Snow (1813–1858) and Sir John Simon (1816–1904). Unfortunately the man who had originally been responsible for the whole of this public health movement, Jeremy Bentham, died shortly after the passing of one of the useful measures for which he had pressed, the Anatomy Act of 1832. This Act had been devised by Dr. Southwood Smith in order to make bodies available to medical students for dissection, and it was characteristic of that practical philosopher Bentham that he should have inserted a special clause in his will, to the effect that his body

should be dissected "so that mankind may reap some small benefit by my decease". His request was duly carried out and his skeleton, dressed in the clothes it wore in life, still stands in the medical museum of University College Hospital.

But the story of Public Health and Preventive Medicine must be interrupted for a little in order to call attention to the rapidly changing background against which these new reforms were being made. During the eighteenth century, life in England was completely transformed by the rapid growth of industry. The invention of industrial machinery led to a steady increase in the size of the towns and to an urbanization of the population, and with this growth of the towns and increase in the population there naturally came an increased demand for food. This necessitated in turn the introduction of improved methods of agriculture, and the better drainage of agricultural land brought about a reduction of malaria, which up to that time was by no means an uncommon complaint in low-lying parts of England. Otherwise, conditions in the rural districts remained as primitive as before. Housing conditions in the country were deplorable, wages so low that it was difficult or impossible for the agricultural labourer to bring up his family, and roads so poor that they became impassable in winter. But it is with life in the rapidly growing centres of industry that we are chiefly concerned.

THE EFFECT OF THE INDUSTRIAL REVOLUTION

The great increase in the population of the towns brought about by the industrial revolution made the need for sanitary reforms still more urgent. During the latter half of the nineteenth century industries were not only growing but were being rapidly transformed by an ever-increasing number of new scientific inventions and machines. More and more people were flocking to the large industrial centres, attracted by the high wages being paid, and in spite of the appallingly high infant mortality rate of that period the total population of Great Britain was rising rapidly. A slow rise had taken place at the beginning of the previous century but nothing in comparison with what was happening now. If housing conditions were bad in the rural districts, those of the workers crowding into the large towns were still worse. The slum districts in all the big industrial centres increased markedly in size. Although by this

time most of the streets in the cities and larger towns of England were paved, drained and lighted, they still lacked good sanitation and a satisfactory water supply. Cesspools were in general use in London in the middle of the nineteenth century, and the first water closets did not appear there until 1828. There existed no way of dealing with London's sewage other than that of allowing it to flow into the nearest river.

In spite of the passing of the First Public Health Act of 1848 and of the establishment of a Central General Board of Health, progress in sanitary measures was so slow that a Royal Commission was appointed in 1860 to review the whole situation. This Commission acknowledged that something had been done to mitigate the worst troubles in the towns and cities but was of the opinion that the work of the Board of Health was very poorly co-ordinated. It recommended that "the fragmentary legislation should be consolidated" and even went so far as to suggest the immediate establishment of a Ministry of Health. But instead of a new Ministry being formed, the Local Government Board came into being. The Royal Commission recommended that this new body should be made responsible for carrying out the following:

(1) The supply of wholesome and sufficient water for drinking and washing purposes.
(2) The avoidance of any pollution of this water supply.
(3) The provision of adequate sewers and the supervision of the proper disposal and utilization of sewage.
(4) The regulation of streets, highways, and new buildings.
(5) Inspection of the healthiness of dwellings.
(6) The removal of nuisances and public refuse and the consumption and disposal of smoke.
(7) The inspection of food.
(8) The suppression of causes of diseases and the adoption of proper measures in the event of epidemics.
(9) Provision for the burial of the dead without injury to the living.
(10) The regulation of markets, etc., and the public lighting of towns.
(11) The registration of deaths and infectious sicknesses.

All these recommendations were eventually incorporated in the Public Health Act of 1875, and the passing of this Act can be looked upon as being a date as important in the history of sanitary reform as the signing of Magna Charta is important in the history of constitutional reform. It is of great significance if for no other reason than that the passing of this Act marks a change-over from a purely negative policy of getting rid of public nuisances to a positive policy of doing everything possible to raise the general level of health.

Supplementary reforms were to follow the passing of this original Act, such as measures for the care of the mother and her child, regulations concerned with housing, town and country planning and the treatment of infectious diseases, mental deficiency, lunacy and tuberculosis. In other words the Act of 1875 was more than a change from a negative to a positive health policy. It represented the title deeds of a new partnership between medical men and the state, a partnership which inaugurated a new era in the history of preventive medicine.

MODERN MAN AND HIS ENVIRONMENT

Advances in technology have permitted of man's bringing about radical changes in his environment and this in turn has had repercussions on his health. Health has been defined as an inner balance of functions, together with the ability of the organism to make satisfactory adjustments to its environment. Nowadays urbanized man maintains this adjustment to a large extent by his clever manipulation of his environment. His aim has been to gain more and more control over his environment so that he may live more comfortably, in other words, make fewer and fewer adjustments to his surroundings. Eighty per cent of modern western men and women have no higher ideal than this, to live more comfortably, safely and easily, and thanks to the discoveries of the scientists, the wealthier classes of the more "highly civilized" western countries have to a great extent achieved this ambition. They have contrived for themselves a comfortable and reasonably secure mode of existence.

But in his search for more comfortable living, modern man sometimes makes for his fellow men and even for himself an

environment which turns out to be highly prejudicial to health. Not only does he become so dependent on his centrally heated houses and his soft way of living that he is liable to fall ill when exposed, through some accident, to natural conditions of living, but he even manufactures new forms of illness. Factory workers in some of our industries spend a third of their lives exposed to the action of certain poisonous substances, whilst miners are liable to suffer from serious pulmonary troubles as the result of inspiring dust. In consequence of this, modern man is exposed to risks unknown to his ancestors and to those living nearer to Nature. Amongst these artificially devised occupational diseases are painters' colic, chimney sweeps' cancer, miners' nystagmus, pneumoconiosis, and divers' cramp or caissons disease. That a man's method of gaining his livelihood has an important bearing on his health is shown by the following table giving the mortality rates for men engaged in different trades, industries and professions.

Occupation				Mortality Rate
For all occupied males	..	..	..	100
Teachers ..	..	..	..	68
Clergymen ..	..	..	..	69
Agricultural Labourers	..	..	..	77
Electrical Workers ..	..	..	..	90
Fishermen ..	..	..	..	96
Textile Workers ..	..	..	..	105
Doctors	..	..	..	106
Coal miners—hewers and getters	..	..		113
Dock labourers ..	..	..	..	137
Underground tin, copper miners	..	..		342

(Taken from the Registrar's Decennial Supplement for England and Wales 1931.)

To protect men from diseases that are the direct result of their occupations a number of Acts of Parliament have been passed which will have to be considered.

LEGISLATION RELATING TO INDUSTRIAL DISEASES

The first Act for the protection of the manual worker was the Health and Morals of Apprentices Act which was placed on the Statute Book as long ago as 1802. It was followed by the Factory Inspectoral Act of 1833 and the Mines Inspectoral Act of 1850. Though these Acts managed to achieve very little they were signs that public opinion was beginning to realize the need for safeguarding the health of factory workers. Since they were passed, conditions in the factories have steadily improved. Increasing recognition of the fact that occupation and health were very closely related has led also to the appointment of a number of medical officers whose sole duty is to look after the health of the workers. There are close on two thousand of these factory doctors in Great Britain at the present time.

Since the passing of the National Insurance (Industrial Injuries) Act of 1946 and of the Disabled Persons (Employment) Act of 1944, the duties of these factory doctors have been increased. They now sit on medical boards and on medical appeal tribunals in order to help to assess claims for compensation. Their advice is also constantly sought by the management on such subjects as the working conditions in the factories and the morale of the factory hands. There can be no doubt that the factory doctors are very important wheels in the cumbersome machinery of State Medicine.

PUBLIC HEALTH AS AN INTERNATIONAL PROBLEM

The earliest recognition of the idea that public health is an international and not merely a national problem can be traced back to the fourteenth century. When the Black Death was rapidly spreading through Europe an agreement was reached by certain nations concerning primitive quarantine regulations. But it has invariably happened that when an international emergency is over, all further co-operation between the nations on the subject of health promptly ceases. No other international collaboration of this nature seems to have taken place until 1851 when an international conference was called in Paris in order to reach some agreement on quarantine regulations in the Mediterranean and the Black Sea areas. Again this proved to be only a fleeting coming

together of the nations and when agreement had been reached the Committee dissolved itself.

The first permanent international body of a sanitary nature to meet was the outcome of a conference of American Republic representatives held at Washington in 1902. The object of the conference was to promote international co-operation in public health measures amongst the nations of the two American continents. Seven years later the field of co-operation was widened further by the opening of an International Office of Public Health in Paris. It was intended that this body should in course of time become world-wide in scope, and forty-six countries actually joined it. The chief aim of this international body was the same as that of its predecessor, the American Sanitary Bureau, that of reaching quarantine agreements which would prevent diseases being transferred from one country to another. It was not really concerned with the health conditions within each of the individual countries for the idea of tackling health problems on a world-wide scale had not as yet been born except in the minds of the controllers of the Rockefeller Foundation. It was indeed in the magnificent work financed or carried out by this Foundation that international co-operation on health problems on a world scale really began.

In 1923 the League of Nations established its Health Organization and also made certain arrangements for attacking specified diseases on a world-wide scale. The central governing body of this Organization was the Health Committee, composed of twelve members, plus certain "expert assessors" or individual men and women nominated by the League itself. Under this supervising Health Committee there worked a secretariat, a staff of experts, and a number of sub-committees dealing with special problems, such as malaria, cancer and housing. The Second World War brought to an end all of these League of Nation's activities.

The story of world co-operation in health problems starts again in the year 1946 when a preliminary International Conference was held in New York at which a constitution for a World Health Organization was drawn up. The Constitution given to this world health organization (W.H.O. for short) shows great breadth of vision on the part of those who devised it. Health was defined as "a state of complete physical, mental and sound well-being, and not

merely the absence of disease or infirmity". The preamble to the Constitution also stated that "the enjoyment of the highest attainable standard of health is one of the fundamental rights of every human being, without distinction of race, religion, political belief, economic or social condition".

This broad statement was amplified later and the actual work of the W.H.O. brought to a clearer focus. Its function was declared to be to promote maternal and child welfare, and to help to improve mental health, and more especially those aspects of mental health on which harmony between human beings depends. Another part of its aims was "to promote, in co-operation with other specialized agencies . . . the improvement of nutrition, housing, sanitation, recreation, economic or working conditions, and other aspects of environmental hygiene. . . . It was also to study and report on . . . administration and social technique, affecting public health and medical care from preventive and curative points of view, including hospital services and social security."

The W.H.O. has its headquarters in the Palais des Nations, built to house the former League of Nations on the shores of Lake Leman. It is governed by a World Health Assembly which meets annually and which, theoretically at any rate, includes representatives from seventy-nine nations. The adverb theoretically has had to be used because the nine police-governed countries behind the Iron Curtain and also China do not at present attend these sessions on Lake Leman.

Already the W.H.O. has accomplished much for world health. It has sent its representatives into the backward countries and has assisted these countries to deal more satisfactorily with their urgent health problems. It has, for example, sent medical commissions into Asia to make frontal attacks on malaria, yaws and venereal diseases. Since the discovery of penicillin and the sulphonamide drugs, the last two of these three diseases can be brought much more quickly under control than was formerly possible and the various commissions not only supply what is required in the way of drugs and equipment but instruct the native inhabitants in their use. Much also has been done for maternal and child welfare by the W.H.O. and this has brought into prominence yet another world problem, that caused by over-population. The steep fall

in infant mortality which has taken place both in Asia and in Africa has aggravated a problem which has long existed in these continents, that of insufficient food supply for the growing population.

THE IMPORTANCE OF THE W.H.O.

The W.H.O. is a body of immense importance to mankind, and not solely because of the valuable work it is doing in matters of health. The W.H.O. is one of man's earliest attempts to co-operate on a world scale and whether it will succeed or whether it will fail and have to be abandoned is still very uncertain. It was very fortunate in its first Director-General, Dr. Brock Chisholm (*b.* 1896), a man of wide vision. His breadth of view is revealed by the inspiring message which is handed to each new member of the secretariat as he takes office, a message full of meaning for others besides newcomers to the W.H.O.:

". . . We must think and act in terms of mankind as a whole. We must be ready to give up old ideas, certainties and devotions in order to place the welfare of all people everywhere on the same level of values, regardless of where on this little earth one happens to have been born himself. In other words, we must try to attain an equal degree of loyalty to all members of the world community, irrespective of race, religion, and colour, and any other group characteristics.

"This does not mean that you will be asked to change those political, economic, social, or religious ideas which you consider the best for yourself or your country. But it does mean that in order to discharge your role in this Organization you must acquire an objective view of the differences between the people of the world. You must realize that the various economic, social, religious systems under which the different nations live are various types of experiments, neither inferior nor superior to each other, and all thoroughly explained by the historical conditions which created them. . . ."

In the past man accustomed himself to living with absolute certainties, absolute orthodoxies, extreme forms of nationalism,

ruthlessness and intolerance, but if humanity is to survive we must emerge successfully from this primitive stage of evolution. Already there are faint signs of this emergence beginning and the W.H.O. is the chief of these portents. That is why its survival and its growth is of such incalculable importance to humanity.

CHAPTER XVIII

Diversion on the Subject of Mind

SO far this book has been concerned only with illnesses of the body and little or nothing has been said about man's mind and its troubles. Yet we all know that the relationship between body and mind is so close that neither can be disturbed without the other being affected. So fully was this realized in the distant past that in the more ancient systems of medicine the emphasis was placed on the mind rather than on the body. It was to the mind that the treatment of the priest-physician and witch-doctor was primarily directed in the hope that if the patient's mind could be restored to health the body would follow suit. Illness was explained in terms of possession by a devil and the first requirement was that this evil intruder should be cast out.

We may smile at these naive ideas but actually the symptoms exhibited by a neurotic patient resemble far more closely possession by an alien and hostile mind than they do a breakage in a piece of machinery, the terms in which doctors of a later age attempted to explain all illnesses. The psychopathic patient behaves precisely as though he was in the power of a devil which is seeking to thwart him in everything he tries to do and which to further its own schemes deliberately upsets the proper working of his body. For example, at his first visit to the doctor the unfortunate patient may complain of various physical troubles, such as headaches and indigestion, but by the time of his next visit his symptoms are likely to have entirely changed. He now reports that he is mentally depressed, that he is losing his memory, that he cannot keep his attention on anything, and that as a result of all these disturbances he is no longer able to carry on his work. At the third visit his symptoms may again have altered. He has become touchy and

irritable, cannot bear the presence of those who are doing their best to look after him and casts on them the blame for everything that goes wrong. It is as though an enemy within him was deliberately frustrating the efforts being made by relatives, friends and doctors to bring about his recovery—in short, as though he were "possessed of a devil".

It is easily understood, therefore, why the ancients saw illnesses in this light and attempted to restore health by means of exorcisms, magical charms and rites. During the Middle Ages the Christian Church subscribed to the ancient view that illness was a punishment for sin and taught that its proper treatment lay in penitence and prayer rather than in physical remedies. Special rituals and services were devised for the casting out of devils and their use was often attended with excellent results. Nor need we be surprised that the patient, deeply moved by these mysteries and completely confident that the officiating saint or priest was invested with supernatural powers, was often cured. Suggestion has always played an all-important part in the work of the doctor, whether he were treating afflictions of the mind or of the body, and in the earlier days of medicine its action was paramount. It will be recalled that when the sick arrived at the *Asklepieia* in ancient Greece they began their cure by making sacrificial offerings and by taking purifying baths. Then, relaxed in muscles and quietened in mind, they lay down on mattresses spread out on the *abaton*. There they were submitted to the constant action of suggestion, for there was little else for them to do but listen to or read the records of the miraculous cures which had been brought about in the very temple in which they were lying. "Oh blessed Asklepios, God of Healing, it is thanks to thy skill that Diophantis hopes to be relieved from his incurable and horrible gout, no longer to move like a crab, no longer to walk upon thorns, but to have sound feet as thou hast decreed."

"Heraicus of Mytilene is bald and entreats the God to make his hair grow. An ointment is applied every night and the next morning he has a thick crop of hair." Such words as these read over and over again sank into the depths of the patient's mind. Suggestion could not have been applied under more favourable conditions than these and the results were frequently entirely satisfactory, as satisfactory as they were when saints cast out devils in the Middle

Ages and as they still are in this century of faith in science and specialists.

It can be accepted therefore that in the earlier periods of medicine some form of psychotherapy played a part in medical treatment. But as medicine became scientific and materialistic, less and less importance was attributed to the mind in the causation of disease so that psychotherapy was almost entirely neglected.

Descartes' severance of man into a material body and an immaterial mind encouraged this tendency on the part of the doctor to direct his attention exclusively to his patient's body and to disclaim all responsibility for his mind. Not only had man been cloven in twain by Descartes but, worse still, the two halves had been handed over for study to different kinds of experts. Scientists and medical men were specialists in matter so it was natural that they should appropriate to themselves man's physical body. Theologians and philosophers were specialists in the mind so it was equally natural that they should make off with his mind. This division and dispersal of spoils would have mattered far less if the scientists (including their camp followers the doctors), and the theologians and philosophers, had understood each other better and had occasionally met together in conference, but unfortunately this very seldom happened. Doctors were so busy that they had no time to keep in touch with the ideas of philosophers and theologians, and the theologians disapproved of scientists and doctors on principle. So as the years passed by medical men thought less and less of their patients' minds and were more and more concerned with their bodies, whilst the theologians lost all contact with scientific progress and not infrequently all relationship with ordinary common sense.

THE MATERIALISTIC OUTLOOK OF MEDICINE

As Sir William Dampier has pointed out, mechanical and spiritual theories of the universe alternate with each other throughout the whole history of science. With each new advance in science and with the subjection of yet another set of phenomena to the rule of mechanical law "the human mind, by an inevitable exaggeration of the power of the new method, tends to think that it is on the point of reaching a complete mechanical explanation of the universe". (Sir William Dampier, *The History of Science.*) This change of

outlook from one age to another is very apparent when we study the history of medicine. Descartes wrote a work on physiology in which he sought to show that living organisms were merely elaborate pieces of machinery which worked in accordance with Newtonian principles. When "animal spirits" were blown through the nerves into the muscles, the latter bulged and became shorter and then, after they had accomplished their work, the animal spirits were carried back again by the blood stream to the great reservoir containing them in the brain and there they remained until more mechanical work was required of them. It was all very simple.

This Cartesian view that everything in life could be explained in terms of machinery was widely accepted in the seventeenth century and, as we have seen, it led to the rise of the Iatro-physical school of physiology, of which Sanctorius and Borelli were prominent members. Then arose the difficulties which always intervene when any single concept has been pushed too far. Baglivi and van Helmont came to the conclusion that life could not be explained by mechanism alone and they founded the new Iatro-chemical school of physiology. Life was now to be interpreted in terms of chemical reactions and great progress was made in this new and more satisfying chemical direction. The Iatro-chemical school prospered for a very long time but eventually it began to run into similar difficulties.

These led to the appearance later of yet another school of physiology, the school of vitalism. The vitalists maintained that life made use of certain processes which could not be explained in terms of physics or chemistry. Another thing that distinguished living organisms from inanimate matter was their dual capacity both to conserve and to reproduce themselves, and these capacities could not, in the opinion of the vitalists, be the result of chemical reactions only. They were manifestations of the intervention in the physical and chemical fields of some intelligent and "living" force to which they gave the name of vital principle.

George Ernst Stahl (1660–1734), Professor of Medicine at the University of Halle, belonged to this vitalist school. For him the source of all vital action was the *anima* or soul. This conserving force prevented the putrefaction which inevitably takes place in the body after the departure of the soul. Consequently the body must be looked upon as being governed not so much by the ordinary laws of

chemistry as by the higher laws of the soul or *anima*, which works on entirely different principles. Stahl's view of physiology was very similar to that of Aristotle, who many centuries previously had defined life as "the power of self-nourishment and of independent growth and decay". Aristotle postulated the existence of three types of vital principle: the lowest or *vegetative*, an intermediate or *animal* principle, and the highest or *intellectual* principle. Stahl's idea of the *anima* was therefore of very ancient origin and it is a theory which has cropped up many times in the history of medicine under a variety of names. It figured, very largely for example, in the teaching of Paracelsus under the name of *archaeus* or *pneuma*.

At the University of Halle, of which Stahl was a very distinguished member, there lived another vitalist whose name is often associated with his own, the physician Dr. Friedrich Hoffman (1660–1742). Hoffman taught that not only the body but the whole universe is pervaded by a vital principle, "finer than all other matter but not exactly spirit, soul or mind". It was this principle which maintained the body in a state of equilibrium and health, and illness might mean either a deficiency or else an excess of this invigorating "tonus", requiring correction by the use of sedatives when present in excess or by tonics in cases of deficiency.

John Hunter (1728–1793), the great English anatomist and zoologist of the eighteenth century, was a vitalist, as were also the two distinguished German biochemists Liebig (1803–1873) and Wöhler (1800–1882). Liebig's system of thought seems at first sight to contain contradictions for he looked upon the processes of fermentation and putrefaction as being entirely physical disturbances. Yet when Lord Kelvin asked him whether "a leaf or flower could be made to grow by chemical forces", he replied: "I would more readily believe that a book on chemistry or on botany could grow out of dead matter by chemical processes." The other great German vitalist Wöhler was famous for his synthesis of urea, a compound which had up till that time been regarded as being obtainable from the action of vital processes alone. Yet in spite of having shown the world by his synthesis of urea that there existed no essential difference between the structural chemistry of life and that of the physical world, Wöhler remained to the end of his life a staunch vitalist.

This brief account of the swing of medical thought on the subject of the relationship existing between the body and the mind has been necessary in order that we may be able to understand the various forms of therapy evolved for the treatment of mental illnesses. We are now in a better position to discuss this subject of the treatment of illnesses of the mind.

CHAPTER XIX

Illnesses of the Mind and their Treatment

IT is against this shifting background of different schools of thought on the body-mind relationship that a strange figure in medical history must be viewed—that of Franz Anton Mesmer. Though a man of much smaller stature than that angry giant Paracelsus, Mesmer had several things in common with him. In the first place Paracelsus and Mesmer were both Swiss by birth, and in the second, Mesmer, like Paracelsus, was convinced that man was influenced by subtle forces which reached him from other parts of the universe. Thirdly Mesmer was regarded by most contemporary physicians as a rogue and a charlatan. Yet in spite of the poor reception of his ideas and of the intense professional hostility he aroused, Mesmer was destined to exert a considerable influence on the subsequent course of medicine. He is worthy therefore of attention.

FRANZ (OR FRIEDRICH) ANTON MESMER (1733–1815)

Little is known about the earlier years of Mesmer's life. We know only that he was born in 1733 in the village of Iznang on Lake Constance, that he received a good education, and that he studied medicine and took his medical degree in Vienna in the year 1766. The fact that he chose for the subject of his academic dissertation so unusual a theme as the influence of the planets on the human body (*De Planetarium Influxu*) shows that his peculiar philosophy was developed very early in his life. The centre of gravity of this philosophy which proved so distasteful to his colleagues was as follows: "that the sun, moon and fixed stars mutually affect each other in their orbits; that they cause and direct on earth a flux and a reflux, not only in the sea, but in the atmosphere; that they influence in a similar manner all organized bodies by means of a

306

mobile fluid, which pervades the whole universe and draws all things together in mutual intercourse and harmony".

So far there is nothing very alarming in Mesmer's philosophy. From the earliest times there have been men who have believed that the universe forms a great whole in which every part is related to, and is influenced by, every other part of it. Mesmer's "mobile fluid which pervades the whole universe and draws all things together in mutual intercourse and harmony" is very similar to Hoffman's pervading principle, "finer than all other matter but not actually spirit, soul or mind". Nor is this all-pervasive principle very different from the "ether" formerly postulated by the scientists.

Whilst at Vienna the young Mesmer made the acquaintance of Professor Hehl, a Jesuit priest and, like many Jesuit priests, also a professor of astronomy. Professor Hehl was particularly interested in the young author of the thesis *De Planetarium Influxu* because he subscribed to a somewhat similar theory himself and had been experimenting with magnets, in the hope that they would have a curative action on certain diseases. He sent Mesmer some of these magnets later, and Mesmer tried them out on a case of heart disease, with apparent benefit to his patient. Later Mesmer came to the conclusion that as his own body was permeated by the same magnetism as that which was present in the magnet, what could be achieved with a magnet could be more readily achieved by means of the hands alone.

Mesmer's next patient was a Baron Hareczky who had been treated for spasms of the throat, without benefit, by most of the leading consultants of Vienna. One of these unsuccessful consultants suggested to the Baron that he should give Mesmer a trial, although he frankly admitted that, as a medical man, he could have no confidence in Mesmer's methods. In due course Mesmer received an invitation to visit the Baron and when he arrived at his Castle of Rohow in Austria he found that the news of his coming had preceded him and that a large crowd of sick villagers was waiting to see him. Mesmer possessed the valuable capacity of keeping his head in difficult circumstances and he now acted very wisely. He agreed to treat one or two patients suffering from troubles of a nervous nature and referred the others back to their own doctors. With his selected cases he had considerable success but the Baron himself,

for whose sake he had made the journey, proved entirely refractory to treatment.

After making a tour of Switzerland Mesmer returned in 1776 to Vienna. There he again brought about many cures by his strange methods, so many indeed that Baron von Stoerck, President of the Faculty of Medicine, Vienna, advised him privately not to make his cures public lest he should incur the enmity of the profession. This excellent advice came too late to save Mesmer for he was already known to and heartily disliked by all of the more orthodox doctors of Vienna. Not only did they refuse to examine any of his successful cases, if they happened to come across them, but they maintained that none of these "cured" people had ever really been ill.

Mesmer's bitterest encounter with his medical colleagues was in connection with the strange case of Mademoiselle Paradis, a *protégé* and *pensionnaire* of the Empress Maria Theresa. This unfortunate young woman had lost her sight from what had been diagnosed as "paralysis of the optic nerve". Yet after a brief course of treatment from Mesmer she had recovered sufficiently to be able to make out the outline of large objects. She was a gifted pianist, who, having learnt to play the piano without sight, now found that piano playing had been rendered more difficult by the partial recovery of her sight. At first, Herr Paradis, her father, was delighted with what Mesmer had done for his daughter but those who had previously treated her without success were determined to get her out of Mesmer's hands. They made a successful appeal to Herr Paradis' well-known avarice, pointing out to him that if his daughter were to regain her sight completely, then she would inevitably lose the pension that had been granted her by the Empress Maria Theresa. The conspiracy succeeded: Mesmer lost his patient, and disgusted with Vienna and its treatment of him he departed to Paris.

At first the Parisians were inclined to laugh at his bizarre methods but Mesmer had immense self-confidence and courage. Reports of his strange treatment and of his cures had preceded him and, the Parisians being by nature a very curious people, his lavishly furnished consulting-rooms in the fashionable Place Vendôme were soon filled with more patients than he could handle. Something had to be done, therefore, to relieve himself of the necessity of treating all of them with "magnetic passes". He got over this difficulty by

inventing the "baguet". This was an oval wooden bath about four feet long and one foot deep, situated in the middle of the salon. In it were laid a number of wine bottles filled with "magnetized" water, disposed radially, their necks directed outwards. Enough water was then poured into the bath to cover the bottles, a few iron filings were flung in "to heighten the magnetic effect" and then the whole contraption was covered with an iron cover pierced by a number of long movable iron rods. The patients were instructed either to hold these rods or else to apply them to the affected region of their bodies, in order that they might receive the "magnetism".

The following is a description of the scene written by the historian Bailly, an eyewitness of it. "The sick persons, arranged in great numbers . . . round the baguet received the magnetism by all these means; by the iron rods which convey it to them from the baguet; by the cords round their bodies, by the connection of the thumb, which conveys to them the magnetism of their neighbours, and by the sounds of a pianoforte, or of an agreeable voice, diffusing the magnetism in the air. The patients are also directly magnetized by means of the finger and wand of the magnetizer . . . above all they are magnetized by the application of his hands and the pressure of his fingers on the hypochondrium and on the region of the abdomen.

"Meanwhile," continues Bailly, "the patients in their different conditions present a very varied picture. Some are calm, tranquil and experience no effect. Others cough, spit, feel slight pains, local or general, heat, and have sweatings. Others again, are agitated and tormented with convulsions. These convulsions are remarkable in regard to the number affected with them, to their duration and force. . . .

"Nothing is more astonishing than the spectacle of these convulsions. One who has not seen them can form no idea of them. The observer is as much astonished at the profound repose of one portion of the patients as at the agitation of the rest—at the various accidents that are repeated and at the sympathies that are exhibited. All are under the power of the magnetizer. It matters not in what state of drowsiness they may be, the sound of his voice, a look, a motion of his hand—brings them out." (Quoted by R. B. Ince in *Franz Anton Mesmer*. Rider, London, 1920.) (*See* Plate 26.)

If Mesmer had hoped that by exchanging Vienna for Paris he

would escape the opposition of the medical profession he must surely
have been disappointed. "It is impossible," writes his contemporary,
Baron Dupotet, "to conceive the sensation which Mesmer's experiments created in Paris. No theological controversy in the earlier
ages of the Church was ever conducted with greater bitterness."
But that Mesmer often obtained astonishing cures could no longer
be denied and the President of the Academy of Sciences, M. Leroi,
proposed that a test of his methods should be conducted along
strictly scientific lines. Mesmer refused this test. "My principal
object," he wrote in reply to M. Leroi, "is to demonstrate the
existence of a physical agent hitherto unobserved. . . . It is as a
natural philosopher . . . and not as a physician, that I call on you,
men of science, requesting you to observe natural phenomena and to
pronounce on my system."

It is interesting to see that Mesmer is still maintaining that his
cures are being effected through the action of a physical agent,
animal magnetism, and that the idea of hypnosis and of suggestion
under hypnosis has never entered his mind. But whatever the
agency by which Mesmer obtained his results, the great bulk of the
medical profession would have nothing to do with him or his methods.
The Royal Society of Medicine even went so far in 1780 as to pass a
decree depriving any qualified doctor of his diploma if he should
advocate or practise Mesmer's treatment by "animal magnetism".

Meanwhile Marie Antoinette had become more than a little
interested in his work and because he was unable to make any headway against the doctors' opposition Mesmer wrote to her, requesting
that a château should be put at his disposal, together with a small
annuity that would allow him to continue his work untroubled by
the persecution of his enemies. This idea met with royal favour
and negotiations were started with the idea of meeting Mesmer's
needs. Later King Louis appointed a Royal Commission to examine
Mesmer's claims on the subject of animal magnetism. Even the
less favourable part of this report did not attempt to deny that
Mesmer had obtained remarkable cures but it declined to regard
them as being due to animal magnetism. The report concluded as
follows: "That which we have learnt . . . by the examination of the
process of Magnetism, is that man can act upon man at any time and
almost at will, by striking his imagination; that the simplest gestures

and signs can have the most powerful effects; and that the action of man upon the imagination may be reduced to an art, and conducted with method, upon subjects who have faith." Considering that little or nothing was known to the Commission of suggestion under hypnosis, the report displays considerable acumen. But the Commission blundered badly in its subsequent actions. Having categorically declared in 1784 that there was no such thing as animal magnetism, in the following year the Commissioners extended an invitation to all foreign and provincial doctors to forward them their own observations on the action of this remarkable force.

There is a limit to the amount of frustration anyone is able to support and by now Mesmer had reached that limit. In 1781 he suddenly left Paris and went off to Spa. There he opened a new clinic to which many of his former Parisian patients came. Mesmer's methods were by now widely known and a few years later the King of Prussia urged him to go to Berlin and work there but Mesmer declined this invitation, excusing himself on the score of his age. His last years were very happy and peaceful ones for he had retired to a country life, devoting himself to his animals for whom, like Edward Jenner, he had always had a great affection. He died in the year of the Battle of Waterloo, 1815.

Mesmer repeatedly affirmed that his sole aim was to demonstrate the existence of the natural force which he believed that he had discovered, the force to which he had given the name of Animal Magnetism. "There is only one disease," he also declared, "and only one cure." For him, disease was the throwing of the natural forces of the body out of balance and cure the bringing of the forces back again into a state of equilibrium. He believed that by discovering how to bring about the "crises" in his patients and how to regulate them, he had found the right means of mobilizing man's inherent curative powers. He believed, in his own words, that he had found the right means of manipulating the Animal Magnetism within man.

Whatever we may think of Mesmer's theory, there is little doubt that he had a salutary influence on the subsequent course of medicine. He complained—and he had good reason for doing so—that his medical colleagues saw only the physical aspects of disease and completely neglected the causes lying in their patient's mind. "To these

physical causes must be added moral causes; pride, envy, avarice, ambition, all the vile passions of the human mind are so many causes of visible maladies. How can the effects of these continually acting causes be radically cured?"

The Parisian Commission appointed to investigate Mesmei's claims agreed that he had brought about many cures but categorically denied the existence of any such thing as "animal magnetism". A committee of modern doctors sifting the same evidence today would probably come to the same conclusion but it might well add a rider to the effect that suggestion in varying degrees of hypnosis played a large part in Mesmer's cures. Yet crude though many of Mesmer's ideas on the subject of Magnetism were, it is quite possible that the day may eventually arrive when some of them will seem less foolish than they seem now. The term "animal magnetism" has completely disappeared out of our vocabulary but it is being slowly replaced by the new word "radiesthesia". This is admittedly a term unacceptable to many medical men but even those who reject it are prepared to admit that an organism constitutes a field of force and this idea of the body acting as a "field of force" is not very distant from Mesmer's queer notion of animal magnetism.

THE MEDICAL INVESTIGATION OF HYPNOTISM

Mesmer's methods of treatment were not completely given up after his death but were carried on for a time by one of Mesmer's disciples, the Count de Puységur. He made three very valuable observations: that patients who were responding well to their treatment heard only what the magnetizer said to them and were oblivious to all else; that they accepted the magnetizer's suggestions without questioning them; and that they could recall nothing of what had happened after their return to an ordinary state of consciousness.

Interest in mesmerism declined after the death of the Count de Puységur and was not revived until the middle of the nineteenth century when James Braid (1795–1861), a Scottish surgeon practising in Manchester, drew the attention of the medical profession to the subject again. He had been present at a public demonstration of "mesmerism" and was at first inclined to believe that the somnambulistic phenomena he had witnessed there were fraudulent and due

to collusion between the lecturer and his subject. Later, and as the consequence of his own personal experiments, he became convinced that a genuine, self-induced sleep could be brought about by staring fixedly at a bright light. He was able also to demonstrate to others this phenomenon of induced sleep which became known as "Braidism". The importance of Braid's work lay in his having produced strong evidence that "mesmerism" was not due to the passage of any mysterious fluid from the operator to his subject but was a subjective psychological state. Braid called his first treatise on the subject *The Rationale of Nervous Sleep* but later he coined the word "hypnotism", deriving it from the Greek word *hypnos*. Braid's new interpretation of the phenomenon formerly called mesmerism was widely accepted by the medical profession, but any doctor who was bold enough to make use of hypnotism for medical purposes met with the most violent opposition. John Elliotson (1791–1868), a London surgeon, published a paper on *Numerous Cases of Surgical Operations without Pain in the Mesmeric state*, and as a result of this he became so unpopular with his colleagues that he was compelled to resign his appointment at University College Hospital. At this point interest in hypnotism as a medical measure might have disappeared had it not been for the use made of it by James Eskdaile who, because he was practising in India, was less vulnerable to criticism. Eskdaile carried out over a hundred painless operations on patients in the hypnotic state and published his results in a pamphlet entitled *Mesmerism in India*.

This renewal of interest in hypnotism spread to Paris and led to events there of considerable importance to the future of medicine. Jean Martin Charcot (1825–1893), who had created at the great hospital of the Salpêtrière a world-famous neurological and psychological clinic, investigated the subject of hypnotism and came to the conclusion that the hypnotic state was a pathological condition akin to, if not identical with, hysteria. He was very sceptical therefore of its being of any value as a method of treating abnormal psychological states. But although Charcot was a brilliant investigator he was a poor clinician. Actually he was not really interested in the treatment of the neurotic patient, as is apparent from Havelock Ellis' masterly thumb-nail sketch of him. "For purely psychological investigation he (Charcot) had no liking, and probably no

aptitude. Any one who was privileged to observe his methods of work at the Salpêtrière will easily recall the great master's towering figure; the disdainful expression, sometimes even, it seemed, a little sour; the lofty bearing, which enthusiastic admirers called Napoleonic. The questions addressed to the patient were cold, distant, sometimes impatient. Charcot clearly had little faith in the value of any results so obtained." He did little to advance medical practice.

SIGMUND FREUD (1856–1939)

Another type of man was required to put into practical use the important discoveries Charcot was making at the Salpêtrière Hospital, and in 1885 this other type of man arrived there. Sigmund Freud, the son of poor Moravian parents, had qualified as a doctor in Vienna and was now visiting Paris before starting to practise. Freud was so deeply impressed by what he saw at the Salpêtrière and by the personalities of Charcot and of Charcot's equally famous pupil Janet, that he decided henceforth to devote himself entirely to the treatment of nervous disorders. At this critical moment of his life Freud happened to fall in with another visitor to Charcot's clinic, Breuer, who was equally enthusiastic about the treatment of neurotic disorders with hypnotism and who gave him an account of a particularly interesting case he had witnessed. The patient in question was a young woman who was suffering from partial paralysis and from a difficulty in speech. Questioned about her trouble when she was in a state of hypnosis, she traced it back to a time of great emotional stress with her father, to whom she was deeply devoted. What was of particular interest to Breuer was that after she had recalled to consciousness the memory of this painful period of her life, her symptoms disappeared. Profiting by this case, Freud and Breuer decided that they would treat a series of cases by this means of questioning whilst the patient was in a state of hypnosis.

As the result of their joint research and of his own later work on this subject, Freud came to the conclusion that "there could be powerful mental processes which nevertheless remained hidden from the consciousness of men". He discovered also that it was unnecessary to hypnotize his patients in order to reveal these hidden,

unconscious mental processes. By getting them to lie relaxed on a couch in a dreamy state in which they gave free utterance to every thought fleeting through their minds, this deeper layer of the mind, "the unconscious", could be tapped. Each idea that was revived called up in turn another one, so that slowly and often painfully the patient could be led back along the tracks of his past life until he reached the beginning of his functional troubles.

From Freud's observations on his patients he was able to make several very useful generalizations on the subject of the unconscious mind and on the phenomena of repression and transference. Freud asserted that in our ordinary waking life, ideas and impulses originate in our unconscious where they are experienced by us as emotions that are never formulated clearly in words. What seemed of special importance to Freud was that many of these unconscious ideas and wishes are repressed, that is to say, they are forcibly prevented from ever becoming conscious. They are repressed by a restraining force which Freud called the "endopsychic censor", a force which allowed only ideas of which it approves to pass over the threshold of the pre-conscious into the realm of the conscious. But any idea of which the censor does not approve it drives back into the unconscious, where it continues its existence still invested with its own quota of life energy or what Freud called "libido". Deprived of an outlet, this repressed idea often manifested itself in neurotic or hysterical symptoms. Freud therefore taught that the patient's failure to remember painful incidents in his past was not due to the fading of memory impressions in his mind but to the action of this defence mechanism. Such events were too painful to be remembered and it was only if the protective mechanism could be put out of action that they were revived and the pent-up energy in them released.

Freud was of the opinion that the majority of deep-seated conflicts responsible for neuroses were of a sexual nature. Society had placed a number of strict taboos on sexual behaviour and, as a consequence of this, a sexual experience was likely to be associated with a strong feeling of guilt. Adler and Jung, Freud's two most brilliant disciples, made use of his analytical methods, but they expressed the view in later years that their teacher had laid too great a stress on the thwarted sexual urge as a cause of neurosis and

sought for other causes of conflict. Adler drew attention to the difficulties encountered by the individual in adjusting himself to society and in his struggle to obtain personal power and he believed that these difficulties were fruitful causes of neurosis. Jung reached the conclusion that nervous breakdowns generally arose from an individual's failure to come to terms with the creative impulses lying in his unconscious. He also developed the idea of the "collective unconscious", that is to say, an unconsciousness of the race as opposed to the "personal unconscious" of the individual. He taught that in order to be properly integrated a man had to adjust himself to this wider unconscious of the race as well as to find a satisfactory relationship with his own "personal unconscious".

Freud's teaching, now familiar to everybody, met at first with considerable opposition and was only slowly adopted. Now the Freudian method of analysis has become so fashionable that many people regard psychotherapy as being synonymous with psycho-analysis. Medicine owes an immense debt to the genius of Freud, but the intense reverence of the Freudians for their master has had the unfortunate effect of hardening Freud's suggestions and ten-tative ideas into a rigid creed from which it is impious to depart. The result has too often been that psychological treatment has been reduced to a single routine procedure, namely the sub-jection of the patient to a lengthy analysis ending in the discovery of the inevitable "Oedipus complex". It was not without reason that Wilfred Trotter once exclaimed: "Let a man beware of his disciples."

It would be an error to regard Freud as the actual discoverer of man's "unconscious". Dr. Carus, a contemporary of Goethe's, wrote: "The key to understanding the nature of the conscious life of the psyche lies in the realm of the unconscious", and Freud's teaching could not have been summarized more clearly than in these few words. Goethe himself expressed the same idea in a slightly different way: "The best in man is formless. I believe everything that genius does, as genius, happens unconsciously. Man cannot stay long in the conscious state; he has to plunge back into the unconscious, for that is where his living roots are." So also was the Neo-Platonist fully aware of the unconscious and of the large part it played in his life. What Freud did was first to stress

the importance of unconscious conflicts in the causation of functional diseases, and second, to demonstrate how these conflicts could be revealed. His great contribution to medicine was his invention of a technique by which the hidden levels of the mind could be explored, the technique of psychoanalysis.

THE TREATMENT OF INSANITY

So far functional disturbances of the mind have alone been discussed; in other words, disturbances of the working of the central nervous system rather than of its structure. But there are also much more serious troubles known as the psychoses, disturbances that are not amenable to the forms of treatment dealt with in this chapter. Something must be said about the history of the treatment of these cases.

In no sphere of human thought and action has man's inhumanity to man been more apparent in the past than in his treatment of the insane. Strange to say, his handling of this admittedly difficult problem of the insane was less callous in the Middle Ages than it became in later centuries. There is evidence that there existed in London, as far back as the thirteenth century, an institute known as Bethlehem in which the insane were housed. In a report issued by a Royal Commission of that date it is stated that only some of the inmates of Bethlehem were "under duress". There is also mention of certain bequests having been made for the treatment and maintenance of the insane. The name Bethlehem was later abbreviated to Bedlam and with the passage of time the lot of the inmates of this asylum deteriorated instead of improving. Even as late as the eighteenth century lunatics were kept in cages or chained to the floor, or if they happened to be harmless, were allowed to run at large as the "Tom o' Bedlams" of England and the "Wizards and Warlocks" of Scotland. Bedlam was a London spectacle and people visited it for amusement, in the same way that they now visit the monkey house at the Zoo. When Steele was saddled with the task of amusing three schoolboys he took them to see "the lions, the tombs, Bedlam and the other places which are entertainment to raw minds, because they strike forcibly on the imagination". Even Dr. Johnson and Boswell once made a tour of Bedlam and stared at raving men and women chained to the floor or exhibited in cages. This must have been a

specially painful and terrifying spectacle to the doctor who all his life cherished a secret dread of madness.

DR. PHILIPPE PINEL (1745–1826)

If the credit for bringing to an end this brutal period in the treatment of the insane is to be accorded to any one man it must be to Dr. Philippe Pinel, physician to the Biûtre Prison in Paris, a prison in which large numbers of lunatics were housed. Pinel was a frail and rather diffident young man who started his career as a student of divinity. Later, at the age of thirty, he decided to study medicine instead and for the rather unusual reason that he had developed a great interest in natural history. It was whilst he was a medical student that an incident occurred which brought to his notice the terrible problem of madness. One of his friends suddenly lost his mental balance and according to custom was promptly locked up in a mad-house. But he contrived to escape from his cage and took refuge in the woods. A week later his body was found there, half devoured by wolves, and this incident made such a painful impression on the sensitive Pinel that he decided to devote himself henceforth to the study of insanity and to the improvement of its treatment.

Even in Pinel's time the insane were regarded as being deliberately malicious and many people still attributed their behaviour to their possession by a devil. If, therefore, exorcism failed to expel the devil, the correct treatment was to punish them for their stubbornness in clinging to evil. Pinel reacted with all his being against this mediaeval idea of possession, for he was convinced that the insane were sick people in need of treatment. He initiated a crusade for the more merciful treatment of the insane by liberating the less violent of his own patients, and after the French Revolution had taken place he petitioned the Commune to allow him to appear before it in order to plead the citizen rights of his patients. Again and again the petition of this ridiculous doctor who wanted to liberate maniacs was refused, but finally Couthon, the fiery leader of the Commune, agreed to see him. Pinel pointed out to him that if it were true, as the Revolutionaries had declared, that all men possessed equal rights, then his poor insane patients in the Biûtre Prison also had their rights. Yet they were kept chained up in

verminous dungeons and were far more cruelly used than the common man had been formerly used by the aristocrats. Couthon regarded Pinel as an impractical visionary but because an appeal had been made to his own favourite theme, the equality of man, he agreed to accompany the doctor back to Biûtre. There he witnessed sights which made an immense impression even on a brutal and cold-blooded Revolutionary leader. As he tramped with his guide through the damp underground corridors of the dark prison he was greeted by the ravings and the curses of three hundred madmen and was deafened by the pounding of their manacles against iron bars. He exclaimed to Pinel: *"Ah, ca! citoyen es-tu fou toi-même de vouloir déchainer de pareils animaux?"* Pinel insisted that this was his wish, to liberate his patients and to accord them their citizen rights. Couthon left hurriedly, his final words being: "Do as you will, but your own life will be sacrificed to this false mercy."

Then came the dramatic and fateful moment. Pinel's first act was to have the manacles knocked off an English captain who had lived in chains for forty years and who in spite of this had managed to kill a prison attendant with a blow from his manacles. Before Pinel freed him, he talked to him sitting alone with him in his cell, offering the captain the freedom of the prison yard in return for his promise "to behave like a gentleman". The promise was given and the chains were knocked off. Within the space of a few days, Pinel had the chains removed from more than fifty men who had hitherto been regarded as dangerous madmen. They still remained insane but because they were being treated kindly they ceased to be rebellious and disorderly.

Pinel's theory that insanity was a mental illness requiring careful study and treatment was not received favourably by the medical profession, but from time to time a more enlightened physician would accept it and as the result of his personal influence some new institution would be opened for the humaner treatment of the insane. But to the public, the madman still remained a man possessed of a devil and almost a hundred years had to pass before this idea was relinquished. That it was given up and that the insane were dealt with more mercifully was due chiefly to the work of a comparatively few humanitarians. The pioneers in this liberal movement were John Conolly (1794–1866), physician to Hanwell Asylum,

William Tuke, the Quaker philanthropist, Henry Maudsley (1835–1918) of London, and Sir Thomas Smith Clouston (1840–1915) of Edinburgh. (*See* Plate 26.) In America the most prominent figure in this Crusade of Mercy was Miss Dorothea Dix of Maine, whose work in ameliorating the treatment of the insane in the United States was as great as was the work in Great Britain of John Howard in the matter of prison reform. She is said to have been instrumental in the founding in America of no less than thirty-two well-run asylums.

THE MODERN TREATMENT OF NEUROSIS AND INSANITY

Many psychiatrists are of the opinion that psychological disturbances of the nature of the neuroses should be treated entirely by psychological means, and that drugs and other physical measures should play only a very small part in treatment. Strong arguments can be marshalled in support of this view, but equally strong arguments can be brought against it, one being that as long as psychotherapy is attended with as many failures as at present we cannot afford to neglect alternative forms of treatment. Convulsive-therapy, or the deliberate provocation of epilephform convulsions, is one of the physical forms of treatment against which many psychiatrists have protested, and pre-frontal leucotomy is another. As both of these methods of treatment are being extensively used, something will have to be said about their history.

CONVULSIVE-THERAPY

Electro-convulsive-therapy is a development of a treatment recommended by Weidkhard as long ago as 1798 in which convulsions were evoked by the injection of a large dose of camphor. This treatment was revived in 1937 by two Italian physicians who substituted the passage of an electric current through the frontal lobes of the brain for the use of camphor. All of these pioneers have claimed that the mental condition of neurotics is often markedly improved by these artificially induced convulsions. In the earlier days of convulsive-therapy accidents frequently occurred in the form of fractures and strains due to the violence of the muscular contraction, but with improvements in technique these accidents have become very rare. The duration of the electrical stimulation of the brain and the number of fits required to bring about a cure varies

widely in different cases so that no general rules can be laid down on the subject. Some patients respond immediately; some only after much treatment; some improve and then relapse so more treatment is required. But that the convulsive-therapy is often effective cannot be denied. It has established for itself a place in medicine.

PRE-FRONTAL LEUCOTOMY

This is a far more drastic method of treatment than convulsive-therapy, a method with such serious consequences for the patient that to resort to it can only be justified when all other forms of treatment have proved of no avail. This operation on the brain has been made possible by the great advances made during the last century in our knowledge of its physiology. By means of experiments on animals and by the study of the effect of different brain lesions on different activities, it has been possible to map out the cerebral lobes into a number of areas controlling our various functions, such as movements, sensations, and impressions reaching us through the special senses. As the result of this research it has been found that there exists what may be called a "silent area" in the forepart of the brain, a region which does not appear to be concerned with any special function and which is now believed to be concerned with man's higher mental processes. These frontal lobe areas are believed to be the meeting-place between emotional impulses arising in the large nuclei at the base of the brain and the purely intellectual processes in which the frontal lobes are engaged. The operation of leucotomy consists of dividing, by means of a fine knife or a needle, the association fibres along which the emotional impulses travel from the basal nuclei towards the frontal areas.

The objection to leucotomy is not that it is a dangerous operation or difficult to perform but that it permanently alters the character of the patient. It is difficult to define the precise changes brought about in him but the operation may be said to remove all his initiative and to render him placid and listless, so that there is something robot-like in his behaviour. He will do what he has been asked to do and what he has been accustomed to do but he will not embark on anything new. What has been gained by the operation is the immense advantage that all violence and anxiety and despair have been

eliminated by it. That the results of leucotomy are in many ways satisfactory is shown by the fact that approximately one third of the asylum patients so treated have been able to return home a few weeks after the operation, and that a large percentage of them have even been able to take up their old jobs again. When it is recalled that previously they were sufficiently serious cases to require certification and confinement in an asylum, the operation cannot be summarily dismissed as never, in any circumstances, justified. But that it must be used with great discrimination and always as a last resort goes without saying.

PSYCHO-SOMATIC MEDICINE

The term psycho-somatic medicine has frequently been heard of late and some people have imagined that it describes yet another new medical speciality. This is not the case. The popularity of the term psycho-somatic is a welcome sign of a saner medical attitude to illness. It is a continual reminder to the medical profession that illness is not what so many doctors of the nineteenth century supposed it to be, a disorderly functioning of one or perhaps two organs, but that it is a disturbance of the equilibrium of the whole man. The word also implies a recognition of the fact that diseases are usually the result of multiple and not of single causes. For example, tuberculosis means more than an invasion of an otherwise healthy body by tubercle bacilli, for tubercle bacilli are everywhere and only a few of us succumb to them. Tuberculosis therefore implies the infection by tubercle bacilli of a body whose resistance to hostile micro-organisms has previously been weakened by a number of unfavourable factors. The term psycho-somatic should also remind us of the need to correlate the physical with the psychological signs and symptoms of the illness. Researchers in this psycho-somatic field of medicine are at present busily engaged in this very important work of bridging the gap between the physical and the psychological symptoms of disease. In the writer's opinion this work is of such importance to further medical progress that something must be said about it.

THE TWO BASIC URGES OF THE UNCONSCIOUS MIND

Towards the end of his life Freud came to the conclusion that

the various primitive urges in the subconscious levels of the mind could be reduced to two great primary urges, a Creative instinct and a Destructive instinct. Because he identified the positive and Creative instinct with love he called it *Eros*. The negative and Destructive instinct he called *Thanatos* or the Death-urge. He pictured these two great primitive instincts as always at war with each other throughout the whole of a man's life, the one gaining the upper hand and then being overcome by the other, the first conferring on us the gift of health and the second burdening us with disease.

Some people find it difficult or even impossible to accept this idea that there exists in us such an anomaly as an instinct for our own destruction, but a dispassionate view of our own lives or those of our friends will help us to see that this is not altogether improbable. Human behaviour is very puzzling, much stranger than is the behaviour of the animals. An animal's actions are far more consistent and logical for they are invariably directed towards its own preservation and its own gain, but the same cannot be said of all human behaviour. There are men and women who prefer to dwell on the negative and the sombre side of life, men and women who have an innate liking for tragedy, illness and unhappiness and who instinctively move, as the candle-seeking moth moves, in the direction of illness and death rather than of health and life. No, this is not a poetic fantasy but a literal account of the behaviour of a by no means rare type of person. Every doctor is familiar with the patient who seems to be possessed with a devil bent on his undoing— in other words, who is controlled by a negative and self-destructive urge. Such patients resist all forms of medical treatment; they take an intense pleasure in defeating the best efforts of their doctors to help them; they cling tenaciously to their own misery, and they die for no other reason than that they possess no will to live.

Dr. Hutschnecker writes of the destructive urge in man as follows: "If we would understand the dynamics of the destructive instinct we must regard it as an active principle checked only by the stronger urge of the creative instinct. . . . We can observe how, in nature, as in man, the destructive instinct gains momentum as the creative powers in an individual are exhausted. This is the

natural progress of all living things towards dissolution and death."
(A. Hutschnecker, *The Will to Live*.)

THE PSYCHO-SOMATIC VIEW OF ILLNESS

The modern doctor tends less and less to divide the illnesses with
which he has to deal into cases of physical illness and cases of
psychological illness. He looks instead at the illness as a process in
which are mingled physical and psychological events, both of which
have to be dealt with. He realizes also, as the homeopathic physician
has long ago realized, that different psychological types of men are
liable to develop different varieties of physical illness, the aggressive
type of man being more disposed to develop cardio-vascular troubles
and the regressive type digestive disturbances. He understands also
that illnesses are very often purposive in character, that they provide
the patient with a way out of a dilemma which cannot be solved in
any other way. This being so, the patient will in all likelihood
continue to develop illnesses until the basic emotional problem from
which they all spring has been uprooted.

To have reached this broader view of illness is a very satisfactory
achievement, but it brings with it new responsibilities for the doctor.
Owing to the decay of religion in the West it is no longer possible
for the physician to urge his patient to take his spiritual and emotional troubles to the priest and to entrust himself to his care.
Whether he likes it or not the modern physician often becomes
responsible for his patient's soul as well as his body and herein lies
the "doctor's dilemma", this realization on the part of the doctor
that he is not fitted to carry out this task. He is unable to do what
Plato seems to have thought a physician should be capable of doing,
to look after his patient's soul as well as his body. By great industry
he can acquire knowledge, but wisdom never came from the reading
of books and it is wisdom that is now needed. Amiel envisaged the
type of doctor that is now required but which is rarely if ever
available, when he made the following entry in his diary in the year
1873. "The principal grievance that I have against the doctors is
that they neglect the real problem, which is to seize the *unity* of
the individual who claims their care: their methods of investigation
are far too elementary; a doctor who does not read you to the
bottom is ignorant of essentials. To me the ideal doctor would be a

man with profound knowledge of life and of the soul, intuitively
divining any suffering or disorder of whatever kind and restoring
peace by his mere presence."

Nobody has pictured better the ideal doctor now required, the
doctor who is capable of ministering to the mind as well as the body
—in a word, the true psycho-somatic physician.

CHAPTER XX

Quackery

THE relationship between the doctor and his patient is a very special one, quite unlike that existing between the parson and his parishioner or the lawyer and his client. The vicar is the representative on earth of Christ and the servant of the Almighty. The solicitor is the exponent and the servant of the law; he interprets it to his client and in a litigation looks after his interests. The doctor's role is more easily described—he is the servant of his patient. It matters not who his patient be; whether he be an unmitigated villain or a saint the doctor's duty is to restore him to health, or if this is impossible, to mitigate his sufferings. If necessary the doctor's own profit and convenience must be sacrificed to those of his patient, for by his Hippocratic oath he has sworn to put the sick man's interests first.

Such should be the relationship between the doctor and his patient, a relationship that must be based on mutual confidence and trust if it is to be of any service. And more often than not an approximation to this lofty ideal was attained prior to the passing of the Health Act. But there are defaulters in the medical profession as there are defaulters in every other walk of life, men who put their own interests first and who are ready to make profit out of their patients' gullibility. Such are the quacks with whom this chapter deals.

But how can we define this word quack? The *Oxford Dictionary* offers us very little help when it tells us that the quack talks "ignorantly and pretentiously". All men talk in this manner occasionally, and the medical man is a frequent offender in this respect. He is sometimes driven to do so by his patients who over-estimate his

326

knowledge and often credit him with powers he does not possess. Faith and confidence in the physician being important ingredients in medicine, the doctor is not infrequently manoeuvred into a position in which he is compelled to talk both "ignorantly and pretentiously".

The *Oxford Dictionary's* second thoughts on this subject are even more misleading. They are to the effect that to be a quack is "to palm off with fraudulent and boastful pretensions"; or "to seek to remedy by empirical and ignorant treatment". Here again the net has been flung so wide that it entangles in its meshes all reasonably honest and competent doctors. Even men so far removed from life as the compilers of dictionaries must realize that if a medicine is to do any good it must be palmed off on the patient with something suspiciously like "boastful pretensions". And as for seeking "to remedy by empirical and ignorant treatment", why, at least eighty per cent of medical treatment is empirical. A medical man prescribes a certain remedy because he recalls that he prescribed it on a previous occasion, in similar circumstances, and found that it did his patient good. In spite of the great aid medicine has received and is still receiving from exact science, it still remains an art, and, as we all know, an art has to advance by the slow method of trial and error.

No sharp line can be drawn between the methods of the *bona fide* physician and those of the quack and the charlatan, and it would be a mistake to attempt to distinguish between these two categories of men by the treatment they prescribe. Some authors would have placed in the latter category characters of whom I have made honourable mention in the earlier chapters of this book. Many medical historians have indeed dismissed Paracelsus as a rogue and a braggart, whilst others have regarded Mesmer as an impostor on the grounds that he dressed in a magician's robe and talked mumbo-jumbo on the subject of magnetic influences, and also that he made the most extravagant of claims. Yet the author of this book has hailed both of these men as important figures in the history of medicine. It is by means of their predominant motive and not by the nature of their treatment that the quack must be distinguished from the physician. In short, the sole main motive of the quack is his own gain whilst that of the physician is the welfare of his patient.

This does not imply that the physician is completely indifferent to his own profit. It means only that his personal gain is not the sole key to his actions.

Francis Bacon wrote: "We see the weakness and credulity of men is such as they will often prefer a mountebank or witch to a learned physician." This is as true of many people today as it was true of people of Francis Bacon's time for the mountebank has this great attraction, that he promises his patient what the learned physician is quite unable to offer him, a quick cure without any trouble to himself. Whereas the learned physician can only recommend an operation for the removal of his stone, the mountebank knows how to dissolve it—an infinitely preferable proceeding. We all seek the primrose path both to heaven and to health, and whereas the honest physician insists on all sorts of inconveniences, such as the abandonment of our bad methods of living, and a course of tedious treatment, including perhaps a stay in an expensive nursing home, the mountebank and the quack know how to avoid all of these unpleasantnesses. Small wonder that they never lack patients.

Strange to say it is not only the uneducated man and the simpleton that is taken in by the quack doctor. The intellectual is particularly partial to him and he is almost always convinced that it is professional jealousy alone which deprives the quack of medical recognition. The late Bernard Shaw and Stafford Cripps both had a very strong bias in the direction of the unorthodox practitioner. Because the medical profession cold-shoulders the unqualified quack, Bernard Shaw accused it, in the preface to *The Doctor's Dilemma*, of being the strongest and the most reactionary of all the trade unions. According to Shaw it is jealousy alone which prevents the Royal Colleges of Physicians and of Surgeons from presenting bone-setters and unqualified men of that kind with licences to practise medicine.

It is strange that men as intelligent as these should so often fail to realize that the law which now makes it obligatory for a man to hold a medical qualification before he practises medicine was made for *their* own protection and not primarily for the profit and the convenience of the medical profession. That the first Act to suppress unlicensed practice which was passed in the year 1511 was badly needed is abundantly clear from the preamble to it: "Forasmuch as the science and cunning of physick and surgery, is

daily within this realm, exercised by a great multitude of ignorant persons, of whom the greater part have no manner of insight in the same, nor any other kind of learning; that common artificers as smiths, weavers and women boldly and accustomably have taken upon them great cures and things of great difficulty in which they partly use sorcery and witchcraft, partly apply such medicines unto the disease as to be noxious and nothing meet, therefore to the High Displeasure of God, great infamy to the Faculty and the grievous hurt and damage and destruction of many of the King's liege people," etc., etc. So runs the preamble to the Act of 1511.

The College of Physicians was founded seven years after the passing of this licensing Act, and the powers that were considered necessary for the suppression of quacks and impostors were conferred upon it. Yet it would seem that these were insufficient for the purpose of stopping quackery, so prevalent had this become, for we find an army surgeon of the name of Thomas Gale complaining in 1544 that whilst he was visiting two great London Hospitals, to wit St. Thomas's and St. Bartholomew's, he saw there "three hundred people that were diseased of sore arms, legs, feet and hands, with other parts of the body so grievously infected, that one hundred and twenty of them could never be recovered without loss of a limb. All these were brought to their mischief by witches, by women, and by counterfeit javels (worthless fellows) that take upon themselves the use of art, not only robbing them of their money, but of their limbs and perpetual health." (Quoted from *The Quacks of Old London* by C. J. S. Thompson, 1928.)

THE LONDON QUACKS

Unlicensed practitioners are very difficult fish to hook and still more difficult to land because they have an aptitude for acquiring powerful patrons who come to their aid in times of trouble. Not that quackery is an easy profession to follow or one unattended with risks. It is true that the eighteenth century was a golden age for "irregular practitioners" but formerly, in the Middle Ages, the citizens of London dealt far more sternly and robustly with their quacks. It is recorded that a "counterfeit physician" of the name of Stowe was arrested in the year 1382, "set on horseback face to the

horse's tail, the same in his hand as bridle, a collar of Jordans about his neck, a whetstone on his breast and so led through the City of London with ringing basons and then banished". Another "counterfeit physician", caught forty years later, fared even worse than Stowe had done, as was testified by an unsightly head exposed to public view on Tower Hill. But in the Elizabethan Age medical buccaneers were far more likely to escape penalties than were their predecessors, thanks to the intervention of their powerful friends, as the following report shows. It refers to a "counterfeit physician" of the name of Charles Cornet who, in 1555, "would not be restrained from his ill-practices, with the bills of his condemnation affixed in the corners of streets; being patronized by Weston, Dean of Westminster, and Robert Charnley, was forced to flee the town and had his unwholesome remedies burnt in the open market at Westminster". (*See* Plate 27.)

Paul Buck is a still more striking example of a medical privateer of the Elizabethan Age who escaped prosecution through the intervention of powerful friends. He is described as "a very impudent and ignorant quack" who was brought up before the College of Physicians but was afterwards discharged because he had in the meantime secured a letter from Queen Elizabeth's private secretary, Sir Francis Walsingham, to the effect that "he had done much good and was otherwise of a verie good and honest disposition". This testimonial stood Paul Buck in good stead, despite the fact that Sir Francis Walsingham could scarcely be regarded as a satisfactory judge of honesty and a good disposition. When arrested a second time, a year or two later, Buck was again freed through the intervention, this time, of Lord Howard, the Lord High Admiral, who wrote praying the College to grant him a licence to practise. Lord Howard even offered twenty pounds to defray the cost of the said licence. The College agreed to set Mr. Paul Buck at liberty again but it could not consent to do what the Lord High Admiral wanted it to do, present Buck with a free licence to practise medicine.

Even before the passing of the Act of 1511 rulers had been forced to adopt their own private measures to suppress the crowd of quacks, mountebanks and charlatans who preyed on the credulity of their subjects. In 1140 Roger II of Sicily issued an edict forbidding anyone from practising medicine without producing satisfactory

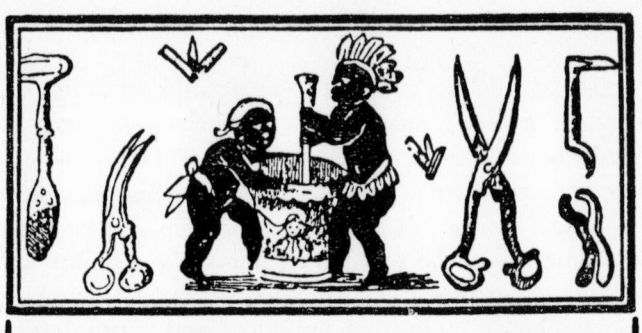

Good News to the Sick.

Veragainſt *Ludgate* Church, within *Black-Fryers* Gate-way, at *Lil-
lies-Head*, Liveth your old Friend
Dr. *Caſe*, who faithfully Cures the
Grand *P-*, with all its Symptoms,
very Cheap, Private, and without the leaſt Hindrance of Buſineſs.   *Note.* He hath been a Phy-
ſitian 33 Years, and gives Advice in any Diſtem
per *gratis.*

All ye that are of *Venus* Race,
Apply your ſelves to Dr. *Caſe*;
Who, with a Box or two of PILLS,
Will ſoon remove your painſull ILLS.

Fig. 15.—A bill printed for the notorious quack John Case
(about 1690)

credentials and punishing infringement of this law by imprisonment.
So also did Mathias, King of Hungary, take care to protect his own
person at a critical moment of his life. He had it proclaimed far and
wide, in the year 1464, that any person who could cure him of his
arrow wound would be richly rewarded, but that if this cure were
undertaken by anybody and proved unsuccessful, then the practitioner himself would be put to death. This was an arrangement

discouraging even to a *bona fide* surgeon and still less attractive to the quack.

As one turns the pages of old treatises and reads the hand-bills of the quack doctors, charlatans, astrologers, nostrum vendors, sham physicians, and beauty specialists of Old London, one is reminded again of what is so often forgotten, that humanity is for ever the same. (*See* Fig. 15.) Thought, customs and emotional conventions change but the essence of humanity remains unaltered. Quackery in olden times was very much the same as is quackery to-day. Take, as an example, that impudent and plausible rogue who practised medicine in the days of King Charles II, Cornelius à Tilbourne. Tilbourne headed his hand-bills with the following description of himself: "Sworn chyrurgeon to King Charles II from whose hands he received a Gold Medal and Chain." Now the public no more thought of investigating Tilbourne's credentials than the people of today think of enquiring into the modern quack's qualifications for treating them. Who is to know whether his account of himself was a true one or not? And even if it were true, it may well have happened that that easy-going monarch, Charles II, amused himself one fine day with the merry jest of appointing a mountebank as his honorary surgeon. But with King Charles's name on the top of his hand-bills, Tilbourne found it easy to attract a large number of patients.

The quack of olden times, like his modern representative, owed much of his success to his clever use of advertisement. Cornelius à Tilbourne's publicity was based on the principle of "no cure, no money", and he also offered his patients lodging and food whilst they were undergoing his treatment. In other words he kept his own very select nursing home. Diffidence was also catered for and those who did not want to be seen going to and coming from Tilbourne's consulting-rooms—and there are always shy people in a quack's clientele—could make use of a back entrance. His rooms were situated in the Blue Flower Pot of Lincoln's Inn Fields and his hand-bill announced: "For the convenience of those that desire privacy, they may come through Red Lion Inn, between the turnstiles in Holborn, which is directly against my back door when you will see the sign of the Blue Bull". So far everything appears to be restrained and seemly in the hand-bill but as soon as the medical

claims are announced these qualities disappear. "I recover and give sight to the blind. I restore sight in a moment. I cure deafness (if curable!), I cure vomiting, rising of the vapours, pain in the milt, stitches in the side and all scorbutick distempers. . . . I can, if any person do by accident or misfortune lose one of his eyes, artificially put in another, not to be discovered as a blemish by anybody." Then follows a list of the nobility he has cured, together with the diseases they suffered from. This list closes with the words: "I could mention a great many more which I have cured, but the paper being too little, Vivant Rex et Regina!"

With so many powerful patrons willing to support him it is not surprising that Cornelius à Tilbourne outlived the King from whose hands he had received a Gold Medal and Chain, and outlived also his brother, James II, so that he was able to head his advertisement with the news that he was now "patronized by King William and Queen Mary".

HIGH REPUTATION OF FOREIGN PRACTITIONERS

It is interesting to note that the Londoner of two hundred years ago had the same partiality for foreign doctors as the Londoner of today. Such is our British modesty that we are disposed to attribute to doctors and quacks hailing from abroad a greater professional skill than that with which our own dull countrymen are endowed. C. J. S. Thomson cites Dr. Abraham of Groningen as a striking example of the special popularity enjoyed by the foreign quack in the seventeenth and eighteenth centuries. Dr. Abraham announced his arrival in London in clarion tones: "Be it known unto all men that to this famous City of London the Renowned and well-experienced Physician, Cutter of Stone and Oculist has arrived. He declares by God's assistance, he hath by his Art and Skill gotten great repute in the United Kingdom of the Netherlands and in several Kingdoms and Dukedoms having by his continual experience acquired many fine and curious manual operations, *not before heard of,* and hath many excellent remedies for curing disease incident to Mankind *which others have not* yet found out." Here we have the distinguishing mark of the quack, that he knows what other doctors do not know and can do what other doctors cannot do. He possesses special knowledge and skill beyond the reach of ordinary men.

An "Eminent Doctor of Physick newly come from Poland" adopted an indirect and more subtle method of attracting a London clientele. Below a portrait of himself he informed the public that "so many persons have flockt to him, that he has been forced to give out these papers by the hands of servants, to desire all persons whatsoever to *forbeare* to come to him, unless it be for the cure of the morbus gallicus". What could be a clearer proof of the Eminent Polish doctor's outstanding attainments than the fact that he had been forced to ration the number of patients permitted to see him, restricting his attention to those suffering from a single specified disease? There can be little doubt that clients who suffered from diseases other than the "morbus gallicus" would manage somehow or other to squeeze through the crowd into the house in Fleet Street, "betwixt the *Golden Lion* and the *Three Golden Bucks*, next door but one to the *Castle Tavern*, where there is a hatch before the entry door".

There was also another foreign visitor to London, a great "Italian Master" who had "brought with him out of Italy, the Right Roman Orvietan which he sells at Half a crown the 3 ounces or 6 ounces for Five shillings, and so you may have as many ounces as you please". This great Italian Specialist, "the Right Medicine Master, that hath cured so many hundreds", implores "all sufferers to come unto him and he will help them, in as short a time as anyone, to the admiration of all people". Different forms of publicity are required for different types of people and the Italian doctor evidently catered for men and women who were far less pushing than those able to gate-crash into the consulting-rooms of the great Polish Physician.

It would seem that the Dutch Chyrurgeon who lodged "at the end of Threadneedle Street at the sign of *The Burnsten Twins*" supplied the needs of a still more reticent type of patient. His hand-bill openly proclaims the following: "If any people are ashamed to come to me, they may have medicines sent them by any messenger, sending but a little note of their condition. I can cure Scal'd heads without pulling the Hare off and draw rotten teeth and stumps with a touch." In other words, the Dutch Surgeon cured by correspondence, a method of treatment which is still being employed on quite a large scale at the present day.

A German physician, who describes himself as a "Doctor beyond other Doctors", also had an attractive dental line to offer his customers. He is a "great artist and draws teethe most artificially, whole teethe, little teethe, the roots of teethe, if they were so fast in the gums they cannot be seen, he knoweth to draw them with great dexterity and without trouble or pain. He puts in artificially teeth of Ivory, Silver, or Gold, as if they were natural. He maketh black teethe white in a moment which taketh a man's heart away to see it and maketh loose teethe fast."

It will be noted that a large number of the quacks of Old London claimed to be under the royal patronage and in at least three cases these claims were fully substantiated. Something must be said of these three privileged rogues, Dr. William Read, the Chevalier John Taylor and Dr. Joshua Ward. The first of these, William Read, was born in the very heyday of quackery, the reign of Queen Anne, and having begun life as a jobbing tailor in Aberdeen he emigrated to Dublin to try his hand in a far more profitable trade. He did fairly well in Dublin but he was ambitious and came to the great city of London, where he settled in rooms in the Strand, advertising that he specialized in eye-strain. The Queen herself suffered from chronic eye weakness and Read's claims to cure all such troubles without any inconvenience to the patient were soon brought to her notice. His infallible eye-wash seemed to have done the royal eyes good so he was knighted by a grateful monarch in the year 1705. Read celebrated his admission to the order of chivalry by paying a hack poet of Grub Street to write an ode about it. Unfortunately another poem was published a few years later in which he figured again, this time bracketed with Sir William Hannes, another recipient of knighthood. The two honours were celebrated in the following verse:

"The Queen, like Heav'n shines equally on all,
Her favours now without distinction fall,
Great Read and slender Hannes both knighted show
That none their honours shall to merit owe."

But Sir William was not the kind of man to be downcast by such lampoonery as this and he remained in his exalted position during

the whole of Queen Anne's reign and even contrived to obtain, after her death, the appointment of sworn-oculist-in-ordinary to His Majesty King George I. After his death he was succeeded as Royal Oculist by a Mr. Roger Grant who had started life as a tinker and an Anabaptist preacher. The Hanoverians, like Queen Anne, had a partiality for "irregular practitioners".

The Chevalier Taylor also had a good line in eye-washes but he was a "specialist" in many other things as well. He had a ready wit and a good appearance and, according to one of his contemporaries, a Dr. King, "no quack ever appeared with fitter and more excellent talents. He has a good appearance, a fine hand, good instruments and performs his operation with great dexterity." The Chevalier also possessed a knowledge of several foreign languages. Thanks to these accomplishments he obtained the post of Oculist to George II who, like George I, had a high regard for unqualified oculists. Dr. Samuel Johnson, who was personally acquainted with both Ward and Taylor, summed them up in the following remark: "Taylor is the most ignorant man I ever knew, but sprightly; Ward is the dullest."

The dull Joshua Ward to whom Dr. Johnson refers flourished in the reign of that somewhat dull monarch, King George II. After starting life as a drysalter, he developed political ambitions and took his seat in the House of Commons as member for Marlborough in the year 1717. But there seems to have been some doubt as to his right to have taken this seat, and a committee appointed to enquire into the matter elicited the fact that he had not received a single vote in the Marlborough election. The spurious member for Marlborough then left hurriedly for France where he learnt to make the pills and drops for which he afterwards became so famous. On his return to London in 1733 he resumed his career as a doctor by advertising the wonderful cures brought about by his various nostrums. An introduction obtained for him to the King set a seal on his success as an advertiser. According to a certain Dr. Henning—and the accuracy of Dr. Henning's report cannot be guaranteed—the first meeting between Ward and George II came about in the following manner. "George II being afflicted with a violent pain of the thumb which baffled the skill of the faculty, sent for the noted Dr. Joshua Ward; who having ascertained the nature of the com-

plaint before he was admitted, provided himself with a suitable
nostrum which he concealed in the hollow of his hand. On being
introduced, he requested permission to examine the affected part
and gave it so sudden a wrench, that the King cursed him and
kicked his shins. Ward bore this very patiently and when the King
was cool, respectfully asked him to move his thumb, which he did
easily and found the pain gone."

Joshua Ward was now what is known as a made man and one
royal favour followed another. The grateful monarch started by
providing him with a room in Whitehall for the treatment of the
poor and also bought him three great houses in Pimlico which were
turned into a hospital. There, assisted by several ladies of quality,
the great Dr. Joshua Ward treated the sick with the special remedies
that he alone possessed. He counted amongst his patients not
only the King, but also such distinguished men as Lord Chesterfield,
Horace Walpole, Gibbon, Fielding and Pope. Ward died in 1761
but, such is the transience of fame, he was not buried—as he had
left clear instructions he should be buried—in front of the altar in
Westminster Abbey, but in a grave so obscure that its very situation
is now unknown to us.

THE BEAUTY SPECIALIST

The last class of quack to be considered is that well-known
variety, the beauty specialist. After the Restoration many beauty
specialists of both sexes returned to London, the bleak city from
which they had fled during the unsightly age of Cromwell. But
now that women were allowed to be women again and to take pains
with their complexions, to attend to their figures, their hair, their
skins and their nails, beauty specialists were needed. They flocked
back from the continent and set up their consulting-rooms in the
neighbourhood of Bond Street, a part of London which their modern
successors still favour.

Nor have the advertisements issued by the beauty specialists
changed very much in the course of the centuries. There were then,
as there still are, hair experts who "cut and curl Ladies' and Gentlemen's Hair extremely fine and after the Fashion". There were, as
there still are, vendors of Beautifying Creams, Vanishing Creams,
Spot Removers, Wrinkle Smoothers, Hair Restorers and Beauty

Elixirs. The lady beauty specialist of the seventeenth century who calls attention to the virtue of her "Roses Balsamack Elixir" uses the same dignified and lady-like language as her twentieth-century prototype of the West End beauty parlour. She assures her clients that it is "the most Noble Medicine that Art can produce. Its incomparable virtues being such that it gives and restores to Nature what is wanting and takes away what is hurtful." Another West End lady of that time wishes to make it known to her clients that "she makes all kinds of Liquers, Salts, Powders, Pills and Opiates, whereby she extracts out of the body all manner of Venoms, poysons, plagues, purple spots etc. . . . and in such a very short time as cant be imagined, nor believed without one sees it". The same lady also understands thoroughly the secret of preserving Youth and Beauty and can even "beautify without recourse to paint".

Of a truth there is nothing new in the modern art of selling cosmetics, beyond the fact that the selling is likely to be done now by middle-aged gentlemen working in the City behind the façade of an attractive lady's name. Publicity methods have advanced but otherwise the quacks and the vendors of beauty parlour preparations remain very much the same. Plate 2 shows a lady of ancient Egypt engaged in giving the final touches to her toilet and in viewing herself, as she does so, in a hand-mirror, very similar in design to those in general use today. What is also striking is that the picture is very much in line with the modern movement in art.

√ "The thing that hath been, it is that which shall be; and that which is done is that which shall be done: and there is no new thing under the sun.

√ "Is there anything whereof it may be said, See, this is new? it hath been already of old time, which was before us." (Ecclesiastes, i, 10–11.)

These are fitting words with which to end a story of medicine.

INDEX

THE STORY OF MEDICINE

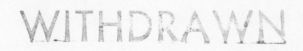